Doxorubicin

MEDICINAL CHEMISTRY

A Series of Monographs

A complete list of titles in this series appears at the end of this volume.

∧

DOXORUBICIN

Anticancer Antibiotics

FEDERICO ARCAMONE

Farmitalia Carlo Erba
Ricerca e Sviluppo Chimico
Milano, Italy

1981

ACADEMIC PRESS

A Subsidiary of Harcourt Brace Jovanovich, Publishers

New York   London   Toronto   Sydney   San Francisco

ACADEMIC PRESS, INC.
111 Fifth Avenue, New York, New York 10003

United Kingdom Edition published by
ACADEMIC PRESS, INC. (LONDON) LTD.
24/28 Oval Road, London NW1   7DX

Library of Congress Cataloging in Publication Data

Arcamone, Federico.
   Doxorubicin.

   (Medicinal chemistry, a series of monographs)
   Includes bibliographies and index.
   1. Adriamycin. 2. Cancer--Chemotheraphy. 3. Antineoplastic agents. I. Title. II. Series. [DNLM:
1. Doxorubicin. 2. Doxorubicin--Analogs and derivatives.
3. Antibiotics, Antineoplastic. W1 ME64 / QV 269 A668d]
RC271.A37A72   616.99'4061   80-1106
ISBN 0-12-059280-0

PRINTED IN THE UNITED STATES OF AMERICA

81 82 83 84   9 8 7 6 5 4 3 2 1

To my Wife and Children

Contents

3 Molecular Interactions

4 Studies with Living Systems

8   New Developments in Biosynthetic Anthracyclines

Preface

The successful development of doxorubicin as a wide-spectrum antitumor antibiotic was the result of a systematic search of the most effective chemical species within a group of biologically active microbial metabolites, namely the anthracycline glycosides. Starting from the classical rhodomycins, an intermediate step was represented by the study of the first *S. peucetius*-derived metabolite, daunorubicin. Important determinants of this development (summarized in Chapter 1) were (a) the involvement of organic chemistry at an early stage (in the elucidation of the detailed structure and stereochemistry of daunorubicin), which allowed the rapid identification of doxorubicin and ensured its prompt availability for the clinical trials; (b) the well-established, pioneering expertise in experimental chemotherapy of Professor Aurelio di Marco and his group at Istituto Nazionale Tumori, Milan, who demonstrated the high therapeutic potential of the new drug; and (c) the highly motivated interest of experienced clinicians whose contributions are clearly visible in the early relevant medical literature in a frame of extensive international cooperation, most importantly, that provided by the United States National Cancer Institute, Division of Cancer Treatment, Bethesda, Maryland.

Chemotherapy as a clinically useful approach to the treatment of human cancer, as an alternative or an addition to surgery and radiotherapy, is now nearly 40 years old; but only in the last decade have its objectives become those of cure or even of prolonged survival of a disease that strikes people at a rate of almost one in four and that represents the second leading cause of death in the United States (as estimated by the American Cancer Society in "Cancer Facts and Figures," 1978). The future of antitumor drug development rests in part on a more rational use of presently known, clinically effective agents and in part on the discovery and selection of new chemical compounds affording a reduction both of host toxicity and of variations in tumor responsiveness. The advantages associated with optimal drug dosage, scheduling, and combination are certainly important, but they lie outside the field of the medicinal chemist. However, the latter have already produced highly active compounds by synthesizing analogues of proven active leads (e.g., methotrexate, doxorubicin itself, CCNU, vincristine, cyclophosphamide). The analogues development approach in the field of anthracyclines is fully justified by the outstanding antitumor activity exhibited by doxorubicin and by the identification of its major side effects, whose dissociation from the therapeutic effects seems, at least in part, possible. Although adequate knowledge of the chemistry involved is a necessary prerequisite for performing appropriate structural variations of the parent drug, the consideration of biochemical and pharmacological properties presumably associated with the clinical effects is of undoubted importance in assisting the medicinal chemist.

Chapters 2 through 8 provide an overview of basic studies in the area of medicinal chemistry and related fields that have been generated as a consequence of doxorubicin development. Such studies have been concerned, on the one hand, with both biochemical and biophysical investigations at the molecular level (the interaction of anthracyclines with DNA having attracted much attention since this cellular constituent appears to be the main receptor of these drugs) and at different levels of biological organization as well. On the other hand, a large body of work whose objective is the development of synthetic procedures for the drug and for new related analogs of potential clinical usefulness has been carried out. New biosynthetic anthracyclines have also been isolated as interest in this family of antibiotics has grown in recent years. This approach remains promising for the identification of new biologically active compounds.

Acknowledgments

The author wishes to acknowledge the very great assistance of Mrs. Domenica Ambroggio who typed most of the manuscript and whose cooperation in the collection of photocopies of many original articles and in checking and listing the literature references was indeed essential to the completion of this work. The author is also grateful to Mrs. Mara Chierichetti for collaboration in the preparation of the typescript.

The author was assisted in the revision of the text by his colleagues and friends—Giovanni Franceschi, Giuseppe Cassinelli, Sergio Penco, Aristide Vigevani and Milena Menozzi—who read large parts of the manuscript. This assistance was particularly valuable since they had each been directly involved in many of the studies reported in this book.

1

Discovery and Development of Doxorubicin

ANTITUMOR ACTIVITY OF AN ANTHRACYCLINE PIGMENT

The history of the antitumor anthracyclines begins in the late 1950s when a pigmented compound originated from a strain of *Streptomyces* sp. was characterized and found to exhibit antitumor properties (*1*). The strain (number 1683 in Farmitalia collection) was isolated from a sample of soil collected in India and displayed a tendency to produce varieties differing phenotypically in the color and the amount of pigmentation. Solvent extraction of both the mycelium and the filtered broth allowed the recovery of the active materials as orange-red or red solids containing one or more hydroxyquinone compounds as shown by the typical absorption spectrum in the ultraviolet and visible regions. The product was purified by the counter-current technique in a Craig's apparatus (chloroform and pH 4.6 acetate buffer) and eventually crystallized as the hydrochloride. It was considered to be closely related to the rhodomycin complex, previously described by Brockmann (*2*). Later work performed in the author's laboratory showed the main pigment produced by strain 1683 to be rhodomycin B, a component of the rhodomycin complex whose structure has been established as **1** by the German authors (*3*).

Biological activity was studied in mice bearing Ehrlich carcinoma or sarcoma 180 both in solid and ascites form. The products were administered intraperitoneally for 5 consecutive days starting the day of ascitic tumor inoculation or subcutaneously in single daily doses for 9 or 10 days starting from day 1 after the transplant of the solid tumors. The crude solids obtained upon *n*-butanol extraction of fermentation fluids allowed a marked

1

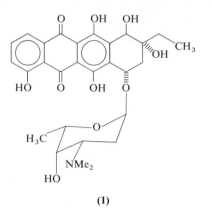

(1)

inhibition of the Ehrlich ascitic tumor when administered at the daily dose of 200 mg to the experimental animals. Survival time of treated animals was, however, not different from that of the controls. Purified pigmented preparations gave similar results at daily doses in the range 0.05–0.25 mg/kg. The latter materials in their water soluble form, i.e., as the intact glycosides, showed also a marked effect on sarcoma 180 in both ascitic and solid form and on Ehrlich adenocarcinoma. In all cases, no favorable effects on survival time were demonstrated, and this was attributed to toxicity of the active principle and especially to the paralyzing effect caused by the substances on intestinal motility. Biological properties of the pigmented substances isolated from strain 1683 indicated, however, that further investigations on new compounds belonging to this class of microbial metabolites would have been of interest. This early conclusion was also supported by the cytostatic and antitumor activity exhibited by the related pigments, the cinerubins (4).

Before dealing with the isolation and structure elucidation of daunorubicin and doxorubicin which took place during the 1960s, a summary of work already done in the preceding decade on this class of glycoside pigments is obligatory. This will be the subject of the following section.

ANTHRACYCLINES AND ANTHRACYCLINONES: THE FIRST DECADE

Starting in 1950 with a publication in *Naturwissenschaften* by Hans Brockmann and Klaus Bauer entitled "Rhodomycin, ein rotes Antibioticum aus Actinomyceten," Brockmann and co-workers at the University of Göttingen had already disclosed in a number of papers the fundamentals of the isolation and chemical structure of the pigmented glycosides named anthracyclines and of the corresponding aglycones, the anthracyclinones [for a comprehensive review of the studies on the classical anthracyclines, see Brockmann (3)]. More precisely, the anthracyclinones identified and studied by these authors belonged to the types known as the rhodomycinones, isorhodomycinones, and pyrromycinones, occuring either free or in water-soluble glycosidated form in the cultures of different *Streptomyces* sp. Both these aglycones and their glycosides are red or orange-red pigments whose color is due to the presence of a polyhydroxyanthraquinone chromophore present on the 7,8,9,10-tetrahydronaphthacene skeleton, the latter being similar to that found in the tetracycline antibiotics and hence the name given to these substances.

Two main groups of pigments had been studied by Brockmann during these years. The first group, including the rhodomycinones, the isorhodomycinones, the rhodomycins, and the isorhodomycins, was isolated from strains of *Streptomyces purpurescens*, while the second, including the pyrromycinones and the glycoside pyrromycin, was obtained from the cultures of *S. DOA* 1205. Typical rhodomycinones are β- and ε-rhodomycinones, corresponding to structures **2** and **4**, the former being the aglycone moiety of both rhodomycins A and B. The corresponding deoxy derivatives **3** and **5**

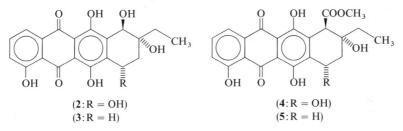

(**2**:R = OH)
(**3**:R = H)

(**4**:R = OH)
(**5**:R = H)

were also isolated and named γ-rhodomycinone (the aglycone of the γ-rhodomycins) and ζ-rhodomycinone, respectively (the different compounds were indicated with the letters of the Greek alphabet on the basis of the chromatographic mobility). A different pattern of hydroxylation of the anthraquinone chromophore was instead found in δ-rhodomycinone (**6**). The

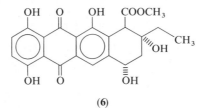

(**6**)

isorhodomycinones are characterized by the presence of four hydroxyl group in the peri positions of the anthraquinone chromophore and were found to possess the same type of substitution of the alicyclic ring as the above-mentioned rhodomycinones. Structures **7**, **8**, **9**, and **10** were attributed,

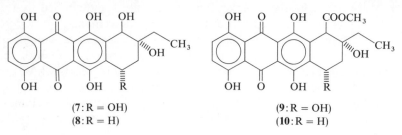

(**7**: R = OH)   (**9**: R = OH)
(**8**: R = H)   (**10**: R = H)

respectively to β-isorhodomycinone (the aglycone of isorhodomycin A), γ-isorhodomycinone, ε-isorhodomycinone, and ζ-isorhodomycinone. Three pyrromycinones were isolated, namely η-pyrromycinone (**11**), ε-pyrromycinone (**12**), the aglycone of the pyrromycins and cinerubins A and B (*4*), and ζ-pyrromycinone (**13**).

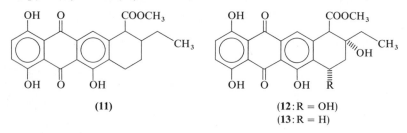

(**11**)   (**12**: R = OH)
                                             (**13**: R = H)

Classical studies carried out in the 1950s allowed the elucidation of the structural features of the above-mentioned anthracyclinones, namely (a) the chromophore moiety, (b) the linear arrangement of the alicyclic ring, and (c) the substitution on the latter portion of the molecule. The details of such studies are reviewed in the already mentioned publication (*3*). Aside from conventional chemical analysis, the UV and visible spectra of the anthracyclinones in, *inter alia*, organic solvents, concentrated sulfuric acid, aqueous alkali, and pyroboracetate containing acetic anhydride, were highly diagnostic for the pattern of hydroxylation of the anthraquinone chromophore. The arrangement of the aglycone basic structure, involving a six-membered ring linearly linked to the anthraquinone chromophore, was deduced from the UV and visible spectra of their bisanhydro derivatives, readily obtained from the anthracyclinone upon acid-, base-, or heat-catalyzed aromatization (the preferred procedure was heating in anhydrous acetic acid in the presence of hydrogen bromide). The tetracyclic structure was not, however, clearly apparent in the initial investigations, as formula **15** was attributed to β-rhodomycinone (*5*).

The subsequent studies allowed the correction of the structure, mainly because of the identification of the product of the reaction of β-rhodomycinone (**2**) with boiling hydrogen iodide as a C_{20} compound of structure **16**.

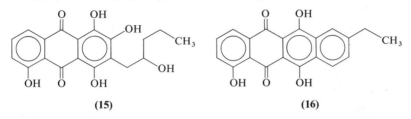

(15)   (16)

The position of the three alcoholic hydroxyl groups of β-rhodomycinone were deduced from the electronic spectrum of its bisanhydro derivative **17**, also compared with that of synthetic naphthacenequinone derivatives, from the behavior toward the periodate oxidation of **2** and of its deoxyderivative

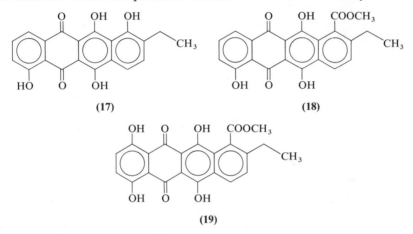

(17)   (18)

(19)

3, and, finally, on the basis of NMR data (6). In the case of ε-rhodomycinone, α-hydroxylation of the corresponding bisanhydro derivative (**18**) with manganese dioxide afforded bisanhydro-ε-isorhodomycinone, identical to η-iso-pyrromycinone, also obtained upon oxidation of η-pyrromycinone, for which structure **19** was established (see above). The position of the ethyl side chain of ε-isorhodomycinone (**9**) had already been clarified on the basis of oxidative degradation of **20**, obtained from **9** upon treatment with hot hydrogen iodide, to β-ethyladipic acid (7). Both ε-rhodomycinone and ε-isorhodomycinone showed two alcoholic groups, one being a tertiary hydroxyl and the other easily removed upon catalytic hydrogenation, in agreement with structures **4** and **9**. The above-mentioned structural investigations were, however, concluded after completion of the studies concerning

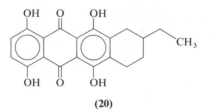

(20)

the pyrromycinones **11** to **13**. Pigment **11**, indicated as η-pyrromycinone, was isolated from a different *Streptomyces* strain together with other pyrromycinones and with the glycoside, pyrromycin, and was identified as a derivative of 1,4,6-trihydroxynaphthacenequinone (**21**) on the basis of the absorption spectra in cyclohexane, in pyridine, and in sulfuric acid. Both reference compounds **21** and 1,6,11-trihydroxynaphthacenequinone (**22**) were prepared for comparison purposes by Brockmann and Müller (*8*). In addition, descarbomethoxy-η-pyrromycinone (**23**) exhibited practically the same absorption spectrum as **21**, and similar identity was found in the spectra of the triacetates of **21** and **23**.

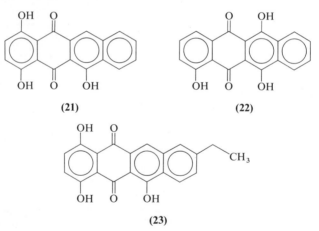

(21)   **(22)**

(23)

Oxidation of **11** and of **23** with manganese dioxide and sulfuric acid afforded, respectively, η-isopyrromycinone (also obtained as mentioned above upon heating of ε-isorhodomycinone) and descarbomethoxy-η-iso-pyrromycinone, the structure of the latter being depicted as **24** because the position of the ethyl group in ε-isorhodomycinone was already known to the German chemists in 1959 (*9*). In the same study, the structures of **12** and **13** were also investigated. The former, identified as a 1,4,5-anthraquinone derivative, was found to give "monoanhydro" derivatives in a variety of conditions, the relationship with **11** being established by dehydration and dehydrogenation of the alicyclic moiety of **12** or by dehydrogenation of the corresponding descarbomethoxy monoanhydro derivative to, respectively, **11** and **23**. The erroneous structure **25** was suggested for ζ-pyrromycinone as,

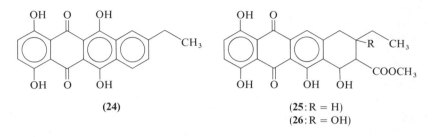

(24)   (25: R = H)
        (26: R = OH)

inter alia, the presence of a tertiary alcoholic group was excluded on the basis of the conversion of **12** to a tetraacetate. Erroneous structure **26** was proposed for ε-pyrromycinone. Pyrromycin was described as the glycoside of **26**, with rhodosamine, the sugar moiety, being placed on the benzylic hydroxyl of **26** (*9*). The compound, ε-pyrromycinone, was also found to be identical with the aglycone of cinerubins A and B, whose structure differed from that of pyrromycin because of the presence of three sugar residues (*4*), and to rutilantinone, the aglycone of the glycoside pigments rutilantins. The latter was investigated by Ollis *et al.* (*10*), who eventually derived the structure **13** also confirmed by the formation of benzene-1,2,3,4-tetracarboxylic acid upon the oxidation with potassium permanganate of the corresponding bisanhydro derivative (**11**). The identity of rutilantinone with ε-pyrromycinone and the revision of the structure assigned to the latter were finally disclosed in a joint publication of the English, the German, and the Swiss chemists (*11*). Conclusion of the investigations concerning ε-isorhodomycinone and ε-rhodomycinone soon followed (*7,12*). The structure of the orange-yellow aklavinone, the aglycone of the pigmented glycoside antibiotic aklavine, was also reported. Aklavinone (**27**) appeared to be clearly related to the above-mentioned rhodomycinones and pyrromycinones, but was found to possess a dihydroxyanthraquinone chromophore (*13*).

As Hans Brockmann (*3*) put it: "Diese Stammverbindung (Ia) [**28** in this book] der Anthracyclinone muss der Nomenklatur-Vorschrift nach als 8-Hydroxy-8-äthyl-7,8,9,10-tetrahydro-tetracenchinon-(5,12) bezeichnet werden. Sie ist dem entgegen. . . . als 9-Hydroxy-9-äthyl-derivat bezeichnet, weil in den meisten Originalarbeiten den Anthracyclinonformeln eine nach (Ia) geschiebene Stammverbindung zugrunde liegt. . . ." On the contrary, the rings were indicated with the letters A, B, C, and D, starting from the alicyclic ring by Brockmann and his group, while the other authors indicated this ring as ring D, because they started the numbering of the rings from the left side of structure **28** (*3,4,14*).

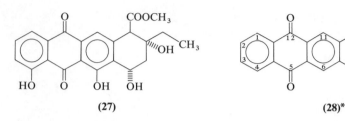

(27)   (28)*

The stereochemistry of the anthracyclinones was not investigated in the 1950s, but the relative configuration of ring A in rhodomycinones, isorhodomycinones, and pyrromycinones was known in 1963 (*3*). Circular dicroism studies demonstrated that all anthracyclinones had the same absolute configuration at C-7 and C-10, the C-7 hydroxyl being trans with respect to the C-10 substituent. The orientation of the hydroxyl at C-9, cis to the one at C-7, was indicated in γ-rhodomycinone on the basis of the slowness of the periodate oxidation of glycol 9,10 and, in ε-isorhodomycinone, on the basis of the reaction of ε-isorhodomycinone tetramethyl ether with 2,2-dimethoxypropane to give a cyclic isopropylidene derivative.

Biogenetic arguments had also been considered in the discussion of the results of the different structural studies, and all early investigators of the anthracyclinones accepted the acetate route (*15,16*) as the basic biosynthetic process leading to this class of compounds. Following these ideas, which were proved by Ollis *et al.* (*17*) in a study of the incorporation of ^{14}C-labeled propionate and acetate into ε-pyrromycinone and its oxidative degradation products (acetic and propionic acid), the different steps in the biosynthesis of the anthracyclinones could be summarized as in Scheme 1. Polyketide precursor **29** represents the hypothetical product of the "head to tail" formal condensation of nine acetate units and one propionate unit. Ring closure by aldol condensation followed by elimination of water would give intermediate **30**, whose reduction at C-2 and C-7 would afford **31**. Elimination of the C-2 hydroxyl in the form of water would give **32**, which would enolize to the chrysazinanthranol derivative **33**, easily oxidized to a direct precursor of aklavinone **27**. Hydroxylation of **27** or of some of its precursor at C-11 or at C-6 would give origin to ε-rhodomycinone or ε-pyrromycinone respectively. The isolation of 7-deoxy compounds such as ζ-rhodomycinone, ζ-isorhodomycinone, and ζ-pyrromycinone indicated that reductive elimination of the C-7 oxygen could take place at some point of anthracycline biosynthesis.

---

* A remark is deserved on the numbering system of the anthracyclinones as used by the above-mentioned authors. All of them had accepted the numbering which indicated as C-9 the carbon atom bearing the ethyl side chain of the base structure **28**.

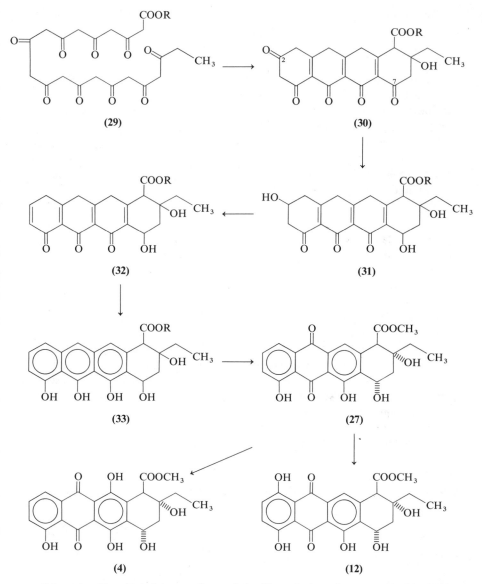

Scheme 1. Hypothetical intermediates of the biosynthetic pathway to aklavinone (**27**), ε-rhodomycinone (**4**), and ε-pyrromycinone (**12**).

The tetraphenolic isorhodomycinone system would arise through enzymic oxidation at the unsubstituted peri position in **4** or **12**, whereas the formation of β-rhodomycinone would involve decarboxylation and hydroxylation at C-10.

The sugar moieties indentified as components of the anthracyclines were rhodosamine (**34**), 2-deoxy-L-fucose, and rhodinose. The structure and stereochemistry of rhodosamine were established as indicated in **34** in 1963 by Brockmann *et al.* (*18*) on the basis of the formation of 2-deoxy-L-fucose and of L-boivinose upon alkaline treatment and of the PMR spectrum of the anomeric diacetates of **34**. To rhodinose, a trideoxyhexose, structure **35** was assigned, because of the formation of succinic dialdehyde and of acetaldehyde on periodate oxidation, by Brockmann and Waehneldt (*19*).

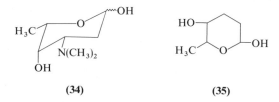

(**34**)   (**35**)

Among this class of pigmented substances, antibiotic activity was exhibited only by the glycosides, i.e., the anthracyclines. In the already cited review (*3*), the following compounds were mentioned (the products of acid hydrolysis or given in parentheses): pyrromycin (ε-pyrromycinone, rhodosamine), the cinerubins A and B (ε-pyrromycinone, rhodosamine, 2-deoxy-L-fucose and rhodinose), the rutilantins (ε-pyrromycinone, unidentified sugars), rhodomycin A (β-rhodomycinone, two rhodosamines), rhodomycin B (β-rhodomycinone, one rhodosamine), γ-rhodomycin I (γ-rhodomycinone, one rhodosamine), γ-rhodomycin II (γ-rhodomycinone, two rhodosamines), γ-rhodomycin III (γ-rhodomycinone, two rhodosamines, 2-deoxy-L-fucose), γ-rhodomycin IV (γ-rhodomycinone, two rhodosamines, 2-deoxy-L-fucose, rhodinose), isorhodomycin A (β-isorhodomycinone, two rhodosamines), aklavin [aklavinone, rhodosamine (?)].

DAUNORUBICIN

The antibiotic daunorubicin was isolated and studied during the early 1960s in the laboratories of Farmitalia where it was named daunomycin, and independently, in those of Rhone-Poulenc (*20*) where it was named rubidomycin. As it was the first antibiotic to show a therapeutic effect in the treatment of acute leukemia in man, the object of extensive chemical investigations and the parent compound of doxorubicin, a detailed account of the studies concerning this compound will be given here.

The preparation of daunorubicin from the cultures of *Streptomyces peucetius* was described by Cassinelli and Orezzi in 1963 (*21*). The pigmented antibiotic was present mainly in the mycelial mass of that microorganism grown in shake flask or in stirred, aerated fermenters in a medium containing glucose, yeast, and inorganic salts. The producing strain was isolated from a soil sample collected at Castel del Monte, in the northern part of Puglie (Italy), whose ancient name was Daunia, hence the name daunomycin given to the antibiotic (*22*). Recovery of the pigments was carried out by extraction of the mycelium with solvents, preferably an acidified mixture of water and acetone, the extract being then neutralized and evaporated to remove the acetone. Alkalinization and shaking with *n*-butanol afforded the transfer of the colored compounds in the organic phase which was reextracted with dilute acid in order to separate the glycosidic bases from the lypophilic pigments and other constituents, among which were polyene antifungal compounds. Reextraction of the glycosides into chloroform at pH between 8 and 9 followed by concentration of the extract allowed the recovery of the crude daunorubicin hydrochloride by addition of methanolic hydrogen chloride and ethyl ether. Purification of the antibiotic was performed by chromatography on a column of cellulose buffered with pH 5.4, 0.1 *M* phosphate buffer which was eluted with *n*-butanol equilibrated with the same buffer. Recovery of the antibiotic from the main elution band was performed in a similar fashion to give daunorubicin hydrochloride as thin red needles. The yields were from 5 to 15 mg per liter of culture broth.

The new antibiotic showed the formula $C_{27}H_{29}NO_{10} \cdot HCl$, melted at 177°C with decomposition, and showed the typical indicator-like behavior of the anthracyclines, its solutions changing from red to blue-violet upon alkalinization at pH 9 or above. The ultraviolet and visible spectra in methanol (maxima at 234, 252, 290, 480, 495, 532 nm) was similar but not identical to that reported for the known anthracyclines, while the spectroscopic behaviour in the presence of metal ions, in concentrated sulphuric acid, and in pyridine were in agreement with the presence of the chromophoric system of the anthracyclinones. Acid hydrolysis afforded a red aglycone, daunomycinone, $C_{21}H_{18}O_8$, showing ultraviolet and visible spectra identical to those of the parent glycoside, but different from those of the aglycone derived from the antitumor anthracycline from strain 1683 and of ε-pyrromycinone.

A detailed report on fermentation, isolation, and characterization of rubidomycin from *Streptomyces caeruleorubidus* was published by Despois *et al.* (*23*). The antibiotic was recovered from the filtered culture broths by adsorption on a cation exchange resin which was eluted with a solution of sodium chloride in aqueous methanol. Concentration of the active fraction, followed by extraction into chloroform, evaporation of the extract, and precipitation with hexane, afforded a mixture of pigmented substances from which crude rubidomycin was obtained by means of a transfer of the active material from a solvent into dilute aqueous acid, then into methylene chloride at pH 7.8 and finally concentration and precipitation to give a mixture of rubidomycin and two other pigments, 13213 RP and 13330 RP. Separation of rubidomycin from the other constituents was carried out by a counter current process using the biphasic system ethyl acetate, methanol, $M/15$, pH 5.6 phosphate buffer (8:3:5), followed by crystallization of the antibiotics as the hydrochlorides from aqueous dioxane. The antibiotic was found to inhibit the growth of Gram positive bacteria and mycobacteria but showed low activity on Gram negative bacteria.

The first report on the antitumor activity of daunorubicin (24) outlined the outstanding pharmacological properties of the new antibiotic. The treatment of mice bearing Ehrlich carcinoma or sarcoma 180 in ascitic form with 1.75 mg of daunorubicin hydrochloride for five consecutive days resulted in remarkable inhibition of tumor growth and increase of survival time of the animals, while disappearance of tumor was recorded in mice bearing Yoshida hepatoma and Walker carcinoma upon treatment with 1 to 2 mg/kg body weight (for 5 days) of the drug. The antibiotic was also found to inhibit the growth of experimental solid tumors such as Ehrlich adenocarcinoma, solid sarcoma 180, Oberling-Guerin-Guerin (OGG) myeloma, Walker carcinoma, and methylcholanthrene transplantable sarcoma, and was found to cause mitotic damages in tumor cells. The mode of action of daunorubicin was also investigated by Di Marco et al. (25), who studied the effect of the antibiotic on normal and tumor cells cultivated in vitro. Reduction of the mitotic index was recorded in rat fibroblasts and in rat and mouse bone marrow cells, the latter showing also profound alterations, including cytolytic phenomena, upon exposure of the cells to $0.01-1$ µg/ml of the drug for 24 hr. Similar effects were found in HeLa, Helius, K13, and rat Walker carcinosarcoma cells at concentrations of the antibiotic higher that 0.01 µg/ml. Strong chromosomal aberrations, and nuclear and nucleolar damages were associated with the said effects. These and other observations, including the finding that daunorubicin was able to form strong complexes with DNA from AH 130 hepatoma ascites, suggested an interference with DNA function as a primer of RNA synthesis and with the ability of DNA to undergo the mitotic process (26).

The knowledge of daunorubicin structure, after the said biological results indicating its superiority over the already known anthracyclines, was considered of paramount importance. It was thought that the elucidation of the structural features inducing the improved pharmacological properties would have represented a further step forward towards the development of a useful anticancer antibiotic. As subsequent events have proved, this view was a correct one.

The first phase of the chemical studies concerning daunorubicin was carried out starting from the available information already described in the preceding section and was concluded with two communications to the editor of the *Journal of the American Chemical Society* (27,28). The antibiotic was found to be the glycoside of a new anthracyclinone, daunomycinone (**36**) with a new aminosugar, daunosamine (**37**), both moieties presenting important variations with respect to the known constituents of the "classical" anthracyclines.

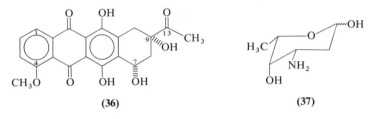

(36)   (37)

The electronic spectra of daunorubicin and of **36**, although not completely superimposable to those of the rhodomycinones, indicated the presence of the 1,4,5-trihydroxyanthraquinone chromophore. As a matter of fact the methoxy group, whose presence was indicated by the Zeisel determination and by the PMR spectrum, did not correspond, as in ε-rhodomycinone, to a methyl ester group, but to the etherification of the C-4 hydroxyl, a new structural feature for an anthracyclinone. Similarly, the carbonyl group giving rise to the 1718 cm^{-1} band in the infrared spectrum of daunomycinone was due to the presence of an acetyl residue replacing the ethyl group as the two-carbon side chain of the already known anthracyclinones. These and other deductions were derived from the results of the analytical determinations, of the degradation studies, and of the PMR investigations on **36** and its derivatives or degradation products such as the trimethyl ether (**38**) and the bisanhydro derivative (**39**). The oxidation of **39** to 3-methoxyphthalic and trimellitic acid allowed the localization of the methoxyl group on ring D, but the position of the group as 1 or 4 would not be established at the time. The structure of **37** was determined on the basis of derivatization and periodate oxidation studies, the formation of *N*-benzoyl-L-aspartic acid from *N*-benzoyldaunosamine upon sodium periodate cleavage followed by ipo-iodide oxidation of the intermediate dialdehyde being the clue to the establishment of absolute configuration of the new aminosugar, as the relative stereochemistry of the two other asymmetric centers was deduced on the basis of PMR determination of the coupling constants and of conformational considerations.

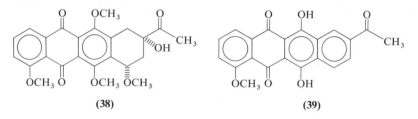

(38)   (39)

The favorable pharmacological properties of daunorubicin induced different groups, both in Europe and in the United States, to perform clinical trials in order to establish the therapeutic effectiveness of the new antibiotic. The first report concerning these studies was presented by Tan and Di Marco in 1965 (*29*), and an overall survey of all different contributions to the clinical evaluation of daunorubicin, together with a review of preclinical knowledge, was the object of an international symposium held in Paris at Hôpital Saint-Louis, on March 11, 1967. The individual reports were published in *Pathologie et Biologie* Volume 15 (1967), but a unified monograph based on the said contributions was also published (*30*). The conclusions were that daunorubicin, when used alone in the treatment of acute leukemias, exhibited great rapidity of action, absence of cross resistance with other drugs such as cortisone, vincristine, folic acid antagonists, 6-mercaptopurine, cytosine arabinoside, methyl glyoxal-bis-guanyl hydrazone, induction of complete remissions in 60% of cases in acute lymphoblastic leukemia and in 35 to 55% of cases in acute myeloblastic leukemia, attenuation of symptoms and frequent remission in acute promyelocytic leukemia. Higher percentages of remissions were obtained when combinations of the drug, such as that with prednisone and vincristine, were used for induction or reinduction treatments. A low efficacy of the drug was recorded in chronic lymphoid leukemias, in lymphosarcomas, in Hodgkin's disease, and in reticulosarcoma and other solid tumors. Major undesirable effects included severe aplasia, immunodepression, and cardiac complications, the latter requiring a limitation of total cumulative dose estimated at 25 mg/kg with consequent impossibility of use of the drug for maintenance treatment.

In the light of the pharmacological results, chemical research on daunorubicin was further developed in the author's laboratory along two lines, having as objectives (a) the elucidation of the still undefined details of the structure and stereochemistry of the antibiotic, and (b) the search of new biosynthetic analogues in cultures derived from the daunorubicin-producing microrganism, *Streptomyces peucetius*. The latter approach, which essentially resulted in the isolation and characterization of doxorubicin, was suggested by the conclusion that limited variations in the anthracycline structure could induce a remarkable improvement of pharmacological properties (as deduced from the comparison of biological properties of daunorubicin and rhodomycin B), by the variety of strictly related structures generally found in acetate-derived microbial metabolites, and by the recurrent observations that antitumor efficacy in mice tests of different crude preparations obtained from *Streptomyces peucetius* or from mutant strains thereof exhibited variations depending on the presence of other pigmented constituents.

Still undefined points of daunorubicin structure were the location of the methoxyl group (if at C-1 or at C-4), the absolute stereochemistry of the aglycone, and the site of attachment and the configuration of the glycoside linkage between daunomycinone and daunosamine. For the determination of the position of the methoxyl group, compound **36** was converted to the corresponding C-7 ketone by chromic oxidation, then aromatized with alkali and O-demethylated to **40** (upon heating with hydrogen bromide in acetic acid) or to **41** (upon treatment with aluminum chloride in benzene at reflux temperature). The pattern of hydroxylation of **40** and **41** was established on the basis of their visible spectra in different solvents (chloroform, concentrated sulfuric acid, dimethylformamide, piperidine) and of the infrared spectra of the corresponding pericarbonates **42** and **43**. As regards the absolute stereochemistry of **36**, once the cis relationship of the C-7 and C-9 hydroxyl groups had been proved by the formation of **44** upon treatment of **36** with 2,2-dimethoxypropane in dioxane in the presence of *p*-toluenesulfonic acid at room temperature, the isolation of $S(-)$-methoxysuccinic

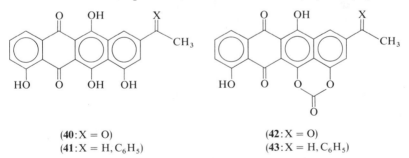

(**40**:X = O)
(**41**:X = H, C$_6$H$_5$)

(**42**:X = O)
(**43**:X = H, C$_6$H$_5$)

acid among the products of periodate–permanganate oxidation of **45** (the product of the oxidation of 4-O-demethyl-7-O-methyl daunomycinone with lead tetraacetate) indicated the $7(S),9(S)$ absolute configuration of the chiral centers of daunomycinone. The position of the attachment of the glycosidic linkage was deduced from the formation of 7-deoxydaunomycinone and of daunosamine upon hydrogenolysis of daunorubicin and from the shift of H-7 in the PMR spectrum of pentaacetyldaunorubicin. Also on the basis of PMR studies the configuration of the glycosidic linkage was shown to be α, as the sum of the coupling constants of H-1$'$($|J_{1'\mathrm{eq},\,2'\mathrm{eq}} + J_{1'\mathrm{eq},2'\mathrm{ax}}| = 5.0$–$5.5$ Hz) in N-acetyldaunorubicin excluded diaxial inter-action, therefore proving the equatorial orientation and the (R) configuration at C-1$'$. Completion of these studies allowed the establishment of

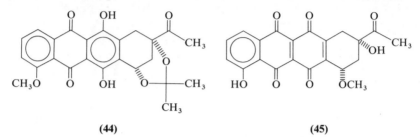

(44)   (45)

structure and stereochemistry of daunorubicin as indicated in **46** (*31–33*). Confirmation of these results stemmed from the X-ray diffraction studies on N-bromoacetyldaunorubicin. The crystallographic analysis of this de-rivative allowed the drawing Fig. 1 as representing the shape and packing of the molecule in the solid state (*34*).

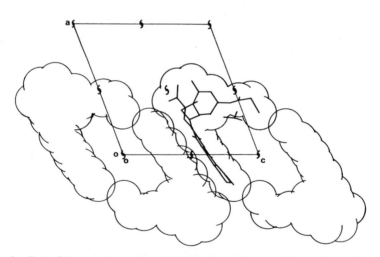

Fig. 1.   Part of the crystal structure of N-bromoacetyldaunorubicin projected down the b axis. The circles were drawn with diameter 3.6 Å. Reproduced from Angiuli *et al.* (*34*).

With regard to the second line of research, it afforded the identification, in addition to doxorubicin which will be dealt with in the following sections, of different daunorubicin-related pigments, both of the glycoside and of the aglycone types. Among the former is 13-dihydrodaunorubicin (**47**) (*33*),

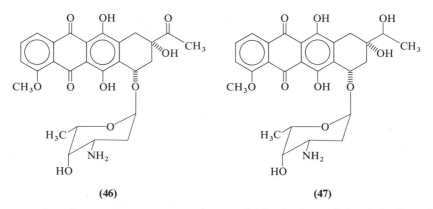

(46)   (47)

possessing the same structure as daunorubicinol, the main metabolite of daunorubicin in different animal species and in man (*35*). Although the conversion of **46** to **47** could be carried out in a number of microbial cultures, it is not yet known if **47** is derived, in the cultures of *Streptomyces peucetius*, by reduction of **46** or if it is an independently produced metabolite arising from the hithero unknown intermediates of daunorubicin biosynthesis. The presence of ε-rhodomycinone (**4**) in the aglycone fraction of *Streptomyces peucetius* pigments (*36*) affords an additional biosynthetic link between the daunomycin and rhodomycin types of pigments, the biogenetic interrelationships among the compounds differing in the degree of oxidation at C-13 (and C-14) being of renewed interest following more recent results in the author's laboratory (see Chapter 8). Another interesting compound isolated from *Streptomyces peucetius* derived strains is the disaccharide 4′-α-daunosaminyldaunorubicin (*37*), whose structure has been confirmed more recently by semisynthesis (Chapter 6). From the lipophilic, free aglycone fraction, the following compounds were also isolated: daunomycinone, adriamycinone, the aglycone of the antibiotic doxorubicin, 13-dihydrodaunomycinone, and 7-deoxydaunomycinone (*36*). A glycosidic compound, to which the structure of rhodinosyldaunorubicin has been attributed, was identified as a cometabolite of daunorubicin in the cultures of *Streptomyces caeruleorubidus* (*38*).

THE ISOLATION OF DOXORUBICIN

The daunorubicin-producing microorganism *Streptomyces peucetius* shows at its isolation a high variability involving mainly the cultural characteristics of the colonies, and this variability is enhanced after mutagenic treatments. Doxorubicin was isolated from the cultures of one of the varieties derived from the original *Streptomyces peucetius* strain, namely *S.*

peucetius var. caesius, the denomination stemming from the blue-green to gray-green color of its abundant aerial mycelium (*39*). This microorganism was grown in shake flask and in stirred aereated fermenters. The best yield in pigmented substances had been obtained using a production medium containing dextrose (60 g), brewer's yeast (25 g), NaCl (2 g), KH_2PO_4 (1 g), $CaCO_3$ (2 g), $MgSO_4$ (0.1 g), $FeSO_4 \cdot 7 H_2O$ (10 mg), $ZnSO_4 \cdot 7 H_2O$ (10 mg) per liter of tap water. The amount of doxorubicin varied from 3 to 11 $\mu g/ml$, depending on the age of the cultures.

Doxorubicin could be separated from daunorubicin by paper or thin layer chromatography in a number of systems, as shown in the Table I, quantitative analysis being possible upon elution from the chromatograms and spectrophotometric reading at 495 nm. However, its isolation in pure form was made difficult by its low stability in aqueous solutions at pH values above neutrality and by the concomitant presence, in the same culture fluids, of the stable 13-dihydrodaunorubicin, behaving indentically to doxorubicin in the chromatographic system used to follow the recovery of the antibiotic.

TABLE I

R_f values of Doxorubicin and Related Compounds in Paper (A, B) and Thin-Layer (C, D, E, F) Chromatography[a]

	Solvent system[b]					
Compound	A	B	C	D	E	F
Doxorubicin	0.1	0.25	0.17	0.33	0.0	0.0
Daunorubicin	0.2	0.5	0.35	0.4	0.0	0.0
Adriamycinone	0.3	0.65	0.9	0.8	0.1	0.25
Daunomycinone	0.75	0.85	0.95	0.85	0.15	0.4

[a] From Arcamone *et al.* (*39*).

[b] The following solvent systems were used: A) *n*-butanol saturated with pH 5.4, $M/15$ phosphate buffer; B) propanol, ethyl acetate, water 7:1:2 by vol.; C) methylene chloride, methanol, water 100:20:2; D) *n*-butanol, acetic acid, water 4:1:5; E) benzene, ethyl acetate, pet. ether (b.p. 80–120°C) 80:50:20; F) benzene, ethyl formate 1:2.

The process for the recovery of doxorubicin is outlined in Scheme 2. The mycelial mass was extracted with a 4:1 mixture of acetone and 0.1 *N* aqueous sulfuric acid, and filtered. The extract was concentrated under reduced pressure, and the aqueous residue was freed from lypophilic pigments upon extraction with chloroform at pH 3. The glycosides were re-extracted at pH 8.6 into a mixture of chloroform and methanol (9:1) which

Whole broth

```
├─────────────────────────────────────────────┐
Mycelial mass                              Filtered medium
  │ Extraction with acetone,
  │ 0.1 N aqueous H₂SO₄ (4:1 by vol.)
  ├─────────────────────────────────────────┐
Acid extract                               Spent solids
  │ Neutralization, concentration (in vacuo),
  │ acidification at pH 3,
  │ chloroform extraction
  ├─────────────────────────────────────────┐
Aqueous phase                              Solvent phase
  │ Extraction with chloroform–
  │ methanol (9:1) at pH 8.6
  ├─────────────────────────────────────────┐
Solvent phase                              Aqueous phase
  │ Concentration, addition of
  │ methanolic HCl and ether
  ├─────────────────────────────────────────┐
Amorphous precipitate                      Mother liquor
  │ Partition chromatography
  │ at pH 5.4
Butanolic eluate
  │ Transfer into water at pH 3, reextraction into
  │ chloroform at pH 8.6
  ├─────────────────────────────────────────┐
Solvent                                    Spent buffer
  │ Concentration in vacuo,
  │ addition of methanolic HCl
  ├─────────────────────────────────────────┐
Crystals                                   Mother Liquor
```

Scheme 2.   Isolation of doxorubicin hydrochloride.

was then concentrated *in vacuo* and treated with methanolic hydrogen chloride and ethyl ether to give a red amorphous precipitate. The crude glycoside hydrochlorides were separated on a column of cellulose powder buffered at pH 5.4 with phosphate using *n*-butanol saturated with the same buffer as the eluting agent. The fractions containing doxorubicin were extracted with water at pH 3, the pH of the aqueous phase being then adjusted to 8.6 to afford reextraction of doxorubicin base into chloroform. The chloroform extract was concentrated and the antibiotic was crystallized as the hydrochloride on addition of an equivalent of methanolic hydrogen chloride (*39*).

Doxorubicin hydrochloride shows the empirical formula $C_{27}H_{29}O_{11}N \cdot HCl$ (M. W. 579.98, free base 93.72%), melts with decomposition at 205°C, and is strongly dextrorotatory ($[\alpha]_D^{20°} = +248°$, c 0.1 in methanol). The ultraviolet and visible spectrum in methanol shows the following absorption maxima ($E_{1cm}^{1\%}$ are given in parentheses) : 233nm (658), 253 nm (440), 290 nm (145), 477 nm (225), 495 nm (223), 530 nm (124). Similarly to the other anthracyclines, the absorption is shifted at longer wavelengths upon alkalinization. A fluorescence emission in the range 520–620 nm is obtained upon excitation at 485 nm. The infrared spectrum in KBr shows, *inter alia*, the following absorptions (in μm) : 2.90, 3.42, 5.79, 6.18, 6.34, 6.92, 7.08, 7.26, 7.42, 7.80, 7.90, 8.05, 8.29, 8.43, 8.72, 8.93, 9.30, 9.88, 10.10, 10.86, 12.32, 12.75, 13.16, 13.70, 14.40. NMR and mass spectra of the antibiotic itself were not available at the time of the structural studies, but a ^{13}C-NMR spectrum of doxorubicin hydrochloride in D_2O and field desorption mass spectra of the free base and of its *N*-trifluoroacetyl derivative have been reported recently (*40*).

THE STRUCTURE AND STEREOCHEMISTRY OF DOXORUBICIN

Acid hydrolysis of doxorubicin afforded the aglycone, adriamycinone, and the aminosugar daunosamine. Adriamycinone (**48**) showed the same ultraviolet and visible spectrum as **36**, and the presence of an additional oxygen atom, in respect to **36**, was indicated by the empirical formula $C_{21}H_{18}O_9$. The carbonyl band in the infrared at 1727 cm^{-1} appeared at higher frequency than the corresponding band in **36**. Acetylation of **48** afforded a pentacetate, and the presence of the additional hydroxyl at C-14 was suggested by the identity of the visible spectrum of bisanhydroadriamycinone (**49**) with that of bisanhydrodaunomycinone (**39**). Further support

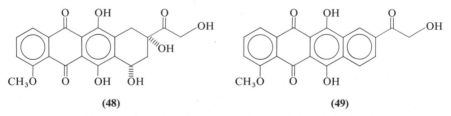

(48)   (49)

to structure **48** was given by the comparison of the electron impact mass spectra of **48** [m/e 414 (M), 396 (M-H_2O), 337 (M-H_2O–$COCH_2OH$), 378 (M-2 H_2O), 347 (M-2 H_2O–CH_2OH), m.u.] and **36** [m/e 398 (M), 380 (M-H_2O), 337 (M-H_2O–$COCH_3$), 362 (M-2 H_2O), m.u.], and by the PMR spectrum of adriamycinone pentacetate showing, *inter alia*, a doublet of doublets at δ 4.83 (2 H, J_{gem} = 16.5 cps) consistent with the presence of the $COCH_2OAc$ group.

In agreement with assignment of structure **50** to doxorubicin, hydrogenolysis of the antibiotic gave 7-deoxyadriamycinone (**51**) and daunosamine. The stereochemistry at C-7 and C-9 appeared to be the same as that of daunorubicin because the CD curve of the former was identical to that of the latter, while the identity of the molar optical rotation of the two antibiotics (and of the corresponding aglycones) allowed the attribution of the same configuration at the glycosidic carbon (*41*).

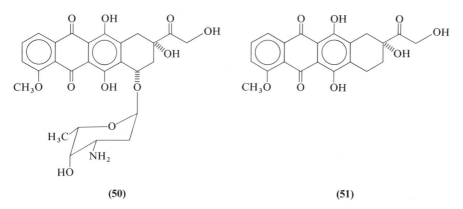

(50)   (51)

Doxorubicin was also correlated chemically to daunorubicin as *N*-trifluoroacetyldoxorubicin (**52d**) was obtained from *N*-trifluoroacetyldaunorubicin (**52a**) upon iodination to **52b** and nucleophilic substitution of the iodine with acetate to give **52c**, whose treatment with bicarbonate afforded **52d**. Protection of the side chain as in **53** followed by removal of the *N*-trifluoroacetyl group with alkalis, and deblocking of the side chain with acid gave

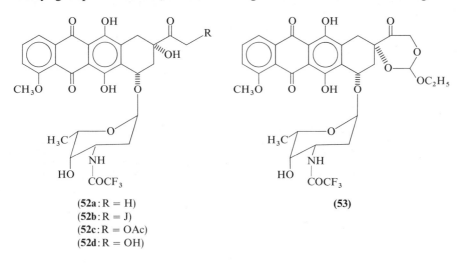

(**52a**: R = H)
(**52b**: R = J)
(**52c**: R = OAc)
(**52d**: R = OH)

(53)

50 (*42*). Of greater preparative value however is the conversion of daunorubicin to doxorubicin, consisting in the treatment of the former with bromine in a mixture of dioxane and methanol, followed by an acid treatment
in order to restore the ketone function which has undergone ketalization
during the bromination reaction, and by a nucleophilic displacement of the
halogen with an hydroxyl in the resulting 14-bromodaunorubicin (*43*).

ANTITUMOR ACTIVITY ON
EXPERIMENTAL TUMORS

The outstanding antitumor properties of doxorubicin were clearly established by Di Marco *et al.* (*44*). These authors reported on the activity of
the antibiotic on different experimental tumors, namely on Ehrlich ascites
carcinoma, a transplantable lymphosarcoma, and sarcoma 180 solid in mice,
and on the OGG myeloma in rats.

Doxorubicin, when administered at doses from 1.25 to 2.50 mg/kg/day
ip, for 5 consecutive days, displayed a marked inhibitory effect on tumor
growth and a considerable increase of survival time of treated mice. The
antibiotic was also found to stop the proliferative activity of the same tumor
for a period of 32 hr after a single injection of a 2 mg/kg dose. When doxorubicin and daunorubicin were compared at the highest dose level of 2.50
mg/kg in the 5 days schedule, the former increased the average survival
time of tumor-bearing mice by 2.8 times, in comparison with the 1.8 figure
exhibited by the latter.

Using mice inoculated ip with a transplantable lymphosarcoma, originally induced by nitrosomethylurea, treatment of the animals intravenously
on days 1 to 8 with a daily dose of 2.50 mg/kg resulted in a noticeable increase (52.8 to 93.4%) of survival time of the treated animals with respect
to the controls, the activity being related to a reduction of the number of
tumor cells, not to a modification of the dissemination characteristics of
the tumor.

Doxorubicin was active on OGG myeloma in rats as treatment with
eight daily doses of 2 mg/kg of the drug iv caused 50% inhibition of tumor
growth. Similarly the antibiotic, when given subcutaneously on days 1 to 8
to mice bearing solid sarcoma 180, markedly inhibited tumor growth at
doses ranging from 1.75 to 7 mg/kg body weight. On this tumor, the activity
was higher than that shown by daunorubicin, the ID_{50} being about 3.3 mg/
kg for daunorubicin but 1.5 mg/kg for doxorubicin, and the therapeutic
index, calculated according to Skipper and Schmidt (*44a*) as the value of
the ratio of maximum tolerated dose (LD_{10}) to the minimum effective dose

(T/C 0.10), was 1.21 for doxorubicin and 0.67 for daunorubicin. Furthermore, after treatment of mice bearing sarcoma 180 with equitoxic doses (i.e., same fractions of the LD_{50}) of the antibiotics intravenously on days 1 to 8 after tumor implantation, a clearly higher inhibition was obtained with doxorubicin than with daunorubicin.

Doxorubicin was more effective than daunorubicin in inhibiting the growth of murine sarcoma virus (Moloney Virus) induced tumors, and pretreatment of mice with doxorubicin did not cause inhibition of the spontaneous regression as instead was the case with daunorubicin (45).

Evidence for the potential of doxorubicin as an inhibitor of solid tumor proliferation stemmed also from the study of its activity against mouse mammary carcinoma (46). When mice bearing spontaneous mammary carcinoma were treated with equitoxic doses of doxorubicin or of daunorubicin in a daily schedule from days 1 to 6 and from day 12 to 17, a consistent inhibition of tumor growth was obtained. At the same cumulative dosage but using an alternate days schedule the effect of doxorubicin was still remarkable. Administration of doxorubicin to normal mice after the subcutaneous inoculation with a cell suspension from the spontaneous mammary carcinomas afforded strong inhibition of tumor growth, a significant increase in survival time, and a high percentage of long-term survivors (Fig. 2).

The above-mentioned results were also presented at the International Symposium on Adriamycin, held in Milan, September 9 and 10, 1971 (47), together with important contributions from other research groups. Schedule dependency of doxorubicin was shown by A. Goldin, who also demonstrated the therapeutic advantage of doxorubicin over daunorubicin for a wide range of dosage schedules in the treatment of leukemia L 1210. According to the author, doxorubicin was considerably more effective than a series of natural products including mitomycin C, vinblastine, and mithramycin on the P 388 experimental leukemia in mice. Because of the dose limitations due to cumulative toxicity of doxorubicin, combination with other drugs, such as methotrexate or DIC, was expected to improve the chemotherapeutic effectiveness of the antibiotic (48). Superiority of doxorubicin over daunorubicin in the test systems represented by rats bearing Yoshida sarcoma and by mice bearing L 1210 leukemia was demonstrated by Hoshino et al. (49), who found cross resistance between the two antibiotics but not with other antitumor agents such as (inter alia) mitomycin C, cyclophosphamide, chromomycin A_3, 6-mercaptopurine, 5-fluorouracil. Hoshino et al. (49) also further developed experimentally the concept of combination therapy. The development of resistance to daunorubicin and doxorubicin in Ehrlich ascites tumor in mice was studied, and doxorubicin

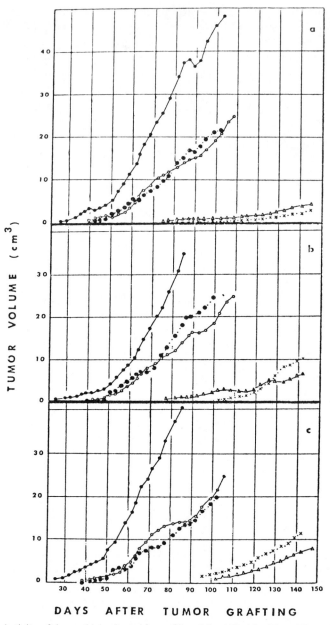

Fig. 2. Activity of doxorubicin, 2 mg (△-----△) or 2.5 mg/Kg/die (X · · · · X), and of daun-orubicin, 2.6 mg (O———O) or 3.25 mg/Kg/die (● · · · · ●) when administered to mice bearing transplanted mammary carcinoma in two cycles of treatment every other day, from day 1 to 11 and from day 17 to 27 after tumor graft. Panel a, whole population; b, females; c, males; (●———●), controls. Reproduced from Di Marco *et al.* (*46*).

was reported to show cross resistance not only with daunorubicin, but also with vincristine, a structurally unrelated antitumor agent of plant origin (*50*).

Subsequently to the above-mentioned investigations, the literature on the effects of doxorubicin in experimental animal systems has grown rapidly and the survey of these studies is beyond the scope of this book. A summary of the most important results has been reported by Goldin and Johnson (*51*).

CLINICAL ACTIVITY OF DOXORUBICIN

In the already mentioned International Symposium on Adriamycin, results of initial clinical trials with this drug were presented. A total of 483 cases had been treated on June 1971 at the Istituto Nazionale per lo Studio e la Cura dei Tumori, Milan, out of which 296 were with doxorubicin alone and the other ones were with the drug given in combination. Toxic side effects were alopecia, stomatitis, myelosuppression, gastroenteritis, and cardiac toxicity, in 1.7% of patients the clinical cause of death being ascribed to cardiac failure. The highest percentage of responses to doxorubicin given alone was observed in malignant lymphomas, in soft tissue sarcomas, and in different solid tumors of children, especially neuroblastomas, Wilms' tumor, and Ewing sarcoma. Tumor regressions were also recorded in testicular tumors and in carcinomas of the lung. Combination therapy including doxorubicin was markedly effective in malignant lymphomas (60 to 84% regression rate) and in pediatric solid tumors. In miscellaneous solid tumors of adults (88 cases), the regression rate was indicated as "significant" in 18% and "overall" in 54% of cases. In acute lymphoblastic leukemia of children, the drug appeared equally effective as daunorubicin, the superiority over the latter being evident particularly in solid tumors. An intermittent dose schedule (3-week interval between courses) and a limitation of total cumulative dose were recommended in order to lower the incidence of toxic manifestations (*52*). The value of doxorubicin in pediatric tumors was demonstrated also at New York Memorial Hospital (172 cases), as doxorubicin produced 43% overall remission rate in previously treated patients with acute leukemia and 78% tumor regression in solid tumors and lymphomas (*53*). Other papers demonstrating the activity of the drug in acute leukemias were those reporting work done at St. Bartholomew's Hospital, London (29 cases) (*54*), at Villejuif, France (90 cases) (*55*), and at Städt. Krankenhaus, München-Schwabing (31 cases) (*56*). Emphasis on the intermittent treatment, favorably compared with continuous treatment with regard to the evolution of toxic side-effects (namely immunosuppression and hematological alterations), was deduced from work performed at M.D. Anderson Hospital, Houston (*57*). The same study (104 evaluable cases) indicated 22% of objective responses in solid tumors in man, most promising applications being identified in bladder carcinoma, lymphomas, soft tissue sarcomas, and breast tumor. Results of clinical trials carried out in Spain (*58*) concerning 64 cases, out of which 51 were solid tumors with metastasis, indicated potential usefulness of the drug in bronchogenic carcinoma and in breast cancer, while those carried out at Roswell Park Memorial Institute (*59*), concerning 44 cases of acute leukemia and 42 solid tumors, confirmed the wide spectrum of antitumor activity of doxorubicin as remission was induced in Wilms' tumor, neuroblastomas, Ewing's sarcoma, reticulum cell sarcomas, and bronchogenic carcinomas. A preliminary report from Institute Jules Bordet (*60*) was based on the study of 27 patients with advanced lung cancer, showing 7 partial remissions with the 75 mg/m^2 dosage every 3 weeks. Favorable objective changes for more than one month in different histological types of advanced lung tumors were recorded at the Clinica Medica, University of Milan (*61*). Other presentations at the same symposium indicated doxorubicin as a potential clinically active agent in different solid tumors (*47*).

The number of clinical papers concerning the effect of doxorubicin, either given alone or in combination therapy, is now exceeding 5000.

As already mentioned, doxorubicin activity in sarcoma patients was already evident from the initial studies, and much of the progress in this area is due to the late Dr. J. Gottlieb (*62*). The treatment of soft tissue sarcomas of the adult, a type of tumor considered refractory to chemotherapy in the early 1970s, has been favorably modified by the use of drug combinations containing doxorubicin (*63,64*). Synergism of doxorubicin with DTIC was demonstrated by Beretta *et al.* (*65*). The effectiveness of this combination for the treatment of metastatic soft tissue sarcomas in adults has also been stressed by Pinedo and Kenis (*66*), good response rate being afforded also with other combinations including doxorubicin, as for instance that with methyl CCNU (*67*). Prolonged disease-free states were obtained in adjuvant therapy with doxorubicin together with amputation in osteogenic sarcomas by Cortes *et al.* (*68*).

Doxorubicin is an useful drug in medical treatment of malignant lymphomas. The drug, used in combination with bleomycin, vinblastine, and DTIC, afforded 70% complete remission rate in advanced Hodgkin's disease (*69*), and alternation of this combination with MOPP gave a 100% complete remission rate and 100% survival at 2 years (*70*). Use of these combinations in a combined modality program with radiotherapy was successful in the treatment of poor-prognosis Hodgkin's disease (*71*). The combination of doxorubicin with bleomycin, DTIC, vincristine, and prednisone was effective in patients with advanced Hodgkin's disease resistant to the established MOPP therapy (*72*). Improved remission rates, positively correlated with survival, have been obtained in advanced non-Hodgkin's malignant lymphomas using drug combinations in which doxorubicin was invariably included (*73–76*). Although favorable therapeutic effects were obtained in children with Burkitt's lymphoma using combination therapy including doxorubicin (*77*), limited efficacy was recorded in adults in Britain (*78*). Doxorubicin as single agent afforded 85% overall response rate in patients with advanced mycosis fungoides (*79*), and the favorable responsiveness of this tumor to combination chemotherapy programs, especially with doxorubicin, has been reported by Grozea *et al.* (*80*). A therapeutic regimen with doxorubicin, epipodophyllotosin (VM 26), cyclophosphamide, and prednisone showed a very high degree of efficacy in lymphosarcoma and reticulosarcoma, the overall response rate being 85% with a complete remission rate of 56%, responsiveness being related to the hystocytological type of the tumor (*81*).

Doxorubicin, as a single agent, has been reported to give high response rates in advanced breast cancer, and doxorubicin-containing drug combinations appear to be the most active. The doxorubicin–cyclophosphamide combination chemotherapy gave 80% objective responses in patients with advanced disease, with a median duration of remission of approximately 10 months (*82*). The association of cyclophosphamide, doxorubicin, and 5-fluorouracil (CAF) compared favorably with an established five-drug combination in metastatic breast cancer, median duration of survival being related to response (*83*). A higher initial response rate was ascribed to CAF than to the corresponding combination containing methotrexate (CMF) (*84*). The use of doxorubicin in adjuvant polychemoimmunotherapy of breast cancer has been reported by Gutterman *et al.* (*85*) and by Buzdar *et al.* (*86*) with promising results in terms of prolonging survival, and increase of duration of complete responses in combined chemotherapy–radiotherapy approaches was recorded using the doxorubicin–vincristine (*87*) or the doxorubicin–cyclophosphamide (*88*) combination. A multidisciplinary treatment including doxorubicin in the chemotherapy cycles has been reported as an effective approach in patients with poor-prognosis locally advanced breast cancer (*89*).

Doxorubicin, which gives about 21% objective response rates as a single agent when used in bronchogenic carcinoma (*90*), has been used in combination with methotrexate, cyclophosphamide, and CCNU in patients with advanced tumors to achieve a 46% response rate, with a median survival of

14 months in the responsive cases, responses being obtained in all hystologi-
cal types of tumor (*91*). In patients with inoperable bronchogenic carcinoma,
an overall objective response rate of 38% was obtained in a combined chemotherapy with doxorubicin and CCNU, best results being recorded with small
cell carcinoma and adenocarcinoma (*92*). The combination of doxorubicin
with vincristine and procarbazine produced a response rate of 59% in small
cell cancer patients no longer responding to cyclophosphamide, CCNU, and
methotrexate chemotherapy, with alternation of the two regimens (not cross-
resistant) being proposed to prolong survival (*93*). Results of a recent study
in this direction (*94*) are encouraging, as are those concerning the use of
doxorubicin together with CCNU, cyclophosphamide, and vincristine in
alternating cycles of intensive combination chemotherapy (*95*) or the treatment with cyclophosphamide, doxorubicin, and vincristine together with
radiotherapy (*96–99*), the overall results remaining, however, still unsatis-
factory as the adverse final course of the disease is not altered. High response
rates in patients with small cell bronchogenic carcinoma were also obtained
using chemoimmunotherapy regimens in which doxorubicin was generally
present (*100–102*). The combination of doxorubicin with cyclophosphamide,
methotrexate, and procarbazine (LAMP) has been found moderately effective in metastatic non-oat cell bronchogenic carcinoma of different histological types, showing lower toxic effects than other combinations (*103,104*).
One of these, containing bleomycin, doxorubicin, CCNU, vincristine, and
nitrogen mustard (BACON), improved survival in responding patients with
inoperable squamous carcinoma of the lung (*105*). The combination of
doxorubicin with cyclophosphamide and *cis*-dichlorodiammine platinum
afforded frequent therapeutic responses in metastatic nonsmall cell bronchogenic carcinoma (*106*), while doxorubicin plus cyclophosphamide was the
most effective out of four different regimens on squamous cell lung cancer
(*107*), a tumor on which the combination of doxorubicin with mitomycin C,
CCNU, and methotrexate also showed partially positive results (*108*). Advanced adenocarcinoma of the lung gave 36% response rates with FAM
(5-fluorouracyl, doxorubicin, mitomycin C) (*109*), and favorable effects with
FAP (ftorafur, doxorubicin, *cis*-diammine platinum) were recorded by
Valdivieso *et al.* (*110*). The use of doxorubicin in adjuvant chemotherapy
(combined surgery and chemotherapy) in lung cancer is expected to be
beneficial (*111,112*).

The effectiveness of chemotherapic agents, including doxorubicin, in the
treatment of acute lymphoblastic leukemia and in relation to the different
aspects of this disease has been reviewed by Frei and Sallan (*113*), Jacquillat
et al. (*114*), Simone *et al.* (*115*), and Woodruff (*116*). Intensification of early
treatment of adults with acute lymphoblastic leukemia also by the addition

of doxorubicin to the vincristine–prednisone combination improved the complete remission rate at St. Bartholomew Hospital, London (*117*). The use of doxorubicin in a chemotherapic combination to increase the remission reinduction rate in children with acute lymphoblastic leukemia was investtigated by Klemperer *et al.* (*118*) and by Rivera (*119*) with promising results. The efficacy of doxorubicin in a maintenance regimen utilizing cycling pulse combination chemotherapy in children with acute lymphoblastic leukemia after induction and consolidation of remission, and central nervous system prophylaxis, has been demonstrated at Sidney Farber Cancer Institute, Boston (*120*). Over 90% of the patients were apparently free of disease at 15 months, when dosage with doxorubicin ceased because of completion of a total cumulative doxorubicin dosage of 450 mg/m^2 (body surface area).

Clinical investigators at Rosewell Park Memorial Institute, Buffalo, found that the combination of doxorubicin and ara-C was an effective treatment in acute myelocytic leukemia, especially in patients less than 40 years old, the dose of the anthracycline being lower than that of daunorubicin used in a similar drug combination (*121*), and possibly even more effective (*122*). The initial leukemic cell-kill due to the daunorubicin plus ara-C treatment was considered to be a determining factor of the improved duration of complete remission (*123,124*), the same combination affording remission more rapidly and more effectively than any other drug combination not containing an anthracycline studied by Chang *et al.* (*125*). The use of the anthracycline antibiotics daunorubicin and doxorubicin in acute myelogenous leukemia has represented, according to Freireich *et al.* (*126*) of M.D. Anderson Hospital, Houston, a major advance in treatment which, combined with results of new strategies of treatment, such as late intensification of chemotherapy, supported an optimistic conclusion about the possibility of long-term control of this disease. A 74% incidence of complete remission was recorded at Memorial Hospital, New York, by Haghbin *et al.* (*127*), in children with acute nonlymphoblastic leukemia who were treated with a combination regimen consisting of ara-C, 6-thioguanine, and doxorubicin. Substitution of doxorubicin or daunorubicin in the TRAP combination (thioguanine, daunorubicin, cytarabine, prednisolone) was considered as a possible improvement of this combination, which is, however, regarded as only palliative treatment for acute myeloid leukemia (*128*). Complete remission rates of greater than 60% are presently achieved in adult acute nonlymphocytic leukemia using drug combinations generally including either daunorubicin or doxorubicin. While increased duration of remission and number of long-term survivors are also recorded, a major obstacle to a high complete remission rate remains the dependency upon considerable therapeutic expertise and extensive support facilities (*129*).

Therapeutic activity was shown by doxorubicin when used as a single agent in patients being treated for advanced acute leukemia in relapse and previously treated with other effective chemotherapic combinations, this result (21% complete remission rate in adequately treated patients) suggesting a further exploration of drug combinations including this antibiotic (130).

Doxorubicin was indicated by Carter and Wasserman (131) as a drug active in urinary tract cancer, and its efficacy in bladder cancer, prostatic and testicular tumors, but not in renal cell carcinoma was deduced from available information by Slavik (132). Intravenous doxorubicin, as a single agent, displayed significant effectiveness against transitional cell carcinoma (133), and indications of activity in advanced cancer of the bladder were reported by Pavone-Macaluso (134). Doxorubicin was compared favorably with 5-FU in systemic treatment of invasive bladder tumors and although the results obtained with doxorubicin appeared more meaningful than those reported for other chemotherapic agents, the true role of the antibiotic in the treatment of bladder cancer needed further clarification according to De Kernion (136) and Yagoda et al. (137). However, combination therapy of doxorubicin and 5-FU, producing a significant remission rate in patients with advanced bladder carcinoma, was reported by the EORTC Urological Group B (138). Adjuvant chemotherapy with the combination of doxorubicin and cyclophosphamide prolonged the interval free of disease in patients after radical cystectomy (139). Topical use of doxorubicin in bladder carcinoma was investigated in Japan (140) and in Sweden (141) with favorable results, and effectiveness of this route of administration in superficial vesical tumors was also recorded by Jacobi et al. (142). Careful analytical control of plasma samples from patients treated with doxorubicin by instillation in the bladder showed no evidence of systemic absorption of the drug (143). The intravesical administration of doxorubicin is apparently an established therapeutic treatment (144,145).

The potential clinical usefulness of doxorubicin for the treatment of digestive tract tumors is presently being actively explored. Most favorable results seem to be obtained in gastric carcinoma, a tumor on which only four drugs (5-FU, mitomycin C, BCNU, and doxorubicin) are known to be active (146). The already mentioned FAM combination has shown favorable effects in advanced gastric cancer (147–149), as did other combinations containing doxorubicin (150). Activity of doxorubicin in hepatocellular carcinoma has been further documented (149,151–153). In contrast with the gastric tumor, colorectal cancer appears not to be affected by doxorubicin treatment, which gave results inferior to those with 5-FU (154). On the other hand, doxorubicin showed efficacy on pancreatic and biliary carcinoma when use in combination with BCNU and ftorafur, a 5-FU derivative (155), on advanced pancreatic tumor in the FAM combination (156), and on inoperable esophageal cancer (*157*). A case of rapid regression induced by doxorubicin in metastatic malignant carcinoid tumor of the intestine has been reported (*158*).

The major dose-limiting side effect in doxorubicin therapy is the development of severe cumulative dose-dependent cardiomyopathy leading to congestive heart failure, which is fatal in the majority of cases. Patients undergoing this cardiotoxicity were 59 (1.7%) of 3461 patients treated with doxorubicin (*159*), or 88 (2%) of 4018 patients entered in clinical trials of eight major cooperative groups (*160*). Incidence of doxorubicin-induced congestive heart failure was correlated with the total cumulative dose administered (*161*), and total cumulative dose limitations at 450 to 550 mg/m^2 have been recommended (*162*). The absence of fully reliable animal models for the study of this effect and of clinical methods for its early diagnosis increases the difficulties of this problem. It appears, however, that conrurrent risk factors exist, related to the patient and to the therapy (*163*), and that this property is probably a characteristic of anthracycline drugs as, for instance, it was observed also with daunorubicin (*159*). More recently, the limitations of noninvasive methods of detecting doxorubicin cardiotoxicity were discussed by different authors (*164–168*), with the histopathologic assessment using endomyocardial biopsy being considered superior to cumulative dose calculation, and to echocardiographic, phonocardiographic, and electrocardiographic evaluation of the cardiac lesion (*169*). The results of a survey of 1273 patients from 12 European cancer centers aimed to define the incidence, characteristics, and possible cofactors of doxorubicin-induced cardiomyopathy has been published recently (*170*).

In conclusion, doxorubicin is a drug with a wide spectrum of antitumor activity. Its development has greatly contributed to present day reevaluation of cancer chemotherapy. Clinical use in responsive tumors has rationally developed from single agent to combination therapy involving other drugs of known activity, allowing both an increase in response rates and a lower incidence of toxic side effects. The progress of clinical studies is expected to allow further improvements in this direction. It is, however, generally felt that the development of analogues with reduced toxicity and enlarged spectrum of activity would eventually make available new anticancer agents of even greater clinical usefulness. A program directed to this objective represents a far from minor challenge to basic scientistis, both in the chemical and the biological disciplines. The former are faced with the manipulation of molecules whose modifications may often require total synthetic approaches in a class of chemical compounds previously largely unexplored from this point of view and involve chemical transformations of carbohydrate derivatives, a field not completely familiar to most medicinal chemists until a few years ago. The latter are requested to derive pharmacological test systems for the proper evaluation of the new potential drugs in the formidable task of predicting the behavior in a complex situation such as that represented by human cancer on the basis of much simpler models such as those conceivably available in the laboratory.

ANALYTICAL DEVELOPMENT AND SYNTHESIS OF RADIOLABELED DOXORUBICIN

The availability of proper analytical methods endowed with adequate specificity and sensitivity for the identification and quantitative determination of doxorubicin has been a matter of concern since the initial clinical results indicating the potential clinical effectiveness of the drug. The importance of such methods for the study of pharmacokinetics and of the metabolism of any drug needs not to be stressed here. In the case of doxorubicin, although some indication both on the methodology and on its applications could be drawn from the previous and concurrent investigations on the related antibiotic daunorubicin, the development of satisfactory analytical procedures was complicated by the lower chemical stability of doxorubicin due to the presence of the hydroxyl group at C-14, as well as by the low concentrations obtained in the body tissues in animal test or in therapeutic treatments and the presence of metabolites.

The first reports dealing with the fluorometric determination of doxorubicin were not specific for the antibiotic, as they could not differentiate it from the possible metabolites. The assay method of Dusonchet et al. (*171*) was based, for the recovery of the drug from biological fluids and tissues, on a procedure previously employed for the tetracyclines. This involved extraction with dilute hydrogen chloride followed by deproteinization steps and reextraction into ethyl acetate. Fluorometric measurements were performed on the organic extract and, although evident quenching phenomena were present, a limit of detection of 10 ng/g of tissue was claimed by the authors. The method used by Rosso et al. (*172*) for blood and urines was based on a procedure already employed for the daunorubicin assay (*173*) involving *n*-butanol extraction of the biological sample followed by fluorometric measurements on the extract itself.

An hydrolytic step and chromatographic separation were introduced by Chan and Harris (*174*) in order to improve the already available methodology. Tissues were extracted with 50% aqueous ethanol containing 0.1 N hydrogen chloride, and the extract was heated in a boiling water both for 20 min. The aglycone, adriamycinone, was extracted with benzene and isolated in higher than 90% yield by chromatography on impregnated glass fiber thin layers using the solvent system chloroform, methanol, acetic acid (100:2:2.5). Elution of the adriamycinone zone with acid ethanol was followed by fluorometric quantitation. A quantitative TLC analysis of chloroform–isopropanol extracts of plasma based on a fluorescence scanning technique has been proposed by Watson and Chan (175).

Chromatographic separations using paper or silica gel plates were performed directly on whole blood, plasma, and artificial perfusates by Mhatre et al. (176,177). Yesair et al. (178) also used thin layer chromatography for the isolation of doxorubicin from the extracts of biological samples. The extracts were prepared by homogenization of the samples with 20 volumes of a mixture of chloroform and methanol (2:1), filtration, and separation of the organic layer upon addition of water. Chromatography was performed using silica-gel plates which were first chromatographed in diethyl ether to separate neutral lipid and subsequently in the system of chloroform, methanol, acetic acid, and water (100:50:14:6). Elution of fluorescent zones with 0.1 N ethanolic hydrogen chloride and fluorometric measurement allowed quantitation of the drug species present in the extract.

For the quantitative assay of doxorubicin and its metabolites in human plasma, Benjamin et al. (179) measured total plasma fluorescence by heating the samples with two volumes of 75% ethanol containing 0.45 N hydrogen chloride, centrifugation, and fluorometric determination. The plasma acid alcohol extracts were hydrolyzed in order to convert glycosidic species to the corresponding aglycones, which were extracted into ethyl acetate and chromatographed on silica-gel plates in a system of chloroform, methanol, and acetic acid (100:2:2.5) allowing separation into two fractions, one constituted by adriamycinone and the other attributed to the aglycones of the metabolites. Account was taken for the presence of artifacts. The assay of doxorubicin and its metabolites in the urines was instead carried out using n-butanol extraction followed by chromatography on thin-layer silica gel in a system of chloroform, methanol, acetic acid, and water (80:20:14:6), elution, and quantitative fluorometric determination of different fractions indicated as doxorubicin, major urinary metabolite, highly polar metabolites, aglycones, and less polar metabolites. Variations to these procedures were introduced in subsequent studies of the Baltimore group. The ice-cold chloroform–methanol (2:1) mixture was used for the extraction of tissue homogenates and blood samples in the rabbit study (180), separation of fluorescent products being performed with the chromatographic procedures already mentioned without previous hydrolysis. Fractions indicated as aglycones, doxorubicin, doxorubicinol, and polar metabolites were separated and quantitated. In a more recent study, acid alcohol extraction of plasma was still used for the assessment of total drug fluorescence, but separation of doxorubicin and its metabolites was carried out chromato-graphically starting from chloroform–isopropanol extracts of plasma samples. Fractionation was achieved using silica-gel thin-layer plates and three sequential developments with (a) ethyl acetate; (b) chloroform, methanol, acetic acid, water (80:20:14:6); and (c) chloroform, isobutanol, acetic acid (100:15:15). Fluorescent areas were identified in UV light, scraped, eluted with 95% ethanol containing 0.6 N hydrogen chloride, and measured fluorometrically. The following fluorescent species were identified and determined in human plasma: doxorubicin, doxorubicinol (adriamycinol), a metabolite less polar than doxorubicin, a metabolite more polar than doxorubicinol, adriamycinone, less polar aglycone, and more polar aglycone. The limit of sensitivity was of the order of a few ng/ml of plasma.

Treatment of tissue samples with a solution of silver nitrate was used by Schwartz (181) to facilitate release of bound drug and its extraction into a water-immiscible alcohol such as isoamyl alcohol or n-butanol. When correction for internal quench of fluorescence was made, recoveries of a total fluorescence higher than 85% were obtained with a lower limit of sensitivity corresponding to 0.2 μg/50 mg cells. A modification of this method was employed by Donelli et al. (182) in the determination of heart levels of doxorubicin in mice. The sensitivity of the method was estimated to be 1 μg/g of tissue or 0.5 μg/ml of serum (total fluorescence). Similarly, Formelli et al. (183), also using the Schwartz procedure for extraction and fluorometric determination of total drug-derived species in mouse tissues, measured levels corresponding to 1 μg/g of tissue or less.

Radioimmunoassay (RIA) procedures offer a sensitive approach for the estimation of drugs especially useful when the levels of the same in biological fluids are low. Such technique was applied by Van Vunakis et al. (184) to the detection of daunorubicin and doxorubicin in plasma or urines. Antisera produced in animals by immunization with doxorubicin–protein conjugates reacted with both antibiotics and also with some derivatives thereof such as N-acetyldaunorubicin and daunorubicin benzoylhydrazone, the aglycone moyeties reacting only 25% as effectively as the parent glycosides. Iodinated N-(p-hydroxyphenylacetyl)doxorubicin was the radiolabeled hapten, and two different procedures, the double antibody technique and the nitrocellulose membrane filtration, were used for the assay. The lower limit of detection appeared to be approximately 1 ng/ml.

The advent of high-performance liquid chromatography (HPLC) as an effective and rapid technique for the separation of molecules of biological interest allowed Langone et al. (185) to develop a combined HPLC–RIA system for the separation and determination of doxorubicin and its metabolites in urines of cancer patients. The n-butanol extracts of urine samples were dried in vacuum and the residues dissolved in 20% ethanol–water for chromatography, a diphenylcorasil column was used, and a linear gradient from 16% acetonitrile–water up to a 1:1 mixture of this solvent and 25% acetonitrile–0.1 % ammonium formate, pH 4.0. Elution was followed by ultraviolet absorption at 254 nm.

The HPLC technique was also used by Hulhoven and Desager (*186*) for the quantitative determination of daunorubicin and daunorubicinol in plasma. Doxorubicin was used as the internal standard. A methylene chloride–isopropanol extract of plasma was injected into the column packed with Zorbax SIL, elution being carried out with a mixture of methylene chloride, methanol, 25% ammonia, and water. Optimal selectivity was achieved using a spectrophotometric detector fixed at 490 nm. The sensitivity was about 10 ng/ml and the recovery approximately 90%. Baurain *et al.* (*187*) have described a method for the extraction of daunorubicin and its metabolites from cell homogenates and their quantitative determination by HPLC to a concentration of 1.5 ng/ml using doxorubicin as internal standard. The extraction mixture was chloroform–methanol (4:1), the stationary phase of the chromatographic separation was silica gel, the mobile phase was chloroform–methanol–acetic acid–water (720:210:35:30), and the detection was fluorometric to allow determination of 1.5 ng/ml of daunorubicin. The retention time was reduced by the addition of 0.3 M aqueous magnesium chloride to the eluent system, and the method was demonstrated to work well also with plasma and urine samples (*188*). A detailed study of reversed-phase liquid chromatography of doxorubicin, daunorubicin, and their metabolites doxorubicinol and daunorubicinol has been reported by Eksborg (*189*). Using surface-modified chromatographic supports derived by treatment of porous silica gel with alkylchlorosilanes, the best separations were obtained with a mobile phase constituted by 10^{-2} M aqueous phosphoric acid containing acetonitrile. When applied to the determination of daunorubicin and its metabolite in plasma of leukemic patients, the concentration of the acetonitrile was in the range 20–30% (v/v). The recovery of the drugs from plasma was carried out by an extraction into a 9:1 mixture of chloroform and 1-heptanol at pH 8.1 followed by reextraction into 0.1 M phosphoric acid in the presence of 5 μg/ml desipramine (to prevent absorption phenomena). Quantitative recoveries and a precision better than 2% at plasma levels greater than 20 ng/ml were reported, quantitation being based on eluate absorbance at 253.7 and 500 nm. Sensitivity to the nanogram level was reached by Israel *et al.* (*190*), who developed an HPLC separation coupled with fluorometric detection for the analysis of plasma, bile, and urine samples containing doxorubicin and doxorubicinol. Two methods were used: one was based on a normal phase liquid chromatography on a column constituted by a cyanoaminoalkyl derivative of silica-gel with the development being carried out with a gradient of the mixture chloroform, methanol, acetic acid, and water (850:150:50:15) mixed with chloroform; the other was based on reverse phase HPLC with a Waters μ-Bondapak/ phenyl column using a gradient of acetonitrile in pH 4 aqueous ammonium formate buffer as developing agent. Extraction of plasma samples was performed with chloroform in the presence of methanol, and that of bile and urine (when necessary) with a 9:1 mixture of ethyl acetate and propanol. The HPLC technique has also been profitably used for the analysis of pharmaceutical preparations containing doxorubicin [see Barth and Conner (*191*), and references cited therein].

Other methods for the analysis of doxorubicin in biological fluids have been described. A differential pulse polarographic method allowing direct recording of the polarograms in a untreated plasma sample and a minimum detectable concentration of the antibiotic of 400 ng/ml has been reported (*192*). GLC–mass spectrometry of a number of pertrimethylsilyl derivatives of the aglycones showed a potential for the identification of doxorubicin metabolites (*193*). A differential light scattering (DLS) bioassay for doxorubicin, significantly more sensitive than the standard disc diffusion microbiological assay procedure, has been developed (*194*). The method was based on DLS patterns corresponding to recorded measurements of the intensity of light, generated by a laser source, which was scattered from a bacterial suspension (in this case of a *S. aureus* strain) as a function of the angle of a detector rotating about the cuvette containing the suspension. The inhibitory effect of the drug, when added to the bacterial culture, represented as a score when a specifically developed computerized device was used, was derived by a comparison of the measured DLS pattern with that of a reference sample. Standard curves were prepared showing a linear dose–response relationship in the range 0.25 to 10 μg/ml of the original doxorubicin-containing fluid (serum or urine).

The synthesis of radiolabeled doxorubicin is a necessary step for the investigation of metabolic transformations, disposition, and tissue distribution of the drug on a quantitative basis. Tritium-labeled doxorubicin was prepared from tritium-labeled daunorubicin obtained by the Wilzbach procedure (*195*) and made available during the last decade to biomedical scientists from the author's laboratory. The product was, however, of limited use, due to the exchange of tritium in buffered aqueous solutions. (A warning suggesting that users take account of this fact was generally included when the product was made available to them.) Typical tritium exchange curves are presented in Fig. 3 and are in agreement with PMR studies of acetyl proton exchange in daunorubicin (*196*).

Doxorubicin labeled with ^{14}C should not present the drawbacks of the tritium-labeled compound. For this reason, processes for the synthesis of

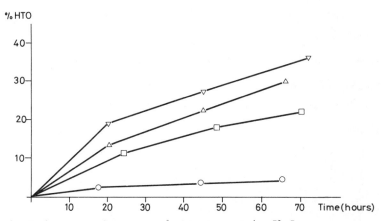

Fig. 3. Exchange rate of tritium at 37°C from $2.6 \times 10^{-4} M$ [³H]doxorubicin hydrochloride, sp. act. 4.25 mC/mM, in distilled water (○), and in $M/150$ (△), $M/15$ (◁) and $M/15$ plus KCL up to ionic strength $\varnothing = 2$ (□), pH phosphate buffer. Data are expressed as per cent of radioactivity recovered in the water after lyophilization (unpublished data from author's laboratory).

[¹⁴C]doxorubicin have been developed in different laboratories. According to the procedure studied in the author's laboratory (*197*), aldehyde **53**, obtained from 13-dihydro-N-trifluoroacetyldoxorubicin upon oxidation with sodium metaperiodate, was treated with [¹⁴C]diazomethane to give [14-¹⁴C]-N-trifluoroacetyldaunorubicin (**54**) and the epoxide **55**. Removal of the N-trifluoroacetyl group by mild alkaline treatment gave [14-¹⁴C]-daunorubicin, which was transformed to [14-¹⁴C]doxorubicin (**56**) in 9% overall radiochemical yield starting from the [¹⁴C]diazomethane precursor, [¹⁴C]methylamine hydrochloride.

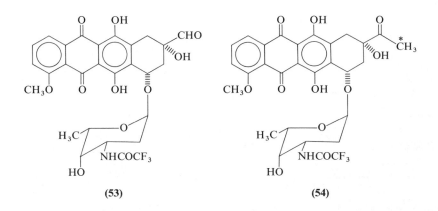

(53)   (54)

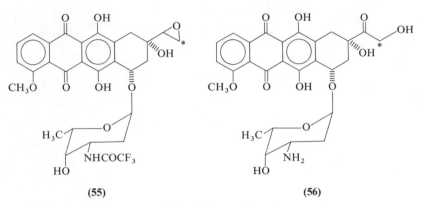

(55)   (56)

Malspeis and his group at Ohio State University (*198*) have reported the synthesis of **56** starting from the acid (**57**) whose mixed anhydride with isobutylchloroformic acid was treated with [^{14}C]diazomethane to give the diazoketone (**58**) in 25% yield, together with the [^{14}C]methyl ester of **57**. Treatment of **58** with hydrogen bromide in dichloromethane afforded 9-*O*-isobutoxycarbonyl-*N*-trifluoroacetyl-14-bromodaunorubicin (**59**), which

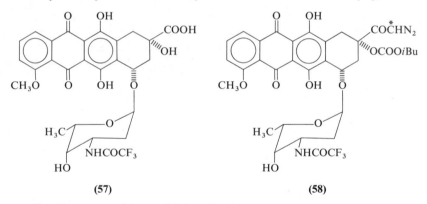

(57)   (58)

gave *N*-trifluoroacetyldoxorubicin (**60**) by reaction with potassium carbonate. Protection of (**60**) as the 14-*O*-*p*-anisyldiphenylmethyl ether allowed alkaline removal of the *N*-trifluoroacetyl group. Subsequent hydrolysis of the trityl ether in 80% acetic acid gave **56** in approximately 2% radiochemical yield from the [^{14}C]diazomethane precursor, [^{14}C]Diazald.

A third synthesis of **56** was carried out in the United States by Chen *et al.* (*199*), who treated adriamycinone with 15 equivalents of [^{14}C]methyl magnesium iodide to give **61** in 5.3% yield from [^{14}C]methyl iodide. Oxidation of **61** with periodate allowed [14-^{14}C]daunomycinone (**62**), whose Koenigs–Knorr glycosidation afforded [14-^{14}C]daunorubicin. Bromination of **62a** and subsequent hydrolysis with alkalis gave [14-^{14}C]adriamycinone (**62b**).

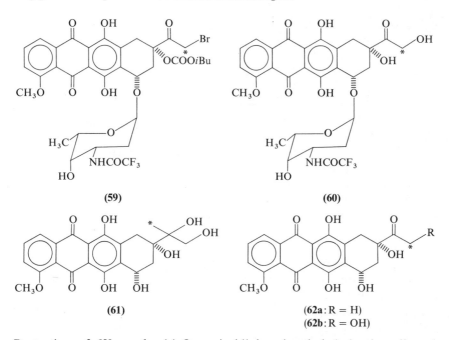

(59)   **(60)**

(61)   **(62a: R = H)**
(62b: R = OH)

Protection of **62b** as the 14-*O*-*p*-anisyldiphenylmethyl derivative allowed glycosidation and N-deacylation in alkaline conditions of the resulting *N*-trifluoroacetyl doxorubicin derivative. Final deblocking with acetic acid afforded **56**.

CONJUGATES AND COMPLEXES OF DOXORUBICIN AS ANTITUMOR AGENTS

The possibility of modifying the unfavorable aspects of doxorubicin therapeutic applications by binding it to other substances in order to increase the selectivity of action has not escaped the imagination of motivated biomedical scientists. Said substances, generally considered as carriers of the cytotoxic drug or of an active fragment thereof, belong to different types, namely proteins, nucleic acids, and even ferric ions.

Linking of daunorubicin or of doxorubicin to immunoglobulins was carried out, according to three different procedures, by Hurwitz *et al.* (*200*). The first method involved oxidation of the drugs with periodate, presumably with the aim of producing an intermediate dialdehyde which is allowed to react with the free amino groups of the protein to give Schiff bases that are finally reduced with sodium borohydride. The second consisted in the reaction of glutaraldehyde with both the drug and the immunoglobulin in order to form cross-linking type compounds. The third procedure involved condensation of carboxyl groups of the protein with the amino group of the drug by the carbodiimide method. The products submitted to a separation using the gel filtration technique and the drug present in the high molecular weight fractions as determined by spectrophotometry were assumed to be covalently bound. However, the same fractions showed *in vitro* effects on nucleic acid synthesis and cell growth whose mechanism remained undefined. In particular, specific cytotoxic effects were exhibited when antibodies specific for different experimental murine tumor cells were used as carriers (*201*). However, conjugates of daunorubicin with specific antitumor-cell antibodies were not more effective than the free drug or than the drug bound with dextrane in *in vivo* tests on a plasmacytoma and lymphoma of the mouse (*202*). Conjugates with concanavalin A (*203*) and with melanotropine (*204*) have been prepared and tested, the periodate–sodium borohydride method being used in both cases.

The use of doxorubicin–DNA complex as a potential less toxic form of the antibiotic (the so-called lysosomotropic approach) was originally proposed by Trouet *et al.* (*205*). This formulation of doxorubicin was extensively investigated. The most recent conclusions are that the doxorubicin–DNA complex behaved like free doxorubicin with regard to efficacy, acute toxicity, and cardiac toxicity (*206*).

The ferric ion complex of doxorubicin, called quelamycin, has been proposed as a less cardiotoxic form of the drug by Gosalvez *et al.* (*207*). No quantitative information is, however, available on the stability and fate of the complex *in vivo*. The results of early clinical trial with quelamycin have been reported (*208,209*).

REFERENCES

1. F. Arcamone, A. Di Marco, M. Gaetani, and T. Scotti, *G. Microbiol.* **9**, 83 (1961).
2. H. Brockmann, Pyrromycines and Pyrromicinones, Rhodomicines and Rhodomycinones, *in* "Sostanze Naturali," pp. 33, 51. Accad. Nazl. Lincei, Rome, 1961.
3. H. Brockmann, *Fortschr. Chem. Organ. Naturst.* **21**, 121 (1963).
4. L. Ettlinger, E. Gäumann, R. Hütter, W. Keller-Schierlein, F. Kradolfer, L. Neipp, V. Prelog, P. Reusser, and H. Zähner, *Chem. Ber.* **92**, 1867 (1959).
5. H. Brockmann and B. Franck, *Chem. Ber.* **88**, 1972 (1955).
6. H. Brockmann, P. Boldt, and J. Niemeyer, *Chem. Ber.* **96**, 1356 (1963).
7. H. Brockmann and P. Boldt, *Chem. Ber.* 94, 2174 (1961).
8. H. Brockmann and W. Müller, *Chem. Ber.* **92**, 1164 (1959).
9. H. Brockmann and W. Lenk, *Chem. Ber.* **92**, 1880 (1959).
10. W. D. Ollis, I. O. Sutherland, and J. J. Gordon, *Tetrahedron Lett.* No. 16, 17 (1959).
11. H. Brockmann, H. Brockmann, Jr., J. J. Gordon, W. Keller-Schierlein, W. Lenk, W. D. Ollis, V. Prelog, and I. O. Sutherland, *Tetrahedron Lett.* No. 8, 25 (1960).
12. H. Brockmann and H. Brockmann, Jr., *Chem. Ber.* **94**, 2681 (1961).

13. J. J. Gordon, L. M. Jackman, W. D. Ollis, and I. O. Sutherland, *Tetrahedron Lett.* No. 8, 28 (1960).
14. W. D. Ollis and I. O. Sutherland, *in* "Recent Development in the Chemistry of Natural Phenolic Compounds," p. 212. Pergamon, Oxford, 1961.
15. R. Robinson, "The Structural Relations of Natural Products" Oxford Univ. Press (Clarendon), 1955.
16. A. J. Birch, *Fortschr. Chem. Organ. Naturst.* **14**, 186 (1957).
17. W. D. Ollis, I. O. Sutherland, R. C. Codner, J. J. Gordon, and G. A. Miller, *Proc. Chem. Soc. London* p. 347 (1960).
18. H. Brockmann, E. Spohler, and T. Waehneldt, *Chem. Ber.* **96**, 2295 (1963).
19. H. Brockmann and T. Waehneldt, *Naturwissenchaften* **50**, 43 (1963).
20. M. Dubost, P. Ganter, R. Maral, L. Ninet, S. Pinnert, J. Preud'Homme, and G. H. Werner, *C. R. Acad. Sci.* **257**, 1813 (1963).
21. G. Cassinelli and P. Orezzi, *G. Microbiol.* **11**, 167 (1963).
22. A. Grein, C. Spalla, A. Di Marco, and G. Canevazzi, *G. Microbiol.* **11**, 109 (1963).
23. R. Despois, M. Dubost, D. Mancy, R. Maral, L. Ninet, S. Pinnert, J. Preud'Homme, Y. Charpentie, A. Belloc, N. de Chezelles, J. Lunel, and J. Renaut, *Arzneim.-Forsch.* **17**, 934 (1967).
24. A. Di Marco, M. Gaetani, L. Dorigotti, M. Soldati, and O. Bellini, *Tumori* **49**, 203 (1963).
25. A. Di Marco, M. Soldati, A. Fioretti, and T. Dasdia, *Tumori* **49**, 235 (1963).
26. A. Di Marco, M. Gaetani, P. Orezzi, B. M. Scarpinato, R. Silvestrini, M. Soldati, T. Dasdia, and L. Valentini, *Nature (London)* **201**, 706 (1964).
27. F. Arcamone, G. Cassinelli, P. Orezzi, G. Franceschi, and R. Mondelli, *J. Am. Chem. Soc.* **86**, 5335 (1964).
28. F. Arcamone, G. Franceschi, P. Orezzi, G. Cassinelli, W. Barbieri, and R. Mondelli, *J. Am. Chem. Soc.* **86**, 5334 (1964).
29. C. Tan and A. Di Marco, *Proc. Am. Assoc. Cancer Res.* **6**, 64, Abstr. 253 (1965).
30. J. Bernard, R. Paul, M. Boiron, C. Jacquillat, and R. Maral, *Recent Results Cancer Res.* **20**, 1 (1969).
31. F. Arcamone, G. Franceschi, P. Orezzi, and S. Penco, *Tetrahedron Lett.* No. **30**, 3349 (1968).
32. F. Arcamone, G. Cassinelli, G. Franceschi, P. Orezzi, and R. Mondelli, *Tetrahedron Lett.* No. **30**, 3353 (1968).
33. F. Arcamone, G. Cassinelli, G. Franceschi, R. Mondelli, P. Orezzi, and S. Penco, *Gazz. Chim. Ital.* **100**, 949 (1970).
34. R. Angiuli, E. Foresti, L. Riva Di Sanseverino, N. W. Isaacs, O. Kennard, W. D. S. Motherwell, D. L. Wampler, and F. Arcamone, *Nature (London), New Biol.* **234**, 78 (1971).
35. N. R. Bachur, *J. Pharmacol. Exp. Ther.* **177**, 573 (1971).
36. A. Di Marco and F. Arcamone, *Arzneim.-Forsch.* **25**, 368 (1975).
37. F. Arcamone, G. Cassinelli, S. Penco, and L. Tognoli, Ger. Patent 1,923,885 (Jan. 29, 1970); *C.A.* **72**, 131086 (1970).
38. G. B. Fedorova, M. G. Brazhnicova, A. S. Mezentsev, and I. Ksheinsky, *Antibiotiki (Moscow)* **15**, 403 (1970).
39. F. Arcamone, G. Cassinelli, G. Fantini, A. Grein, P. Orezzi, C. Pol, and C. Spalla, *Biotechnol. Bioeng.* **11**, 1101 (1969). F. Arcamone, G. Cassinelli, A. Di Marco, and M. Gaetani, S. African Patent 68/02,378 (Dec. 30, 1968), C.A. **72**, 20607 (1970).
40. F. Arcamone, *in* "Topics in Antibiotic Chemistry" (P. G. Sammes, ed.) Vol. 2, Part C, pp. 100–239. Ellis Horwood, Chichester, England, 1978.
41. F. Arcamone, G. Franceschi, S. Penco, and A. Selva. *Tetrahedron Lett.* No. 13, 1007 (1969).
42. F. Arcamone, W. Barbieri, G. Franceschi, and S. Penco, *Chim. Ind. (Milan)* **51**, 834 (1969).

43. F. Arcamone, G. Franceschi, and S. Penco, Ger. Patent 1,917,874 (Nov. 6, 1969); *C. A.* **73**, 45799 (1970).

44. A. Di Marco, M. Gaetani, and B.M. Scarpinato, *Cancer Chemother. Rep.* **53**, 33 (1969).

44a. H. E. Skipper and L. H. Schmidt, *Cancer Chemother. Rep.* **17**, 179 (1962).

45. A. M. Casazza, A. Di Marco, and G. Di Cuonzo, *Cancer Res.* **31**, 1971 (1971).

46. A. Di Marco, L. Lenaz, A. M. Casazza, and B. M. Scarpinato, *Cancer Chemother. Rep.* **56**, 153 (1972).

47. S. K. Carter, A. Di Marco, M. Ghione, I. H. Krakoff, and G. Mathé (eds.), "International Symposium on Adriamycin." Springer-Verlag, Berlin and New York, 1972.

48. A. Goldin, see ref. 47, p. 64.

49. A. Hoshino, T. Kato, H. Amo, and K. Ota, see ref. 47, p. 75.

50. K. Danø, see ref. 47, p. 90.

51. A. Goldin and R. K. Johnson, *Cancer Chemother. Rep.* **6**, 137 (1975).

52. G. Bonadonna, S. Monfardini, M. De Lena, F. Fossati-Bellani, and G. Beretta, see ref. 47, p. 139.

53. C. Tan, E. Etcubanas, N. Wollner, G. Rosen, M. L. Murphy, and I. H. Krakoff, see ref. 47, p. 204.

54. J. A. M. Whitehouse, D. Crowther, and J. A. Malpas, see ref. 47, p. 213.

55. G. Mathé, J. L. Amiel, M. Hayat, F. de Vassal, L. Schwarzenberg, M. Schneider, C. Jasmin, and C. Rosenfeld, see ref. 47, p. 168.

56. H. Begemann and G. Wernekke, see ref. 47, p. 135.

57. E. Frei, III, J. K. Luce, and E. Middleman, see ref. 47, p. 153.

58. C. Rozman, E. Simŏ Camps, M. Ribas Mundŏ, F. Solsona, I. Dantart, A. Raichs, and M. Giralt, see ref. 47, p. 188.

59. L. S. Sinks, E. Cortes, J. J. Wang, and J. F. Holland, see ref. 47, p. 195.

60. Y. Kenis and J. Michel, see ref. 47, p. 161.

61. C. Praga, see ref. 47, p. 173.

62. J. A. Gottlieb, L. B. Baker, M. O'Bryan, J. K. Luce, J. G. Sinkovics, and J. M. Quagliana, *Biochem. Pharmacol., Suppl.* **2**, 183 (1974).

63. E. Frel, III, R. Blum, and N. Jaffe, *in* "Immunotherapy of Cancer: Present Status of Trials in Man" (Terry and D. Windhorst, eds.), pp. 245–255. Raven, New York, 1978.

64. R. S. Benjamin, L. H. Baker, R. M. O'Bryan, T. E. Moon, and J. A. Gottlieb, *Med. Clin. North Am.* **61**, 1039 (1977).

65. G. Beretta, G. Bonadonna, E. Bajetta, G. Tancini, M. De Lena, A. Azzarelli, and U. Veronesi, *Cancer Treat. Rep.* **60**, 205 (1976).

66. H. M. Pinedo and Y. Kenis, *Cancer Treat. Rep.* **4**, 67 (1977).

67. S. E. Rivkin, J. E. Gottlieb, T. Thigpen, and I. Elsebai, *Proc. AACR/ASCO* **19**, Abstr. C-97 (1978).

68. E. P. Cortes, J. F. Holland, and O. Glidewel, *Cancer Treat. Rep.* **62**, 271 (1978).

69. G. Bonadonna, R. Zucali, M. De Lena, and P. Valagussa, *Cancer Treat. Rep.* **61**, 769 (1977).

70. G. Bonadonna, V. Fossati, and M. De Lena, *Proc. AACR/ASCO* **19**, Abstr. C-227 (1978).

71. D. Straus, C. Young, B. Lee, L. Nisce, D. Case, Z. Arlin, M. Sykes, and B. Clarkson, *Proc. AACR/ASCO* **19**, Abstr. C-45 (1978).

72. J. J. Lokich, E. Frei, III, N. Jaffe, and J. Tullis, *Cancer (Philadelphia)* **38**, 667 (1976).

73. G. Bonadonna, S. Monfardini, and E. Villa, *Cancer Treat. Rep.* **61**, 1117 (1977).

74. V. Rodriguez, F. Cabanillas, M. A. Burgess, E. M. McKelvey, M. Valdivieso, G. P. Bodey, and E. J. Freireich, *Blood* **49**, 325 (1977).

75. P. S. Schein, V. T. De Vita, S. Hubbard, B. A. Chabner, G. P. Canellos, C. Berard, and R. C. Young, *Ann. Intern. Med.* **85**, 417 (1976).

76. G. Bonadonna, E. Villa, R. Canetta, and S. Monfardini, *Proc. AACR/ASCO* **19**, Abstr. 861 (1978).

77. J. Barbosa, E. Hvizdala, and P. Smith, *Proc. AACR/ASCO* **18**, Abstr. C-323 (1977).
78. R. L. Brearley, T. A. Lister, J. M. A. Whitehouse, and A.G. Stansfeld, *Br. J. Cancer* **35**, 484 (1977).
79. J. A. Levi, C. H. Diggs, and P. H. Wiernik, *Cancer (Philadelphia)* **39**, 1967 (1977).
80. P. N. Grozea, S. E. Jones, and E. M. McKelvey, *Proc. AACR/ASCO* **19**, Abstr. 262 (1978).
81. J. L. Misset, P. Pouillard, D. Belpomme, L. Schwarzenberg, M. Delgado, M. Gil, C. Jasmin, M. Hayat, and G. Mathé, *Eur. J. Cancer* **13**, 411 (1977).
82. S. E. Jones, B. G. M. Durie, and S. E. Salmon, *Cancer (Philadelphia)* **36**, 90 (1975).
83. R. V. Smalley, J. Carpenter, A. Bartolucci, C. Vogel, and S. Krauss, *Cancer (Philadelphia)* **40**, 625 (1977).
84. J. M. Bull, D. C. Tormey, S.-H. Li, P. P. Carbone, G. Falkson, J. Blom, E. Perlin, and R. Simon, *Cancer (Philadelphia)* **41**, 1649 (1978).
85. J. U. Gutterman, J. O. Cardenas, G. R. Blumenschein, G. Hortobagyi, M. A. Burgess, R. B. Livingston, G. M. Mavligit, E. J. Freireich, J. A. Gottlieb, and E. M. Hersh, *Br. Med. J.* **ii**, 1222 (1976).
86. A. U. Buzdar, G. R. Blumenschein, C. K. Tashima, J. U. Gutterman, G. N. Hortobagyi, H. Y. Yap, L. T. Campos, T. L. Smith, E. M. Hersh, E. J. Freireich, and E. A. Gehan, *Proc. AACR/ASCO* **19**, Abstr. C-109 (1978).
87. M. De Lena, R. Zucali, G. Viganotti, P. Valagussa, and G. Bonadonna, *Cancer Chemother. Pharmacol.* **1**, 53 (1978).
88. N. Hammond, S. E. Jones, S. E. Salmon, G. Giordano, R. Jackson, R. Miller, and R. Heusinkveld, *Proc. Int. Conf. Adjuvant Ther. Cancer* p. 153 (1977).
89. G. Hortobagyi, G. Blumenschein, C. Tashima, A. Budzar, J. Gutterman, and E. Hersh, *Proc. AACR/ASCO* **19**, Abstr. C-219 (1978).
90. O. S. Selawry, *Cancer Chemother. Rep.* **6**, 349 (1975).
91. P. Chahinian, D. J. Arnorl, J. M. Cohen, D. P. Purpora, I. S. Jaffrey, A. S. Teirstein, P. A. Kirschner, and J. F. Holland, *J. Am. Med. Assoc.* **237**, 2392 (1977).
92. R. C. Trowbridge, B. J. Kennedy, and G. J. Vosika, *Cancer (Philadelphia)* **41**, 1704 (1978).
93. M. H. Cohen, L. E. Broder, B. E. Fossieck, M. Bull, D. C. Ihde, and J. D. Minna, *Cancer Treat. Rep.* **61**, 485 (1977).
94. M. H. Cohen, D. C. Ihde, B. E. Fossieck, Jr., P. A. Bunn, M. J. Matthews, S. E. Shackney, A. V. Johnston, and J. D. Minna, *Proc. AACR/ASCO* **19**, Abstr. C-209 (1978).
95. S. J. Ginsberg, G. B. King, R. W. Tinsley, and A. Fitzpatrick, *Proc. AACR/ASCO* **19**, Abstr. 284 (1978).
96. F. A. Greco, R. L. Richardson, S. F. Schulman, S. Stroup, and R. K. Oldham, *Br. Med. J.* **ii**, 10 (1978).
97. P. Y. Haloye, *Proc. AACR/ASCO* **18**, Abstr. 278 (1977).
98. R. B. Livingston, T. N. Moore, L. Heilbrun, R. Bottomley, D. Lehane, S. E. Rivkin, and T. Thigpen, *Ann. Intern. Med.* **88**, 194 (1978).
99. R. K. Oldman, F. Greco, R. L. Richardson, and S. L. Stroup, *Proc. AACR/ASCO* **18**, Abstr. C-59 (1977).
100. T. F. Tenczynski, M. Valdivieso, E. M. Hersh, K. G. Khall, C. F. Mountain, and G. P. Bodey, *Proc. AACR/ASCO* **19**, Abstr. C-277 (1978).
101. J. McCraken, J. White, R. Reed, R. Livingston, and B. Hoogstraten, *Proc. AACR/ASCO* **19**, Abstr. C-354 (1978).
102. L. Israel, A. Depierre, C. Choffel, B. Milleron, and R. Edelstein, *Cancer Treat. Rep.* **61**, 343 (1977).
103. J. B. Bitran, R. K. Desser, T. R. Demeester, M. Colman, R. Evans, A. Billings, M. Grien, L. Rubenstein, C. Shapiro, and A. M. Golomn, *Cancer Treat. Rep.* **60**, 1225 (1976).
104. J. D. Bitran, R. K. Desser, T. Demeester, and H. M. Colomb, *Proc. AACR/ASCO* **19**, Abstr. C-63 (1978).

105. R. B. Livingston, *Cancer (Philadelphia)* **37**, 1237 (1976).

106. R. J. Gralla, E. Cvitkovic, and R. B. Golbey, *Proc. AACR/ASCO* **19**, Abstr. C-188 (1978).

107. L. Hyde, W. C. Lowe, R. Phillips, and J. Wolf, *Proc. AACR/ASCO* **18**, Abstr. C-38 (1977).

108. L. Israel, A. Depierre, and J. Aguilera, *Proc. AACR/ASCO* **19**, Abstr. C-247 (1978).

109. J. MacDonald, T. Butler, L. Smith, F. Smith, and P. Schein, *Proc. AACR/ASCO* **18**, Abstr. C-160 (1977).

110. M. Valdivieso, M. A. Burgess, and G. P. Bodey, *Proc. AACR/ASCO* **19**, Abstr. C-411 (1978).

111. H. Takita, A. C. Hollinshead, and S. Bjornsson, *Proc. AACR/ASCO* **19**, Abstr. C-50 (1978).

112. S. S. Legha, F. M. Muggia, and S. K. Carter, *Cancer (Philadelphia)* **39**, 1415 (1977).

113. E. Frei, III and S. E. Sallan, *Cancer (Philadelphia)* **42**, 828 (1978).

114. C. Jacquillat, M. Weil, M. F. Auclerc, C. Chastang, G. Flandrin, V. Izrael, G. Schauson, L. Degos, M. Boiron, and J. Bernard, *Cancer Chemother. Pharmacol.* **1**, 113 (1978).

115. J. V. Simone, R. J. A. Aur, H. O. Hustu, M. S. Verzosa, and D. Pinkel, *Cancer (Philadelphia)* **42**, 839 (1978).

116. R. Woodruff, *Cancer Treat. Rev.* **5**, 95 (1978).

117. T. A. Lister, J. M. A. Withhouse, M. E. J. Berad, R. L. Breardley, P. F. M. Wrigley, R. T. D. Oliver, J. E. Freeman, R. K. Woodruff, J. S. Malpas, A. M. Paxton, and D. Crowther, *Br. Med. J.* **i**, 199 (1978).

118. M. Klemperer, P. Coccia, V. Albo, I. Ertel, M. Donaldson, and D. Hammond, *Proc. AACR/ASCO* **19**, Abstr. C-429 (1978).

119. G. Rivera, *Proc. AACR/ASCO* **19**, Abstr. C-432 (1978).

120. S. E. Sallan, B. M. Camitta, J. R. Cassady, D. G. Nathan, and E. Frei, III, *Blood* **51**, 425 (1978).

121. H. D. Preisler, S. Bjornsson, and E. S. Henderson, *Cancer Treat. Rep.* **61**, 89 (1977).

122. H. Preisler, Y. Rustum, E. Henderson, S. Bjornsson, and D. Higby, *Proc. AACR/ASCO* **19**, Abstr. C-330 (1978).

123. P. A. Cassileth and M. E. Katz, *Cancer Treat. Rep.* **61**, 1441 (1977).

124. R. P. Gale and M. J. Cline, *Lancet* **i**, 497 (1977).

125. P. Chang, P. H. Wiernik, J. L. Lichtenfeld, and C. A. Schiffer, *Proc. AACR/ASCO* **19**, Abstr. C-254 (1978).

126. E. J. Freireich, M. J. Keating, E. A. Gehan, K. B. McCredie, G. P. Bodey, and T. Smith, *Cancer (Philadelphia)* **42**, 874 (1978).

127. M. Haghbin, M. L. Murphy, and C. T. C. Tan, *Cancer (Philadelphia)* **40**, 1417 (1977).

128. A. S. D. Spiers, J. M. Goldman, D. Catovsky, C. Costello, D. A. G. Galton, and C. S. Pitcher, *Br. Med. J.* **ii**, 544 (1977).

129. C. D. Bloomfield, *Arch. Intern. Med.* **138**, 1334 (1978).

130. H. E. Wilson, G. P. Bodey, T. E. Moon, M. Amare, R. Bottomley, A. Haut, J. S. Hewlett, F. Morrison, and J. H. Saiki, *Cancer Treat. Rep.* **61**, 905 (1977).

131. S. K. Carter and T. H. Wasserman, *Cancer (Philadelphia)* **36**, Suppl. p. 729 (1975).

132. M. Slavik, *Cancer Chemother. Rep.* **6**, 297 (1975).

133. S. H. Weinstein and J. D. Schmidt, *Urology* **8**, 336 (1976).

134. M. Pavone-Macaluso, *Eur. Urol.* **2**, 138 (1976).

135. P. H. Smith, *in* "Tumours of Genito-Urinary Apparatus" (M. Pavone-Macaluso, ed.), pp. 241–248. (Cofese, Palermo,) 1977.

136. J. B. De Kernion, *Cancer Res.* **37**, 2771 (1977).

137. A. Yagoda, R. C. Watson, W. F. Whitmore, H. Grabstald, M. P. Middleman, and I. H. Krakoff, *Cancer (Philadelphia)* **39**, 279 (1977).

138. M. R. G. Robinson, P. H. Smith, M. Pavone-Macaluso, J. H. Mulder, J. A. Martinez-Pineiro, L. Cifuentes-Delate, A. Bono, and R. W. Glashan, *Eur. Urol.* **3**, 276 (1977).

139. C. Merrin and S. Beckley, *J. Urol.* **119**, 62 (1978).
140. T. Niijima, *in* "Diagnostic and Treatment of Superficial Urinary Bladder Tumors," pp. 37–44. Who, Collab. Cent. Res. Treat. Urinary Bladder Cancer, Stockholm, 1978.
141. F. Edsmyr, T. Berlin, J. Bonam, M. Ducher, P. L. Espositi, H. Gustafson, and H. Wikstrom, see ref. 140, pp. 45–53.
142. G. H. Jacobi, K. H. Kurth, K. F. Klippel, and R. Hohenfellner, see ref. 140, pp. 83–94.
143. S. Eksborg, see ref. 140, pp. 55–58.
144. M. Pavone-Macaluso, see ref. 140, pp. 21–36.
145. M. D. Banks, J. E. Pontes, R. M. Izbicki, and J. M. Pierce, *J. Urol.* **118**, 757 (1977).
146. S. K. Carter and R. L. Comis, *J. Natl. Cancer Inst.* **58**, 567 (1977).
147. J. MacDonald, P. Schein, W. Ueno, and P. Woolley, *Proc. AACR/ASCO* **17**, Abstr. C-111 (1976).
148. P. Schein, J. MacDonald, P. Woolley, and L. Widerlite, *Gastroenterology* **70**, Part 2, p. 963 (1976).
149. P. Woolley, J. MacDonald, S. Rosenoff, P. Olmert, and P. Schein, *Proc. AACR/ASCO* **18**, Abstr. C-151 (1977).
150. M. J. O'Connel, C. G. Moertel, and P. T. Lavin, *Proc. AACR/ASCO* **19**, Abstr. C-146 (1978).
151. L. H. Baker and V. K. Viatkevicius, *Proc. AACR/ASCO* **17**, Abstr. 859 (1976).
152. G. Falkson, C. G. Moertel, and P. T. Lavin, *Proc. AACR/ASCO* **17**, Abstr. 84 (1976).
153. D. C. Ihde, R. C. Kane, M. H. Cohen, and J. D. Minna, *Proc. AACR/ASCO* **17**, Abstr. 236 (1976).
154. S. Frytak, C. G. Moertel, A. J. Schutt, R. J. Hahn, and R. J. Reittemeier, *Cancer Chemother. Rep.* **59**, 405 (1975).
155. S. W. Hall, R. S. Benjamin, M. A. Burgess, and G. P. Bodey, *Proc. AACR/ASCO* **18**, Abstr. C-250 (1977).
156. D. Haller, P. Woolley, B. Levin, W. Ueno, J. MacDonald, and P. Schein, *Proc. AACR/ ASCO* **19**, Abstr. C-144 (1978).
157. K. Kolaric, Z. Maricic, A. Roth, and I. Dujmovic, *Tumori* **63**, 485 (1977).
158. A. Solomon, T. Sonoda, and F. K. Patterson, *Cancer Treat. Rep.* **60**, 273 (1976).
159. L. Lenaz and J. A. Page, *Cancer Treat. Rep.* **3**, 111 (1976).
160. D. Von Hoff, M. Rozencweig, and M. Slavik, *Adv. Pharmacol. Chemother.* **15**, 2 (1978).
161. R. A. Minow, R. S. Benjamin, and J. A. Gottlieb, *Cancer Chemother. Rep. Part 3* **6**, 195 (1975).
162. R. S. Benjamin, *Cancer Chemother. Rep.* **6**, 191 (1975).
163. R. A. Minow, R. S. Benjamin, T. E. Lee, and G. A. Gottlieb, *Cancer* (*Philadelphia*) **39**, 1397 (1977).
164. R. A. Minow, R. S. Benjamin, E. T. Lee, and G. A. Gottlieb, *Cancer Treat. Rep.* **62**, 931 (1978).
165. I. Craig-Henderson, L. J. Sloss, N. Jaffe, R. H. Blum, and E. Frei, III, *Cancer Treat. Rep.* **62**, 923 (1978).
166. F. A. Greco, *Cancer Treat. Rep.* **62**, 901 (1978).
167. G. A. Ewy, S. E. Jones, M. J. Friedman, J. Gaines, and D. Cruze, *Cancer Treat. Rep.* **62**, 915 (1978).
168. P. K. Fulkerson, R. Talley, D. Kleinman, S. K. Weaver, C. V. Leier, S. P. Balcerzak, and R. P. Lewis, *Cancer Treat. Rep.* **62**, 881 (1978).
169. J. W. Mason, M. R. Bristow, M. E. Billingham, and J. R. Daniels, *Cancer Treat. Rep.* **62**, 857 (1978).
170. C. Praga, G. Beretta, P. L. Vigo, G. R. Lenaz, C. Pollini, G. Bonadonna, R. Canetta, R. Castellani, E. Villa, C. G. Gallagher, H. Von Melchner, M. Hayat, P. Ribaud, G. De

Wasch, W. Mattson, R. Heinz, R. Waldner, K. Kolaric, R. Buehner, W. Ten Bokkel-Huynink, N. I. Perevodchikova, L. A. Manziuk, H. J. Senn, and A. C. Mayr, *Cancer Treat. Rep.* **63**, 827 (1979).

171. L. Dusonchet, N. Gebbia, and F. Gerbasi, *Pharmacol. Res. Commun.* **3**, 55 (1971).
172. R. Rosso, C. Ravazzoni, M. Esposito, R. Sala, and L. Santi, *Eur. J. Cancer* **8**, 455 (1972).
173. J. M. Finkel, K. T. Knapp, and L. T. Mulligan, *Cancer Chemother. Rep.* **53**, 159 (1969).
174. K. K. Chan and P. A. Harris, *Res. Commun. Chem. Pathol. Pharmacol.* **6**, 447 (1973).
175. E. Watson and K. K. Chan, *Cancer Treat. Rep.* **60**, 1611 (1976).
176. R. M. Mhatre, E. Herman, A. Huidobro, and V. Waravdekar, *J. Pharmacol. Exp. Ther.* **178**, 216 (1971).
177. R. M. Mhatre, E. H. Herman, V. S. Waravdekar, and I. P. Lee, *Biochem. Med.* **6**, 445 (1972).
178. D. W. Yesair, E. Schwartzbach, D. Shuck, E. P. Denine, and M. A. Asbell, *Cancer Res.* **32**, 1177 (1972).
179. R. S. Benjamin, C. E. Riggs, Jr., and N. R. Bachur, *Clin. Pharmacol. Ther.* **14**, 592 (1973).
180. N. R. Bachur, R. C. Hildebrand, and R. S. Jaenke, *J. Pharmacol. Exp. Ther.* **191**, 331 (1974).
181. H. S. Schwartz, *Biochem. Med.* **7**, 396 (1973).
182. M. G. Donelli, A. Martini, T. Colombo, A. Bossi, and S. Garattini, *Eur. J. Cancer* **12**, 913 (1976).
183. F. Formelli, A. Di Marco, A. M. Casazza, G. Pratesi, R. Supino, and A. Mariani, *in* "Current Chemotherapy," Proceedings of the 10th International Congress of Chemotherapy (W. Siegenthaler and R. Luthy, eds.), p. 1240. Am. Soc. Microbiol., Washington, D.C., 1978.
184. H. Van Vunakis, J. J. Langone, L. J. Riceberg, and L. Levine, *Cancer Res.* **34**, 2546 (1974).
185. J. J. Langone, H. Van Vunakis, and N. Bachur, *Biochem. Med.* **12**, 283 (1975).
186. R. Hulhoven and J. P. Desager, *J. Chromatogr.* **125**, 369 (1976).
187. R. Baurain, A. Zenebergh, and A. Trouet, *J. Chromatogr.* **157**, 331 (1978).
188. R. Baurain, D. Deprez-De Campeneere, and A. Trouet, *Anal. Biochem.* **94**, 112 (1979).
189. S. Eksborg, *J. Chromatogr.* **10**, 638 (1978).
190. M. Israel, P. M. Wilkinson, W. J. Pegg, and R. Frei, III, *Cancer Res.* **38**, 365 (1978).
191. H. G. Barth and A. Z. Conner, *J. Chromatogr.* **131**, 375 (1977).
192. L. A. Sternson and G. Thomas, *Anal. Lett.* **10**, 99 (1977).
193. K. K. Chan and E. Watson, *J. Pharm. Sci.* **67**, 1748 (1978).
194. C. Woolley, L. B. Mellett, and P. J. Wyatt, *Res. Commun. Chem. Pathol. Pharmacol.* **21**, 531 (1978).
195. F. Arcamone, G. Cassinelli, G. Franceschi, S. Penco, C. Pol, S. Redaelli, and A. Selva, *in* "International Symposium on Adriamycin" (S. K. Carter, A. Di Marco, M. Ghione, I. H. Krakoff, and G. Mathé, eds.) p. 9. Springer-Verlag, Berlin and New York, 1972.
196. D. R. Philips and G. C. K. Roberts, *J.C.S. Chem. Commun.* p. 436 (1979).
197. S. Penco, G. P. Vicario, F. Angelucci, and F. Arcamone, *J. Antibiot.* **30**, 773 (1977).
198. B. R. Vishnuvajjala, T. Kataoka, F. D. Cazer, D. T. Witiak, and L. Malspeis, *J. Labelled Compd. Radiopharm.* **14**, 77 (1976).
199. C. R. Chen, M. Tan Fong, A. N. Fujiwara, D. W. Henry, M. A. Leaffer, W. W. Lee, and T. H. Smith, *J. Labelled Compd. Radiopharm.* **14**, 111 (1978).
200. E. Hurwitz, R. Levy, R. Maron, M. Wilchek, R. Arnon, and M. Sela, *Cancer Res.* **35**, 1175 (1975).
201. R. Arnon, *in* "Biotechnological Applications of Proteins and Enzymes (Z. Bohak and N. Sharon, eds.) pp. 247–265. Academic Press, New York, 1977.
202. E. Hurwitz, R. Maron, A. Bernstein, M. Wilchek, M. Sela, and R. Arnon, *Int. J. Cancer* **21**, 747 (1978).
203. T. Kitao and L. Hattori, *Nature (London)* **265**, 81 (1977).

204. J. M. Varga, N. Asato, S. Lande, and A. B. Lerner, *Nature* (*London*) **267**, 56 (1977).
205. A. Trouet, D. Deprez-De Campeneere, A. Zenebergh, and R. Hullhoven, *in* "Adriamycin Review," Eortc International Symposium (M. Staquet *et al.*, eds.), pp. 62–69. Eur. Press Medikon, Ghent, 1975.
206. R. S. Benjamin, J. W. Mason, and M. E. Billingham, *Cancer Treat. Rep.* **62**, 935 (1978).
207. M. Gosalvez, M. F. Blanco, C. Vivero, and F. Valles, *Eur. J. Cancer* **14**, 1185 (1978).
208. A. Brugarolas, N. Pachon, M. Gosalvez, A. P. Llanderal, A. J. Laclave, J. M. Buesa, and M. G. Marco, *Cancer Treat. Rep.* **62**, 1527 (1978).
209. H. Cortés-Funes, M. Gosalvez, A. Moyano, A. Nanas, and C. Mendiola, *Cancer Treat. Rep.* **63**, 903 (1979).

2

Total Synthesis of Doxorubicin
and Related Compounds

Remarkable chemical interest has arisen on the total synthesis of doxorubicin and of the anthracycline glycosides in general. Major efforts have been directed towards the synthesis of the aglycone moiety in which the problems related with functionalization, regiospecificity, and stereospecificity represent an attractive challenge for organic chemists. However, different syntheses of daunosamine starting from more readily available sugar precursors, and also from nonsugar precursors, have been published. The study of the synthesis of the glycosidic linkage has resulted in the development of efficient glycosidation procedures. The aim to develop a method, alternative to the biosynthetic process, for the production of doxorubicin appears to be generally interwoven with that of providing practical routes towards new structurally related analogues. In this chapter, synthetic studies directly concerning the synthesis of doxorubicin, as well as general approaches to the solution of the above-mentioned problems, will be reported. Total syntheses specifically aimed at new analogues will be dealt with in more detail in Chapters 7 and 8.

WONG'S SYNTHESIS OF DAUNOMYCINONE

The classical reaction of a substituted tetralin with a phthalic acid derivative (*1,2*) was used in the first studies of antracyclinone synthesis, namely those leading to **1** (*3*) and to **2** (*4*), the C-7 hydroxyl (or methoxyl) group being introduced via a benzylic bromination and subsequent nucleophilic displacement. The preparation of 4-demethoxy analogues on the basis of an improved version of Wong's scheme for the synthesis of **2** will be presented

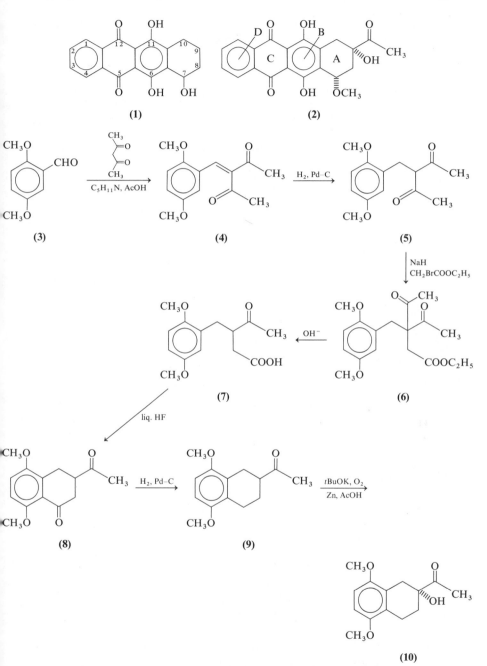

Scheme 1. The synthesis of 6-acetyl-1,4-dimethoxy-6-hydroxytetralin (*4,5*).

in Chapter 7. On the other hand, Wong's application of the same procedure to the synthesis of racemic daunomycinone represented the first total synthesis of this compound and of a biosynthetic anthracyclinone as well (5).

Starting materials were racemic 6-acetyl-1,4-dimethoxy-6-hydroxytetralin (**10**), also used for the synthesis of **2** and obtained in seven steps starting from 2,5-dimethoxybenzaldehyde (Scheme 1) and 3-acetoxyphthalic acid monomethyl ester, whose condensation, upon heating in trifluoroacetic anhydride, afforded a mixture of diaryl ketones that was saponified and cyclized in hydrogen fluoride to give the mixture **11a** and **11b** (overall yield 19%). The mixture was methylated and the side-chain ketone protected as in **12**; then selective bromination with bromosuccinimide, methanolysis, and TLC separation afforded the two epimeric mixtures, **13a,b** and **14a,b**. Acid hydrolysis of **13a,b** followed by TLC separation gave daunomycinone

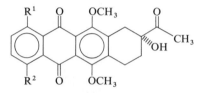

(**11a**: R^1 = H, R^2 = OH)
(**11b**: R^1 = OH, R^2 = H)

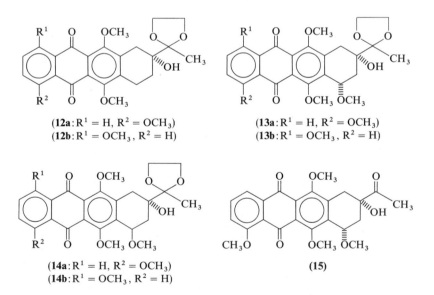

(**12a**: R^1 = H, R^2 = OCH$_3$)
(**12b**: R^1 = OCH$_3$, R^2 = H)

(**13a**: R^1 = H, R^2 = OCH$_3$)
(**13b**: R^1 = OCH$_3$, R^2 = H)

(**14a**: R^1 = H, R^2 = OCH$_3$)
(**14b**: R^1 = OCH$_3$, R^2 = H)

(**15**)

trimethylether (**15**) and isodaunomycinone trimethylether (**16**), both compounds being transformed to (±)-daunomycinone (**18**) and to (±)-isodaunomycinone (**19**) by demethylation of the phenolic groups with aluminum chloride, oxidation to the diquinone form (e.g., **17** from **15**), and remethylation of C-4 with methyl sulfate, the benzylic methoxyl group being substituted with a hydroxyl via the 7-*O*-trifluoroacetate and treatment of the latter with ammonium hydroxide.

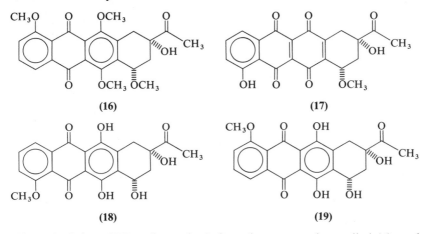

(16)   (17)

(18)   (19)

The principles of Wong's synthesis have been recently applied (*6*) to the preparation of (±)-7-deoxycarminomycinone (**24**). In this study, two alternative procedures for the synthesis of tetralin derivative **10** were provided. The first involved acylation of 1,4-dimethoxybenzene with succinic anhydride and AlCl₃ followed by catalytic hydrogenation and polyphosphoric acid treatment to give **20** in 45% yield (*7*). Acylation of **20** with acetic anhydride and boron trifluoride afforded **21**, which was hydrogenolyzed to Wong's intermediate (*9*). Hydroxylation of **9** as described by Wong *et al.* (*4*) gave **10** in 21–22% overall yield from 2,4-dimethoxybenzene (six steps).

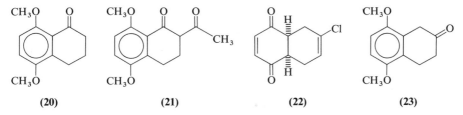

(20)   (21)   (22)   (23)

According to the second route, β-tetralone (**23**) was obtained from benzoquinone, whose Diels–Alder adduct **22** was methylated with dimethyl sulfate and potassium carbonate and then treated with sulfuric acid to give

23. The latter compound was submitted to a Grignard reaction with ethinyl magnesium bromide and the ethinyl hydroxy derivative thus formed was hydrated to give **10** in 35% overall yield from benzoquinone (five steps).

Acylation of **10** with 3-acetoxyphthalic acid half ester followed by alkaline treatment and ring closure in liquid hydrogen fluoride afforded the mixture of regioisomers **11a** and **11b** in 33% yield. Demethylation of the mixture and chromatographic separation allowed the isolation of **24**. Transformation of **24** to (±)-7-deoxydaunomycinone (**25**) in reasonable yield (60%) was carried out by selective methylation with an excess of diazomethane in methylene chloride. The selective methylation was indicated as a general reaction of compounds containing the 1,4,5-trihydeoxyanthraquinone system and its application for the conversion in 45% yield of carminomycinone (**26**) to daunomycinone (**18**) was also reported.

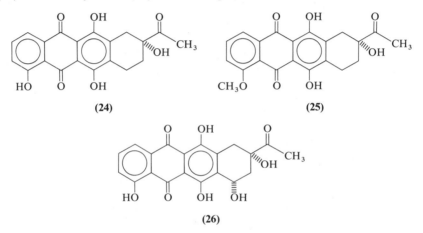

(24)   (25)

(26)

The important intermediate **10** has been resolved in the two enantiomeric forms by crystallization of the Schiff base of racemic **10** with (−)-1-phenylethylamine, thus allowing the synthesis of optically active anthracyclinones (8). Recently, an asymmetric synthesis of **10** has been described (9). According to this work, the ester **27**, prepared with known procedures and in three steps from 1,4-dimethoxybenzene, was first condensed with ethylformate in the presence of sodium hydride and then cyclized in strong acid conditions to give **28** in 43% yield. The corresponding acid, obtained upon alkaline hydrolysis of **28**, was condensed with S-(−)-ethyl prolinate by the diethyl phosphorocyanidate–triethylamine method to give **29** in quantitative yield. Basic hydrolysis of ester **29** afforded the corresponding acid that was converted by treatment with N-bromosuccinimide and potassium *tert*-butoxide to a mixture of bromolactone (**30**) and its 5,6-diepi diastereoisomer in the ratio 98.5 to 1.5 in 87% yield. Debromination of the

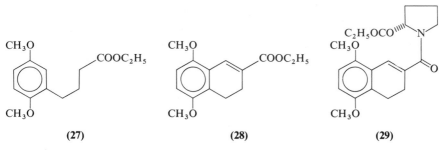

(27)   **(28)**   **(29)**

mixture with tributyltin hydride and a trace of azobisisobutyronitrile followed by crystallization allowed the isolation of **31**. Acid hydrolysis of **31** followed by resterification with diazomethane afforded **32**, which was

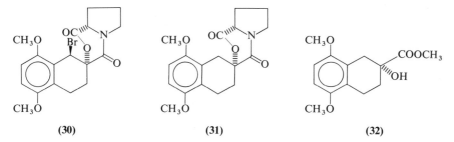

(30)   **(31)**   **(32)**

then hydrolyzed to the corresponding hydroxy acid whose treatment with excess methyllithium gave levorotatory **10**. The authors had also carried out a parallel series of transformations starting from acid **33**, prepared by acylation of **28** with O-methoxycarbonylbenzoyl chloride, alkaline hydrolysis and cyclization in hydrogen fluoride. However treatment of optically active **34** with methyllithium failed to give the corresponding methyl ketone derivative (4-demethoxy-7-deoxydaunomycinone).

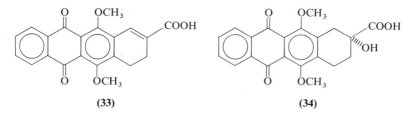

(33)   **(34)**

OTHER SYNTHESES STARTING FROM 3-METHOXYPHTHALATE AND A TETRALIN OR THEIR EQUIVALENTS

The synthesis of (±)-9-deoxydaunomycinone (**35**) reported by Kende *et al.* (*10*) consisted in the preparation of **36** by condensation of 2-cyano-3-methoxybenzoic acid with **37** (the latter synthon being obtained from Wong's tetraline (**8**) in four reaction steps) and subsequent photo Fries rearrangement of **36** to give, regiospecifically, **38**. Basic hydrolysis of the latter followed by cyclization and deblocking with liquid hydrogen fluoride at room temperature afforded **35**. Yield of **35** from **36** was 11%, including a final chromatographic purification.

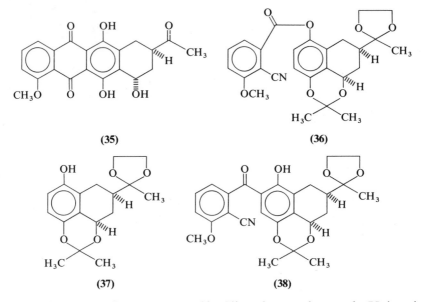

(35)   (36)

(37)   (38)

A similar approach was attempted by Sih and co-workers at the University of Wisconsin, but probably unexpected difficulties were encountered and regioselectivity was not obtained. The approach was based on a model study (*11*) in which compound **39** was cyclized in 60 to 80% yield to **40** by reaction with boron trifluoride etherate, apparently via Fries rearrangement followed by ring closure. However, cyclization of **41** (obtained upon selective acylation of 2-acetyl-5,8-dihydroxy-4-tetralone with 2-carbomethoxy-3-methoxybenzoic acid) and of **42a** in the same conditions was not successful. On the other hand **42b** gave the regioisomeric mixture of **43a**

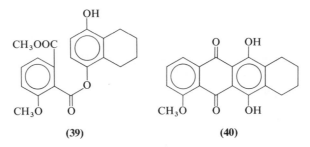

(39)   (40)

and **43b** in 37% yield upon heating at 100°C for 75 min with the above-mentioned reagent, but it appeared clearly that the cyclization process did not proceed regiospecifically as had been hoped. The likely intervention of a Hayashi rearrangement (intermediate formation of **44**) was suggested for the explanation of the unfavourable result. In the same study hydroxylation at C-9 of compounds **43a** and **43b** was achieved in an original four-step procedure involving conversion to the enolacetate by refluxing with acetic anhydride and *p*-toluenesulfonic acid, epoxidation with *m*-chloroperbenzoic acid, and an alkaline and an acid treatment. The resulting compounds (±)-7-deoxydaunomycinone (**25**) and (±)-7-deoxyisodaunomycinone (**45**), were obtained in 50% overall yield from, respectively, **43a** and **43b**.

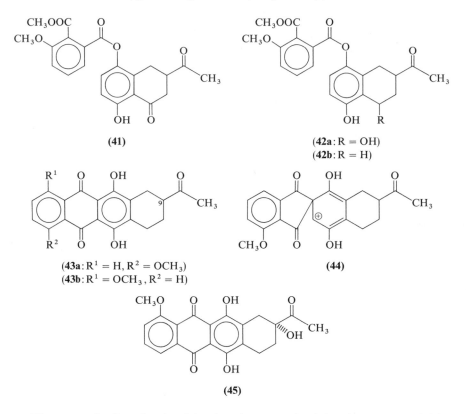

(41)

(42a: R = OH)
(42b: R = H)

(43a: R^1 = H, R^2 = OCH$_3$)
(43b: R^1 = OCH$_3$, R^2 = H)

(44)

(45)

The control of regioselectivity has been attained by Swenton and his group by allowing dimethyl 3-methoxyphthalate to react with a metalated tetrahydronaphthoquinone ketal derivative in order to obtain, after cycliza-tion, only the desired substituted tetracyclic compound (*12,13*). Bromode-rivative **54**, used for the preparation of key intermediate **55a**, was obtained

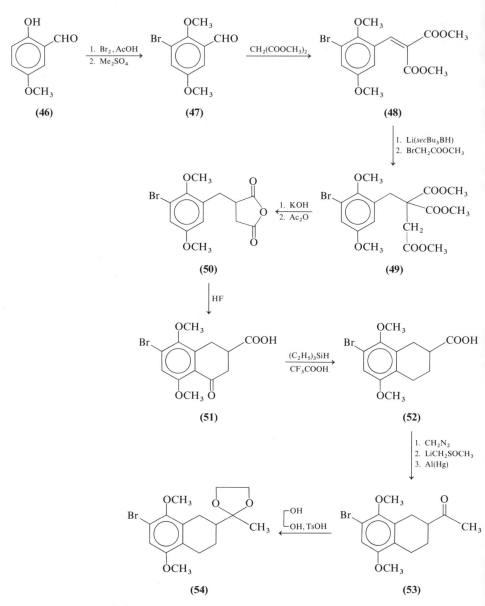

Scheme 2. Synthesis of **54** according to Swenton and Raynolds (*13*).

as indicated in Scheme 2 starting from 2-hydroxy-5-methoxybenzaldehyde (**46**). Compound **54** was converted to **55a** by electrochemical oxidation in methanolic potassium hydroxide at a platinum anode in 85% yield, the reaction being performed at $-3°C$, as at higher temperatures a concomitant debromination took place. Compound **55a** could be metalated with *n*-butyllithium in tetrahydrofuran at $-90°C$, thus giving rise to carbanion derivative **55b**, in which the polarity of the reactive center is reversed in respect to that of the corresponding quinone. In fact, addition of dimethyl 3-methoxyphthalate to the solution of **55b** gave **56**, isolated in 69% yield after chromatographic separation. Compound **56** was converted to **58**, preferably without isolation of pure intermediates, by reductive hydrolysis

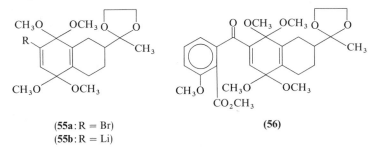

(**55a**: R = Br)
(**55b**: R = Li)

(**56**)

with stannous chloride and trifluoroacetic acid to give **57a**, which was saponified to **57b** and cyclized in methanesulfonic acid or in hydrogen fluoride to ($\pm$)-7,9-dideoxydaunomycinone **58**.

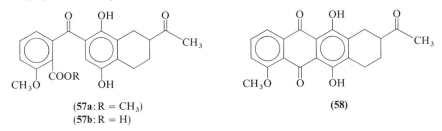

(**57a**: R = CH$_3$)
(**57b**: R = H)

(**58**)

A similar reaction sequence was also carried out starting from **59**, but compound **60** appeared to be highly unstable as it oxidized rapidly to **61**

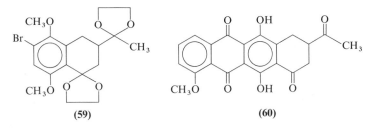

(**59**)

(**60**)

and could not be isolated as a single product, notwithstanding precautions that were taken to avoid contact with air. In the same study, the use of aryl-lithium derivative **62** as the nucleophilic reagent was explored. Reaction of **62** with dimethyl 3-methoxyphthalate gave **63** in 40% yield. The following steps, namely the conversion of **63** to **64a** or **64b** and that of the latter to **58**

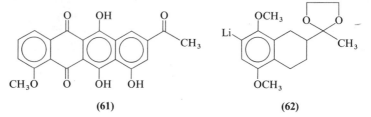

(61)   (62)

by oxidation with silver oxide followed by reduction with sodium dithionite, were performed with 37 and 68% yield, respectively.

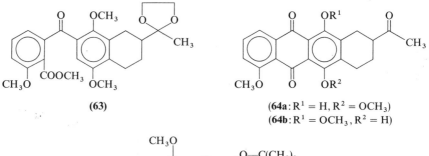

(63)   (64a: R¹ = H, R² = OCH₃)
                                             (64b: R¹ = OCH₃, R² = H)

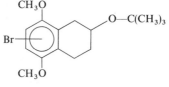

(65)

Synthon **65** has been used by Alexander and Mitscher (*14*) in an approach to tetracyclic intermediates useful for anthracyclinone synthesis according to a procedure similar to that mentioned above, that is, metalation with butyllithium and nucleophilic condensation with dimethylphthalate, follow-ed by ring closure. As **65** was used as a mixture of the two regioisomers for the purpose of preparing ring D symmetrically substituted analogues of the known anthracyclinones, this approach will be dealt with in Chapter 7. Compound **65** was obtained by the authors in a five-step reaction sequence from benzoquinone, each step showing a yield higher than 90%.

The synthetic approach developed by F. Johnson and his group at New York State University represents a further refinement of the synthetic principles outlined above. The regiospecific approach to unsymmetrically substituted anthraquinones (*15*) was based on the finding that 3-bromo-4-methoxyphthalide (**66**) reacted in 70 to 85% yield with compounds of structure **67**, where R was H, Cl, Br, or CH_3 to give the corresponding 3-aryl-phthalides (**68**). The favorable course of the reaction (occuring also with

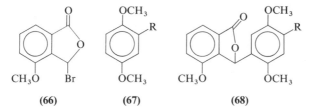

(66)   (67)   (68)

structural variants of **66** and **67**) was ascribed to a deactivation induced by the 3-phthalido group which inhibited further alkylation of the aromatic substrate. Conversion of **68** to islandicin (**71**) was carried out in good yield. The steps involved were reduction of **68** (R = CH_3) with triethylsilane in trifluoroacetic acid to give **69**, ring closure with trifluoroacetic anhydride in trifluoroacetic acid to **70**, oxidation of the latter with chromium trioxide in acetic acid, and finally O-demethylation with aluminum chloride in nitrobenzene at 90°C.

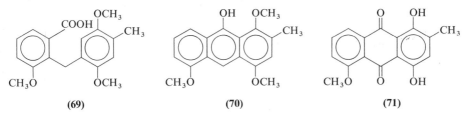

(69)   (70)   (71)

This approach allowed the same group (*16*) to elaborate a regioselective synthetic procedure for racemic 7,9-dideoxydaunomycinone (**58**) (Scheme 3). According to this procedure, which was carried out in the **a** (R = CH_3) and **b** (R = C_2H_5) series, compound **73** was selectively hydrolyzed to **74** and the latter cyclized to **75**, which afforded the acid (**76**) upon stepwise reduction of the benzylic ketone and the lactone groups. Cyclization of **76** afforded the tautomeric mixture of **77** and **78**, whose oxidation gave the anthracyclinone derivative **79**. Saponification of **79** to **80** and decarboxylation gave the acid **81**, which was converted to **82** upon reaction of the chloride with lithium dimethyl cuprate. Final dealkylation was performed in two steps (via oxidation to the anthradiquinone and subsequent reduction) when R was an ethyl group. Overall yield was 20% as all reactions showed yields in the range 80 to 98%, with the exception of Jones reagent oxidation of **78** to **79** (62%).

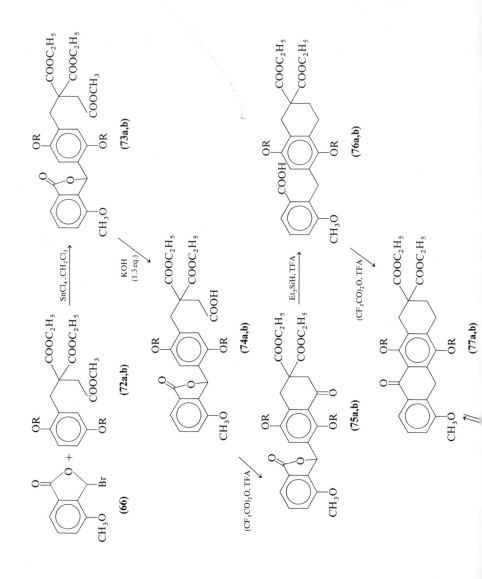

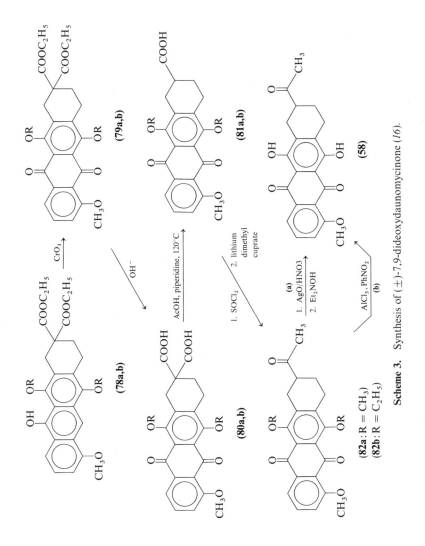

Scheme 3. Synthesis of (±)-7,9-dideoxydaunomycinone (*16*).

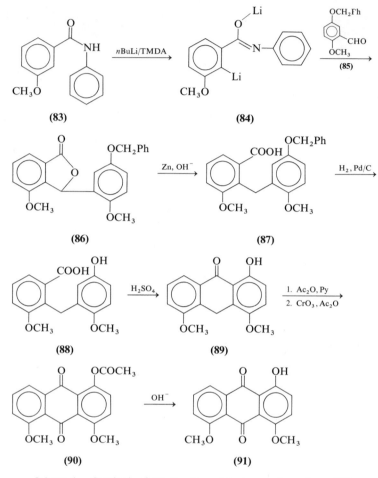

Scheme 4.   Synthesis of 4,5-dimethoxy-1-hydroxyanthraquinone (*17*).

In this section two studies, whose aim was the development of a regio-selective synthetic scheme to doxorubicin aglycone formally similar to those already described, but by a reversed approach, are included. According to these approaches, a synthon corresponding to ring D is the carbanionic species in the key coupling reaction, whereas an electrophilic center is a carbonyl function substituting the aromatic ring which will become ring B in the final tetracyclic product.

The first study, concerned with the approach to the anthraquinone system via a phthalide intermediate and allowing regioselective synthesis of an anthracyclinone, was reported by Baldwin and Bair (*17*). The MIT chemists carried out quantitatively the metalation of *N*-phenyl-*m*-anisamide (**83**) to the dilithium salt (**84**), whose reaction with 4-benzyloxy-2-methoxybenz-aldehyde afforded phthalide **86** in nearly quantitative yield (Scheme 4). Selective reduction of **86** to **87** followed by debenzylation gave **88** in 94% yield. The four steps necessary to convert **88** into the desired asymmetrically substituted anthraquinone **91** were: (a) a cyclization in concentrated sulfuric acid to anthrone derivative **89**; (b) conversion of the latter to the acetate; (c) chromic acid oxidation to **90**; and (d) deacetylation, the total yield (not optimized) from **88** to **91** being 20% of theoretical. Utilization of these reactions in the synthesis of anthracyclinones has been announced by the authors.

In the second study Forbes *et al.* (*18*) treated *N-tert*-butyl-3-methoxy benzamide (**92**) with two equivalents of *n*-butyllithium in tetrahydrofuran to obtain **93**, which was allowed to react with electrophilic **94** to give the

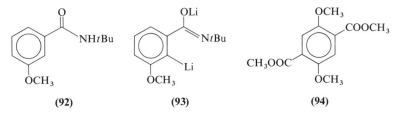

(92)   (93)   (94)

ketoamide **95** together with the corresponding lactol tautomer **96**. Cyclization of **97**, derived from the hydrolysis of the mixture, with acid catalyst,

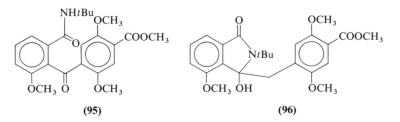

(95)   (96)

followed by remethylation gave the anthraquinone derivative **98**, a Hayashi rearrangement being considered unlikely because of the substitution pattern of **97**.

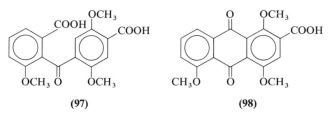

(97)   (98)

CLOSURE OF RING A IN SUBSTITUTED ANTHRAQUINONES AND THEIR DERIVATIVES

Different studies concerning the regioselective synthesis of adriamycinone and related anthracyclinones have been based on the formation and closure of a proper side chain in anthraquinone derivatives. Such approaches are in principle endowed with regioselectivity and are therefore useful ones, provided that substituted anthraquinones be readily available for starting.

A total synthesis of anthracyclinones via intramolecular base-catalyzed cyclization of a suitable anthraquinone derivative, also allowing regiospecific preparation of the biosynthetic aglycones, has been carried out by Suzuki et al. (19). The synthesis has been applied in both the 4-demethoxy and the 4-methoxy series. Bromination of **99** with bromosuccinimide followed by alkylation with ethyl 3-acetyllevulinate gave **100**. Treatment of the latter with alkalis afforded **101**, from which **102** was prepared in three steps. Overall yield of **102** from 2-methylhydroquinone, the precursor of **99**, was 23%, with one chromatographic separation.

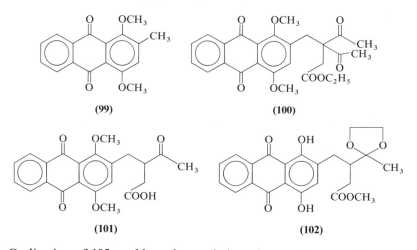

(99)   **(100)**

(101)   **(102)**

Cyclization of **102** could not be carried out in a variety of acid and basic conditions. On the other hand, compound **103**, the diketo form of the yellow 1,4,9,10-tetrahydroxyanthracene derivative obtained from **102** upon reduction with zinc dust in glacial acetic acid, was cyclized in rather restricted experimental conditions, as **103** showed a high tendency to reoxidize to **102** in the basic medium required for the reaction. The best procedure consisted in the treatment of **103** with calcium oxide in ethylene glycol–diglyme and in the presence of zinc dust at $-78°C$ in a nitrogen atmosphere, followed by heating for 3 min at 140°C. The yield was 54% of **104**, whose formation involved the air oxidation of an intermediate cyclization product.

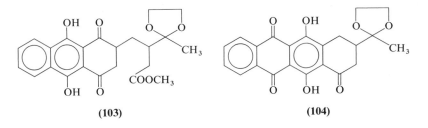

(103)   (104)

As a more practical alternative the authors converted **102** to the aldehyde (**105**) by a five-step procedure including (a) benzylation of the phenolic hydroxyl groups; (b) hydrolysis of the ester; (c) reduction of the free carboxylic acid to a primary alcohol with borane in tetrahydrofuran; (d) removal of the benzyl groups by catalytic hydrogenation; and (e) oxidation of the primary alcoholic group to an aldehyde with pyridinium chlorochromate (overall yield 35%).

Cyclization of **105** was performed using sodium hydrosulfite and sodium hydroxide in aqueous dioxane to give **106** in 50% yield. Ring closure of an intermediate reduction product of **105** to give **106** is a resonable step in the reaction, the final product apparently being formed from **107** by hydrogenolysis of the benzylic hydroxyl followed by air reoxidation to the anthraquinone system or, as suggested by the authors, by dehydration and tautomerization. 4-Demethoxy-7,9-deoxydaunomycinone (**108**) was obtained upon deketalization of **106**.

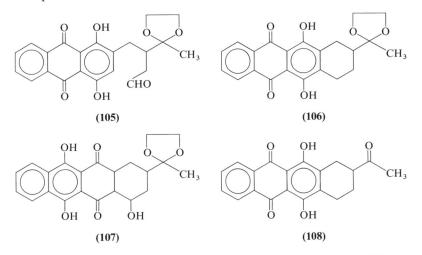

(105)   (106)

(107)   (108)

Application of this approach to the 4-methoxy series proved laborious, but the final objective was reached as follows. The starting material, 1-hydroxy-5-methoxyanthraquinone (**109**), was methylated by a Marschalk reaction and acetylated to **110**. Radical bromination of **110** and separation of the monobromide from the dibromide, followed by alkylation with ethyl-3-acetyl levulinate, afforded **111**, from which **112** was obtained upon treatment with alkalis. The overall yield of the five-step procedure was 52%, including two chromatographic separations.

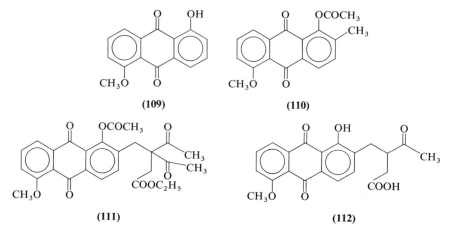

(109)

(110)

(111)

(112)

Conversion of **112** to **113** was carried out with potassium persulphate in alkaline solution (yield 42%), and **113** was then submitted to esterification and ketalization to give the desired **114**. The latter compound was reduced to **115** with dithionite and, as **115** was cyclized, at best, in 8% yield in conditions similar to those used with **103**, **114** was transformed to **116** in five steps and 42% overall yield.

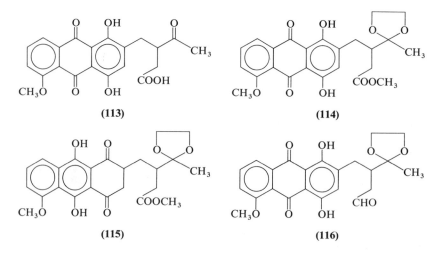

(113)

(114)

(115)

(116)

Cyclization of **116** with basic sodium dithionite afforded **117** in 55% yield. Deketalization of **117** to 7,9-dideoxydaunomycinone (**83**) followed by hydroxylation at C-9 upon (a) enol acetylation, (b) epoxidation, (c) alkaline hydrolysis, and (d) acid rearrangement gave (±)-7-deoxydaunomycinone (**25**).

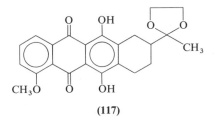

(117)

An anionic equivalent of the Friedel–Crafts cycloacylation that shows some promise as a synthetic entry into the anthracycline antibiotics has been reported (*20*). This reaction was studied on a number of *o*-bromophenyl-alkanoic acids which were converted to the corresponding benzocyclo-alkenones with *n*-butyllithium in tetrahydrofuran at temperatures ranging from −110° to 0°C. When **118** was used as the starting compound, cycliza-tion to **119** was recorded to occur in 55% yield. Compound **119** was also

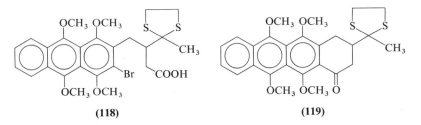

(118)   **(119)**

obtained upon treatment of the methyl ester of **118** with *tert*-butyllithium at −100°C. On the other hand, anthraquinone derivative **120** did not afford cyclization in similar conditions because of the deactivating effect of the quinone and interaction of the reagent with the quinone carbonyl. Com-pound **118** was obtained from **120** in good yield by treatment with sodium dithionite and dimethylsulfate in the presence of potassium hydroxide. Anthraquinone **120** was prepared from 3-bromo-1,4-dimethoxy-2-methyl-anthraquinone in four steps, and 70–79% overall yield. The authors pointed out the efficacy of reductive methylation of anthraquinone derivatives for the production of useful intermediates such as **121**, whose cyclization to **119** took place in quantitative yield upon treatment with trifluoroacetic anhy-dride at −40°C.

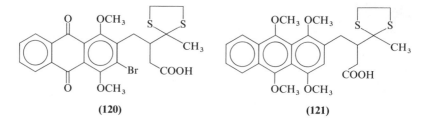

(120)   (121)

The use of the Marschalk reaction (21) allowed Morris and Brown (22) to obtain naphthacenequinone derivative (40) by dithionite reduction of 1,4-dihydroxy-5-methoxyanthraquinone (122) (prepared by methoxylation of 1,4,5-trichloroanthraquinone followed by selective oxidative demethylation with argentic oxide and subsequent reduction at positions 1 and 4) to give the leuco derivative 123 and reaction of the latter with succindialdehyde in the presence of sodium carbonate and in an oxygen-free atmosphere, followed by oxygenation. Analogues 124a,b,c were prepared starting from 1,4-dihydroxy-, 1,4,5-trihydroxy-, and 1,4,5,8-tetrahydroxyanthraquinone. The authors pointed out the usefulness of the Marschalk reaction for the regioselective synthesis of anthracyclinones.

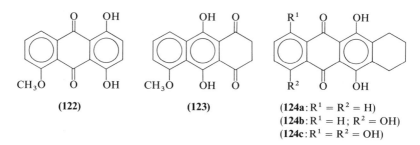

(122)   (123)   (124a: $R^1 = R^2 = H$)
                                          (124b: $R^1 = H$; $R^2 = OH$)
                                          (124c: $R^1 = R^2 = OH$)

Other synthetic approaches to anthracyclinone derivatives according to principles analogous to those already described are those of Krohn (23). As these studies were more precisely aimed to the synthesis of new compound related with rhodomycinones, they are reported in Chapter 8.

The conversion of the β-methyl group into a formyl group in easily accessible, either natural (morindone, rubiadin 1-methyl ether) or synthetic (1-hydroxy-2-methyl anthraquinone, 1,4-dihydroxy-2-methylanthraquinone) α-hydroxyanthraquinones by benzylic dibromination of the corresponding O-methyl ethers followed by heating of the geminal dibromo derivative with aqueous acetic acid was carried out by Roberts et al. (24). Roberts and Rutledge (25) also introduced the β-formyl group in 1-hydroxyanthraquinone by means of a Claisen rearrangement of the allyl ether, isomerization of the resulting 2-allyl derivative into the 2-prop-1′-enyl isomer with base, and finally ozonolysis.

APPLICATIONS OF THE DIELS–ALDER REACTION FOR THE CONSTRUCTION OF RING A

The obvious application of the Diels–Alder reaction to build up the tetracyclic ring system of the anthracyclinones has been widely explored, and it represents one of the most, if not the most, attractive routes leading to economically feasible preparations of such compounds. The first approach is that involving the use of linear tricyclic derivatives, bearing a quinone system in the ring that will become ring B in the final tetracyclic compound, as the philodiene, and a proper butadiene derivative as the diene. A single interesting exception to this principle will also be considered.

Lee *et al.* (*26*) succeeded in the preparation of the desired adducts **126a** and **126b** resulting as the major products of the reaction of quinizarinequinone (**125**) with, respectively, 1,3-butadiene and 1-acetoxy-1,3-butadiene. Other substituted butadienes gave mainly the undesired "internal" addition. Model compounds **126a** and **126b** were further transformed, *inter alia*, to, respectively, **127** and **128** both in six-step reaction sequences.

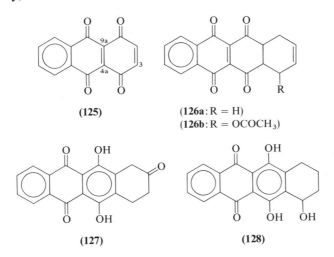

(**125**)

(**126a**: R = H)
(**126b**: R = OCOCH$_3$)

(**127**)   (**128**)

The second now classical (after that of Wong) total synthesis of (±)-daunomycinone was instead carried out by Kende *et al.* (*27*), starting from 5-methoxy-1,4,9,10-anthradiquinone (**129**) that was allowed to react with 2-acetoxybutadiene to give the 1:1 mixture of **130a** and **130b** in 71% yield. Tautomerization and acid cleavage of the enol acetate function gave the mixture of the corresponding ketones from which the desired regioisomer **131** was isolated. The C-9 side chain was built in two steps and 20% yield (first reaction with a tenfold excess of ethynyl magnesium bromide, then hydration with mercuric oxide and sulfuric acid) to give ($\pm$)-7-deoxydauno-mycinone (**25**). The benzylic hydroxyl was introduced by radical bromination at C-7 followed by hydrolysis, with ($\pm$)-7-epidaunomycinone (**132**), co-produced as the major product with ($\pm$)-daunomycinone (**18**), being epi-merized to the latter by solution in trifluoroacetic acid and aqueous work-up. As an additional application of this synthetic approach, Kende and Tsay (*28*) devised the conversion of ketone **131** to racemic rhodomycin aglycones, namely γ-, α-, and β-rhodomycinone (see Chapter 8).

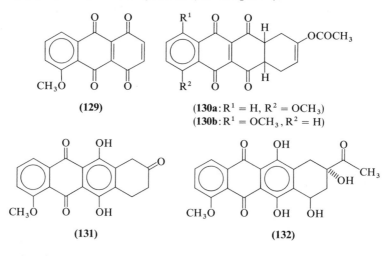

(129)

(130a: R^1 = H, R^2 = OCH_3)
(130b: R^1 = OCH_3, R^2 = H)

(131)

(132)

Starting from interesting findings of previous workers (*29*), Kelly *et al.* (*30*) were able to obtain the mixture of **136a** and **136b** upon reaction of **135** with 3-ethyl-1-methoxybutadiene, intermediate **135** being prepared by Diels–Alder condensation of naphthazarin **133** with 1-methoxycyclohexa-1,3-diene to give **134**, whose oxydation afforded **135**. As in Kende's syn-thesis presented above, the regioselectivity problem was not considered in this approach. However, the relative amounts of the two regioisomers **136a** and **136b** were estimated by aromatization of ring A with oxygen and alkalis followed by elimination of ethylene by heating to give **137a** and **137b**. De-methylation of the latter mixture with boron tribromide at $-70°C$ afforded the mixture of **138a** and **138b** which was found to contain more than 80% of the latter unfavorable isomer by comparison of the IR spectrum of the mixture with that of authentic samples of the two regioisomers. The partial regioselectivity of the Diels–Alder reaction was tentatively ascribed to a different electron-withdrawing effect of the two quinone carbonyls in the

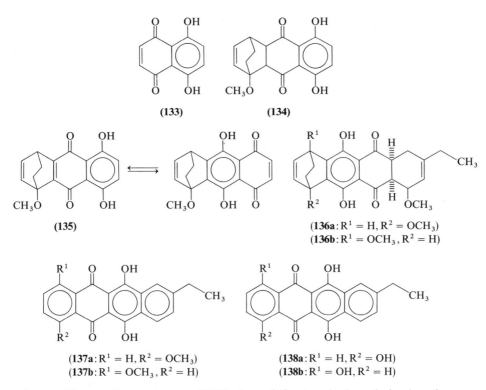

(133) **(134)**

(135) **(136a:R¹ = H, R² = OCH₃)**
(136b:R¹ = OCH₃, R² = H)

(137a:R¹ = H, R² = OCH₃) **(138a:R¹ = H, R² = OH)**
(137b:R¹ = OCH₃, R² = H) **(138b:R¹ = OH, R² = H)**

less stable reactive tautomer of **135**. One of the two hydroxyls having the possibility to chelate with the methoxyl group, the corresponding carbonyl group is less strongly hydrogen-bonded than the other one.

An improved approach to the Diels–Alder route has been developed by Chandler and Stoodley (*31*). Limitations of the standard condensation of substituted butadienes to the diquinone **125** were circumverted by the conversion of **125** to the epoxide **139** with *m*-chloroperbenzoic acid in reasonable (50%) yield, followed by the reaction of **139** with an appropriate diene.

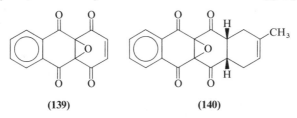

(139) **(140)**

Reaction of **139** with isoprene, already reported to give the 4a,9a adduct when allowed to react with **125** (*31,32*), gave **140** in 90% yield. Treatment of **140** with sodium dithionite afforded **141** in 35% yield. Transformation of **141** to **142** was performed by reaction of the former with lead tetraacetate in acetic acid followed by treatment with base (80% yield). Similar reaction sequences utilizing cyclopentadiene and cyclo-hexa-1,3-diene as reactants in the Diels–Alder step afforded compounds **143a** and **143b**.

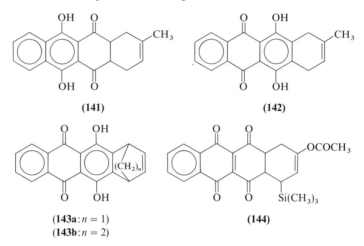

(141)   (142)

(143a: $n = 1$)   (144)
(143b: $n = 2$)

It can be deduced from the results of these studies that the DCB → DCBA Diels–Alder route has not met the requirements of regioselectivity necessary for the development of a reasonable synthesis of doxorubicin. For this reason, this approach is expected to give best results when the objective is the synthesis of ring D symmetrically substituted anthracyclinones, as it is the case of the 4-demethoxy analogues. Other recent investigations have in fact been directed towards the synthesis of the said analogues which represent a new class of potentially useful antitumor drugs. One investigation is that of Garland *et al.* (*33*) at Searle Laboratories, based on the reaction of **125** with *trans*-4-(trimethylsilyl)-2-acetoxy-1,3-butadiene to give **144** in which the trimethylsilyl group functions as a precursor of the benzylic hydroxyl and represents a remarkable solution of the functionalization at C-7 in synthetic anthracyclinones. Another approach, that of Kerdesky and Cava (*34*), differs from the other mentioned, as intermediate **145**, generated by zinc debromination of 2,3-dibromomethyl-1,4-dimethoxyanthra-

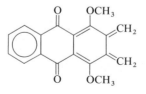

(145)

quinone, is the reacting species in the Diels–Alder condensation with methyl vinyl ketone to give **108**. Further details on these approaches will be given in Chapter 7.

OTHER SYNTHESES BASED ON DIELS–ALDER CONDENSATION

The construction of rings A and D starting from a precursor representing rings C and B, together with a solution of the problem of regioselectivity, are essential features of the remarkable synthetic study of Kelly *et al. (35)*.

According to this study, compound **147** was regioselectively obtained by reaction of naphthazarin monopivalate (**146**) with 3-ethyl-1-methoxybutadiene. The favorable course of the reaction was ascribed to the opposite effects of the *peri*-hydroxyl group and of the *peri*-acyloxy group on the two carbonyls which make the C-4 carbonyl the most electron-withdrawing substituent on the C-2,C-3 double bond, thus allowing the orientational control of the Diels–Alder addition of the substituted butadiene. Compound **147** was epoxidized and then oxidized with lead dioxide to give **148**,

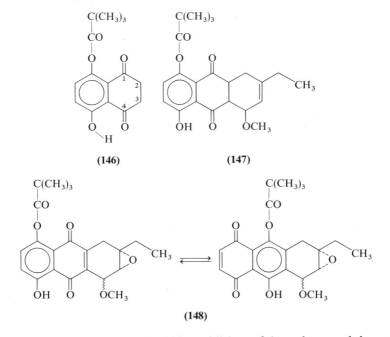

(146)　　　　**(147)**

(148)

on which regioselective Diels–Alder addition of 1-methoxycyclohexa-1,3-diene was carried out exploiting the same orientational effects as above. The resulting tetracyclic derivative **149** was treated with base to give **150**, and the latter was transformed to the interesting highly functionalized anthracyclinone derivative **151**. The reported overall yield of **149** from **146** was 45%.

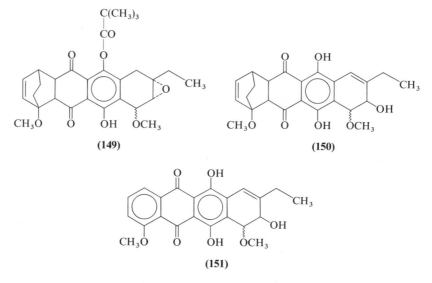

(149)   (150)

(151)

In their syntheses of 4-deoxy-γ-rhodomycinone (*36*) and of 4-demethoxy-daunomycinone (*37*), Krohn and his coworkers also used the principle of the stepwise construction of rings A and D on the two-ring precursor, naphthazarin (**133**). Basically, naphthazarin was condensed with the proper butadiene derivative to give either **152a** or **152b**, the former being then converted to **153a** and the second functionalized to **153b**. Reaction of both **153a** or **b** with 1-acetoxybutadiene allowed the tetracyclic derivatives (see Chapters 7 and 8).

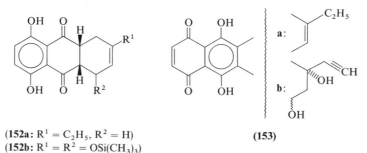

(152a: $R^1 = C_2H_5$, $R^2 = H$)   (153)
(152b: $R^1 = R^2 = OSi(CH_3)_3$)

A different strategy is exemplified by the synthesis of ($\pm$)-7-deoxydauno-mycinone (**25**) developed by the group at the University of Rochester, the so called "isobenzofuran route to anthracyclinones" (*38*). The synthesis is

based on the Diels–Alder condensation of isobenzofuran derivative, originated by thermolysis of the mixture of **154a** and **154b** with tetrahydronaphthoquinone derivative **155** giving rise to the mixture of the corresponding
adducts **156a** and **156b**. The latter was aromatized to the mixture of **157a**
and **157b**. Reductive acetylation of regioisomeric mixture **157a,b** gave the

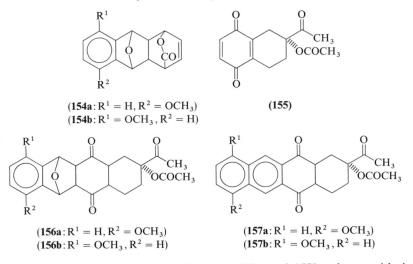

(**154a**: R^1 = H, R^2 = OCH$_3$)   (**155**)
(**154b**: R^1 = OCH$_3$, R^2 = H)

(**156a**: R^1 = H, R^2 = OCH$_3$)   (**157a**: R^1 = H, R^2 = OCH$_3$)
(**156b**: R^1 = OCH$_3$, R^2 = H)   (**157b**: R^1 = OCH$_3$, R^2 = H)

corresponding mixture of quinol diacetate **158a** and **158b**, whose oxidation
with chromic anhydride in acetic acid led to **159a** and **159b**. Hydrolysis
with acid of the latter gave (±)-7-deoxydaunomycinone and (±)-7-
deoxyisodaunomycinone.

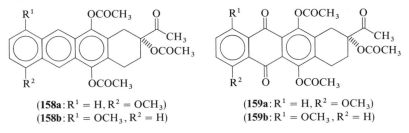

(**158a**: R^1 = H, R^2 = OCH$_3$)   (**159a**: R^1 = H, R^2 = OCH$_3$)
(**158b**: R^1 = OCH$_3$, R^2 = H)   (**159b**: R^1 = OCH$_3$, R^2 = H)

An intermolecular cycloaddition reaction of the *o*-quinodimethane **161**,
generated *in situ* by heating benzocyclobutenol (**160**), with tetrahydronaphthoquinone (**162**) (prepared by treatment of 1,4-dihydroxy-6-tetralone with
ethylene glycol in refluxing acetonitrile in the presence of a catalytic amount
of *p*-toluenesulfonic acid and concomitant air oxidation), allowed Kametani
et al. (*39*) to obtain a product which was apparently the mixture of **163a**
and **163b**. This reaction opens a new approach to tetracyclic compounds

related with daunomycinone, and other condensations of the same type were reported in the same and in a subsequent paper (*40*). Interestingly,

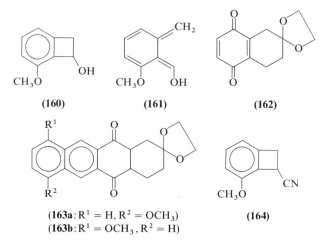

(160)   (161)   (162)

(163a: R¹ = H, R² = OCH₃)
(163b: R¹ = OCH₃, R² = H)   (164)

the possibility that this reaction may be endowed with regioselectivity stemmed from the conclusion that the product **166**, obtained in the thermolysis of 1-cyano-6-methoxybenzocyclobutene (**164**) in the presence of 6-ethoxy-4a,5,8,8a-tetrahydro-1,4-naphthoquinone (**165**), was constituted by a single regioisomer (sharp melting point, single peak of methoxy group in the PMR spectrum). It was, however, not known if the regioisomer was **166a** or **166b** (*39*).

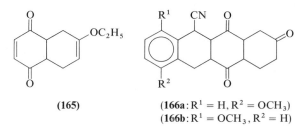

(165)

(166a: R¹ = H, R² = OCH₃)
(166b: R¹ = OCH₃, R² = H)

Two studies reported by Jung and Lowe (*41,42*) were concerned with other new approaches to the total synthesis of anthracyclinones. The first was an exploration of the possibilities offered by the Diels–Alder condensation of photochemically generated bisketenes with olefinic compounds. The reaction of **167** with different benzoquinone derivatives and with naphthoquinone gave low yields of the expected condensation products, apparently because of the intense absorption of irradiation by the quinone reagent, together with a lack in regioselectivity. The second study showed that 6-

methoxy-4-methyl-α-pyrone (168) reacted readily with naphthoquinone to give pachybasin (169a) after oxidation and demethylation of the condensation product. The pyrone (168) reacted regiospecifically with juglone to give similarly, after oxidation and demethylation, chrysophanol (169b) in overall 62% yield, while reaction with juglone acetate was not regiospecific. Reaction with naphthazarin led to helminthosporin (169c). Pyrone 168 was obtained from β-methylglutaconic anhydride by reaction with diazomethane.

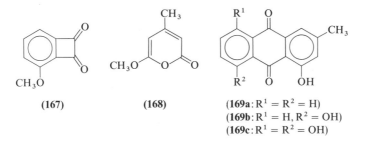

(167)   (168)   (169a: R^1 = R^2 = H)
                                                  (169b: R^1 = H, R^2 = OH)
                                                  (169c: R^1 = R^2 = OH)

SYNTHESES BASED ON DIFFERENT PRINCIPLES

Recently a regioselective synthesis of ketone 131 has been carried out by Kende et al. (43). This synthesis is based (Scheme 5) on the Michael addition of 1,4,5-trimethoxynaphthylacetonitrile (170) to cyclohexene derivative 171, with formation of 172 as a mixture of diastereoisomeric compounds, in 94% yield. Compound 170 was obtained in four steps and 63% yield from 2-allyl-5-methoxynaphthoquinone. This approach is very similar to that independently developed by Parker and Kallmerten (see below). Hydrolysis of the ester group in 172, followed by cyclization and reketalization, afforded the tetracyclic compound 173 (mixture of diastereoisomers) in 75% yield. Reaction of the enolate of 173 with oxygen and subsequent reduction gave quinone 174 in 70% yield after a chromatographic separation step. Conversion of 174 to 175 by the oxidative demethylation procedure of Snyder and Rapoport (44) and deprotection of the latter with acid gave the desired 131 in 70% yield from 174.

The regioselective synthesis of Parker and Kallmerten (45) started from naphthylacetonitrile 176 and ester 177, whose condensation by a Michael addition reaction in the presence of sodium hydride gave 178 in 77% yield. Compound 178 was submitted to a basic hydrolysis, then to an intramolecular Friedel–Crafts acylation in the presence of trifluoroacetic acid and trifluoroacetic anhydride followed by reketalization to give 179 in 61% yield. The quinone function was generated (82% yield) upon treatment of 179 with two equivalents of lithium diisopropylamide and then with oxygen

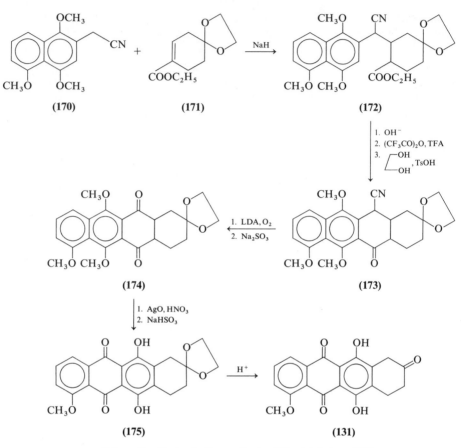

Scheme 5.   Regioselective synthesis of Kende's ketone (**131**).

gas and sodium bisulfite. Conversion of the resulting quinone **180** to adriamycinone is presently investigated by the authors. Starting compounds **176** and **177** were prepared respectively from 1,5-dihydroxynaphthalene (six steps) and from perillartine (four steps).

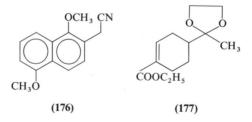

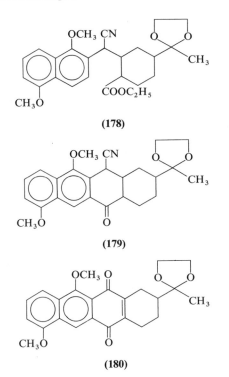

(178)

(179)

(180)

The most recent work published by Sih *et al.* (*46*) is concerned with a "naphthalene route" to anthracyclinones. According to this new approach, tetracyclic ester **189** was obtained from naphthalene derivative **184** in which the norbornene side chain was the precursor of ring A and of the C-9 substituent (Scheme 6). Compound **184** was prepared from **181** via the selenide **182**, whose oxidation afforded 1,5-dimethoxy-2-naphthylvinyl ketone (**183**), the philodiene reagent in the Diels–Alder reaction with 1,3-cyclohexadiene, giving rise to **184**. Alternatively, this intermediate could be obtained from 1,5-dimethoxynaphthalene or from 5-methoxytetralone **185**, the latter route being also shown in Scheme 6. The transformation of **184** into **189** required a four-reaction-step conversion to **187** in 34% yield, the hydroxylation of **187** to **188** in 45% yield, and finally cyclization and reesterification in 41% yield.

A new synthesis of anthracyclinone precursors based on the stepwise construction of rings B and A starting from naphthoquinone as the source of rings D and C is that of O'Connor and Rosen (*47*). The Diels–Alder reaction of naphthoquinone with 1,1,3-trimethoxy-2,4,5-trichlorocyclopentadiene (**190**) gave **191** in 80% yield. Acid hydrolysis and acetylation of **191** afforded **192**, which was treated with sodium hydride and with methyl

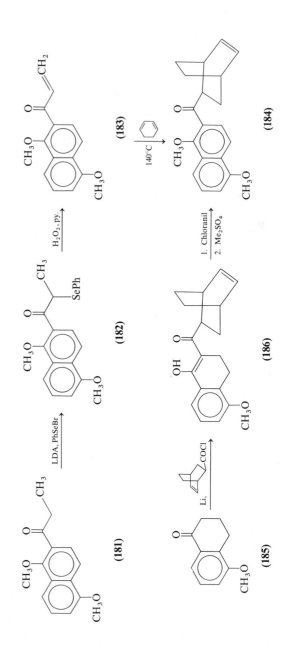

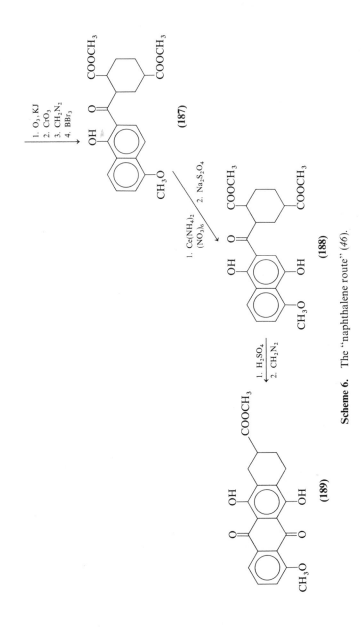

Scheme 6. The "naphthalene route" (46).

vinyl ketone, followed by ring closure with pyrrolidine in anhydrous acetic acid to give **193** in almost 50% yield from **191**.

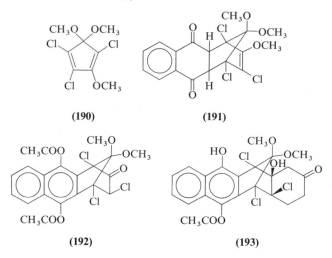

The two-carbon-atom sidechain was introduced in **193** upon reaction with ethinyl magnesium bromide followed by a mercuric acetate treatment to produce **194** in 60% yield from **193**. The last two steps of the synthetic sequence were the oxidation of **194** with Ag₂O and the hydrolysis of the resulting product with aqueous trifluoroacetic acid to give **195a**, possessing an orthoacetate grouping whose presence was proved by different physicochemical methods on **195a** and on its crystalline acetate **195b**.

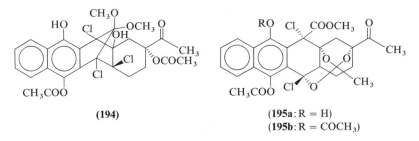

THE CARBOHYDRATE MOIETY

The first synthesis of daunosamine started from L-rhamnal (**196**), a compound obtained from commercially available L-rhamnose in four reaction steps (*48*). Methoxymercuration followed by potassium borohydride reduction afforded methyl 2-deoxy-α-L-rhamnoside (**197**), which was monotosylated to **198**. Sodium methoxide treatment of **198** gave epoxide **199**, and treatment of the latter with sodium azide afforded **200**, whose mesylation to **201** followed by nucleophilic displacement with sodium benzoate gave **202**. Saponification of **202** and subsequent catalytic hydrogenation and acid hydrolysis afforded daunosamine (**203**).

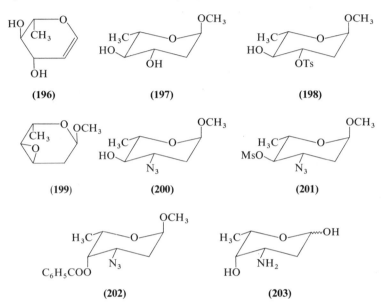

(196)	(197)	(198)

(199)	(200)	(201)

(202)	(203)

A nine-step reaction sequence for the synthesis of daunosamine starting from methyl α-D-mannopyranoside (**204**) has been reported by Horton and Weckerle (*49*). Treatment of **204** with benzaldehyde dimethylacetal and *p*-toluenesulfonic acid gave **205** which was treated with butyllithium at −30°C to afford **206**. The yield of this step in a preparative scale was 91%. Compound **206** was converted to the oxime, which afforded mainly **207** upon

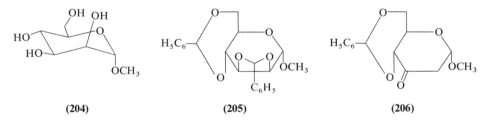

(204)	(205)	(206)

reduction with lithium aluminum hydride followed by acetylation. Bromination of **207** according to the procedure developed by Hanessian (*50*) gave **208**, which was converted to **209** with silver fluoride in pyridine. Debenzoylation followed by catalytic hydrogenation led stereospecifically to methyl

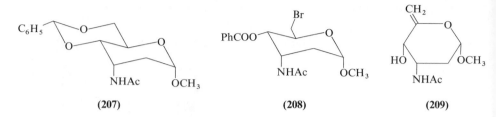

(207)   (208)   (209)

N-acetyl-β-daunosaminide **(210)**, from which **203** was obtained upon deacetylation with barium hydroxide and subsequent hydrolysis with aqueous acid. Overall yield of **203** from **204** was 40%.

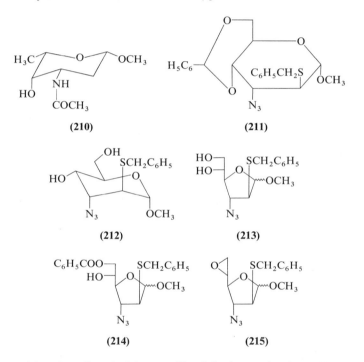

(210)   (211)

(212)   (213)

(214)   (215)

Yamaguchi and Kojima (*51*) have utilized the isomerization of hexopyranoside derivatives having an S-substituent at C-2 to the corresponding furanosides for the conversion of D-glucose derivatives into L-sugars. As a matter of fact, the study of the products of treatment of **211** (*52*) with a polymeric acid indicated **212** and **213** as the major products, their mixture being obtained as a syrup in 86.5 to 71.1% yield. Benzoylation of the syrup afforded a mixture of benzoates from which monobenzoate **214** was obtained in yields up to 47% (from the syrup). Tosylation afforded a monotosyl derivative which was converted to the epoxide **215** with sodium methoxide. Treatment of **215** with lithium aluminum hydride gave the mixture of methyl 3-amino-2-*S*-benzyl-3,6-dideoxy-2-thio-α- and β-L-galactofuranosides (**216**). Desulfurization of **216** with Raney nickel afforded methyl 3-amino-2,3,6-trideoxy-α- and β-L-lyxo-hexofuranosides (**217**) (also obtained from **215** upon treatment with Raney nickel under hydrogen), whose hydrolysis with dilute acid gave daunosamine (**203**).

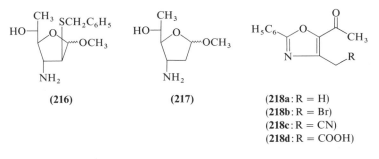

(216)   (217)   (218a: R = H)
                (218b: R = Br)
                (218c: R = CN)
                (218d: R = COOH)

Two syntheses of daunosamine from nonsugar precursors are now available. The first was reported by Wong *et al.* (*53*) and started from oxazole derivative **218a**, whose bromination to **218b** followed by displacement of the halogen atom with cyanide gave **218c**. Transformation of **218c** into **218d** and ring closure with thionyl chloride gave **219**, whose conversion to **203** took place in six reaction steps, namely hydrogenation to **220** using rhodium on alumina as catalyst, then reduction of the lactone carbonyl by sodium di(2-methoxyethoxy)aluminum hydride, followed by acetylation and further catalytic hydrogenation to **221**. Removal of the benzylidene group with acid and reacetylation gave triacetyldaunosamine.

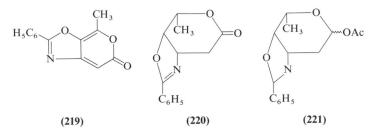

(219)   (220)   (221)

The second synthesis has been elaborated by Dyong and Wiemann (*54*), and involved the sigmatropic (Claisen) rearrangement of allyl vinyl ether (**222**) to give *trans*-hexenal (**223**), whose protected variant **224** was submitted to an allylic amination with selenium and anhydrous chloramine T leading to 3-tosylamino derivative **225**. Detosylation with sodium in liquid ammonia followed by N-acetylation and cis-hydroxylation with a catalytic amount of osmium tetroxide and in the presence of *N*-methylmorpholin *N*-oxide afforded **226** as a mixture of diastereoisomers from which isopropyl *N,O*-diacetyl-DL-daunosaminide (**227**) and -acosaminide (**228**) were obtained.

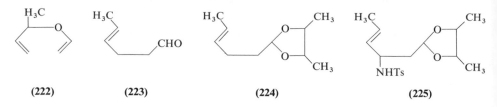

(222)   (223)   (224)   (225)

Compound **227** was identified on the basis of the 100 Mc PMR spectrum and mass spectrum, which were found in agreement with published data of the corresponding methyl glycoside (*55,56*).

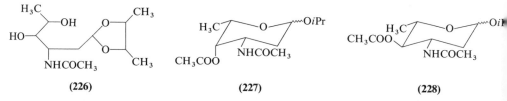

(226)   (227)   (228)

The first coupling of daunomycinone with daunosamine was reported by Acton *et al.* (*57*). According to these authors, the reaction of daunomycinone with 3 molar equivalents of *O-p*-nitrobenzoyl-*N*-trifluoroacetyldauno-saminyl bromide (**229**) in boiling tetrahydrofuran and in the presence of mercuric cyanide, mercuric bromide, and molecular sieve afforded, stereoselectively, the α-glycoside **230** in 50% yield. Daunorubicin was obtained from **230** by alkaline treatment. A somewhat different procedure was

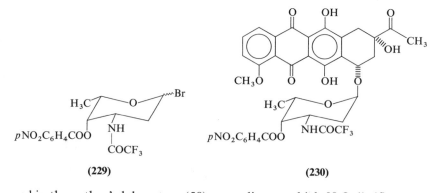

(229)   (230)

used in the author's laboratory (*58*), according to which *N,O*-ditrifluoroace-tyl-α-daunosaminyl chloride was used as the glycosylating agent, the reaction being carried out in dichloromethane and in the presence of mercuric oxide, mercuric dibromide, and molecular sieve. Methanolysis of the reaction product gave N-trifluoroacetyl daunorubicin (**231a**), together with the corresponding β-glycoside **232a** in the ratio 7 : 3. Chromatographic separation and removal of the N-trifluoroacetyl group by a mild alkaline treatment afforded daunorubicin (**231b**) and its β-anomer **232b**.

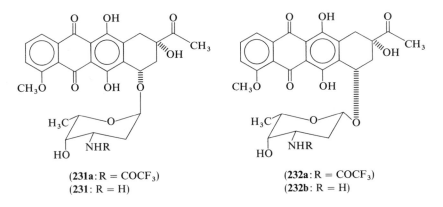

(**231a**: R = COCF₃)
(**231**: R = H)

(**232a**: R = COCF₃)
(**232b**: R = H)

The coupling of adriamycinone with daunosamine has also been carried out in similar conditions, protection of the C-14 hydroxyl group in the former being, however, necessary in this case. In the author's laboratory, adriamycinone was converted to the dioxolane derivative **223**, which was condensed with N-O-ditrifluoroacetyl-α-daunosaminyl chloride to give, after removal of the O-trifluoroacetyl group with methanol, glycosides **234** and **235**. Removal of the protecting groups from the latter compounds using first an alkaline and then an acid treatment afforded respectively doxorubicin (**236**) and its β-anomer **237** (*58*).

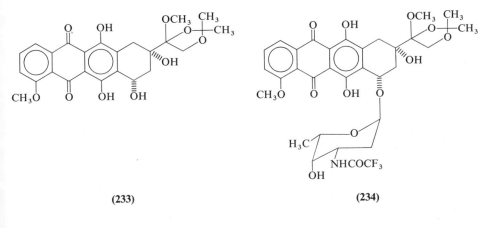

(233)

(234)

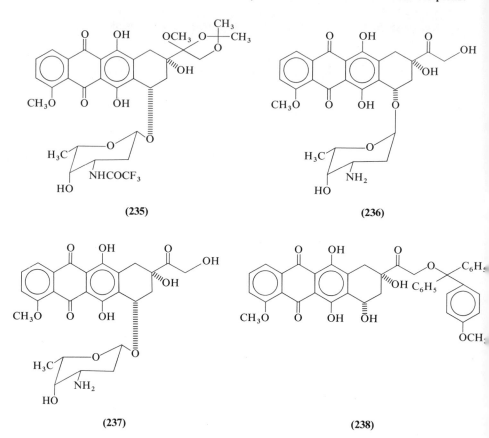

(235)   (236)

(237)   (238)

In their synthesis of [14-^{14}C]doxorubicin, Chen *et al.* (*59*) converted adriamycinone to the 14-monomethoxytrityl ether **238** before glycosidation, the protecting group being removed at the last step with aqueous acetic acid.

In addition to the Koenigs–Knorr type condensations outlined above, other methods have been used for the coupling of daunomycinone with daunosamine. The acid-catalyzed direct condensation of the aglycone and N, O-dithrifluoroacetyldaunosamine was carried out in anhydrous dioxane in the presence of hydrogen chloride and at room temperature to give, stereoselectively, only the α-glycoside, namely 3′,4′-ditrifluoroacetyldaunorubicin (*60*). Acid-catalyzed addition of daunomycinone or of **233** to the glycal **239** was also found to proceed stereoselectively, as only the α-glycosides **231a** and **234** were recovered after methanolysis of the O-trifluoroacetyl group (*61*).

Silver triflate assisted glycosidation of daunomycinone with sugar halides has been proved to be a particularly useful procedure for the preparation

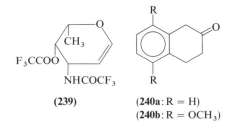

(239)   (240a: R = H)
                 (240b: R = OCH₃)

of daunorubicin and of daunorubicin-related glycosides (62,63). According to this procedure, daunomycinone was allowed to react in a suitable solvent (usually methylene chloride) with the protected sugar halide and silver trifluoromethanesulfonate, in the presence of molecular sieves and at room temperature, to give, after working up and purification, predominantly the α-anomeric glycoside in reasonable yields, the reaction showing the possibility of substantial variation in the relative ratio of the aglycone and sugar reagents according to the necessity of optimizing the yields on one or the other of the starting products. In its application for the synthesis of N-trifluoroacetyldaunorubicin, a twofold molar excess of the aglycone was allowed to react with N,O-trifluoroacetyl-α-daunosaminyl chloride to give, after O-deacylation and chromatographic purification, 63.5% of N-trifluoroacetyldaunorubicin, which in turn was converted quantitatively to the free aminoglycoside by the usual procedure (62).

OTHER STUDIES RELATED TO RING A FUNCTIONALIZATION

Because of the availability of ketone 127 and of 131, the latter a synthetic precursor of daunomycinone, a different route for the elaboration of the dihydroxyacetone side chain was investigated by Smith et al. (64). Reductive cleavage of daunorubicin with sodium dithionite gave 7-deoxydaunomycinone (25), whose reduction at C-13 with lithium aluminum hydride followed by periodate cleavage of the resulting glycol gave 131. Model studies, performed on simpler ketones 240a and 240b, had indicated that reaction of the said substrates with the sodium derivative of triethyl phosphonoacetate or diethyl cyanomethylphosphonate, as well as with carbethoxymethylenetriphenylphosphorane, afforded mainly or exclusively the endocyclic olefin derivative. On the other hand, the reaction with vinyl magnesium chloride, or even less so with the more basic vinyllithium and other similar reagents, took place partially or not at all because of the easy enolization of the starting ketone. However the cyanohydrin route proved successful and was applied to **131**. The latter was readily converted to **241a**, and this intermediate was first protected as the tetrahydropyranyl derivative **241b**, then allowed to react with an excess of methylmagnesium iodide, to give ($\pm$)-7-deoxydauno-mycinone after treatment with hot aqueous acetic acid and a chromatograph-ic separation. The overall yield from **131** was 36%.

In the same study, the introduction of the hydroxyl groups at C-7 and C-14 was also investigated. The former transformation was achieved by reaction of ($\pm$)-7-deoxydaunomycinone with 1.5 equivalents of bromine in

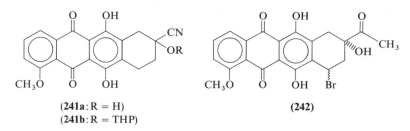

(**241a**: R = H)   (**242**)
(**241b**: R = THP)

the presence of a radical initiator to give **242**, which was converted into **243b** as the major product via formation of **243a** and subsequent methanolysis. The stereochemical course of the reaction was ascribed to the more favorable approach of the trifluoroacetate anion from the side trans to the axial hydroxyl at C-9 during the nucleophilic displacement of bromine with so-dium trifluoroacetate. However, epimerization of **243a** in trifluoroacetic acid before methanolysis afforded mainly ($\pm$)-daunomycinone in 35% yield

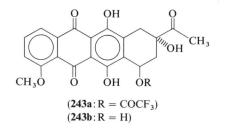

(**243a**: R = COCF$_3$)
(**243b**: R = H)

from ($\pm$)-7-deoxydaunomycinone. Adriamycinone was obtained from daunomycinone via bromination at C-14, followed by a treatment with diluted sodium hydroxide, in 87% yield. In the same paper, the protection of the 14-hydroxyl of adriamycinone as the 14-*O*-*p*-anisyldiphenylmethyl derivative and its glycosidation to give doxorubicin after deblocking are described in detail.

REFERENCES

1. G. Schroeter, *Chem. Ber.* **54**, 2242 (1921).
2. C. Dufraisse and R. Horclos, *Bull. Soc. Chim. Fr.* **3**, 1880 (1936).
3. J. P. Marsh, R. H. Iwamoto, and L. Goodman, *Chem. Commun.* p. 589 (1968).
4. C. M. Wong, D. Popien, R. Schwenk, and T. Raa, *Can. J. Chem.* **49**, 2712 (1971).
5. C. M. Wong, R. Schwenk, D. Popien, and T. L. Ho, *Can. J. Chem.* **51**, 466 (1973).
6. R. J. Blade and P. Hodge, *J. C. S. Chem. Commun.* p. 85 (1979).
7. J. A. Moore and M. Rahm, *J. Org. Chem.* **26**, 1109 (1961).
8. F. Arcamone, L. Bernardi, B. Patelli, and A. Di Marco, *Ger. Patent* 2,601,785 (July 29, 1976).
9. S. Terashima, S.-S. Jew, and K. Koga, *Tetrahedron Lett.* No. 49, 4937 (1978).
10. A. S. Kende, J. Belletire, T. J. Bentley, E. Hume, and J. Airey, *J. Am. Chem. Soc.* **97**, 4425 (1975).
11. D. G. Miller, S. Trenbeath, and C. J. Sih, *Tetrahedron Lett.* No. 20, 1637 (1976).
12. P. W. Raynolds, M. J. Manning, and J. S. Swenton, *Tetrahedron Lett.* No. 28, 2383 (1977).
13. J. S. Swenton and P. W. Raynolds, *J. Am. Chem. Soc.* **100**, 6188 (1978).
14. J. Alexander and L. A. Mitscher, *Tetrahedron Lett.* No 37, 3403 (1978).
15. K. S. Kim, M. W. Spatz, and F. Johnson, *Tetrahedron Lett.* No. 4, 331 (1979).
16. K. S. Kim, E. Vanotti, A. Suarato, and F. Johnson, *J. Am. Chem. Soc.* **101**, 2483 (1979).
17. J. E. Baldwin and K. W. Bair, *Tetrahedron Lett.* No. 29, 2559 (1978).
18. I. Forbes, R. A. Pratt, and R. A. Raphael, *Tetrahedron Lett.* No. 41, 3965 (1978).
19. F. Suzuki, S. Termbeath, R. D. Geeim, and C. J. Sih, *J. Am. Chem. Soc.* **100**, 2272 (1978).
20. R. J. Boatman, B. J. Whithlock, and H. W. Whithlock, Jr., *J. Am. Chem. Soc.* **99**, 4822 (1977)
21. C. Marschalk, F. Koening, and N. Ourosoff, *Bull. Soc. Chim. Fr.* **3**, 1545 (1936).
22. M. J. Morris and J. R. Brown, *Tetrahedron Lett.* No. 32, 2937 (1978).
23. K. Krohn, *J. Chem. Res. (S)* p. 394 (1978); *(M)* 4762 (1978).
24. J. L. Roberts, P. S. Rutledge, and M. J. Treblicock, *Aust. J. Chem.* **30**, 1553 (1977).
25. J. L. Roberts and P. S. Rutledge, *Aust. J. Chem.* **30**, 1743 (1977).
26. W. W. Lee, A. P. Martinez, T. H. Smith, and D. W. Henry, *J. Org. Chem.* **41**, 2296 (1976)
27. A. S. Kende, Y. Tsay, and J. E. Mills, *J. Am. Chem. Soc.* **98**, 1967 (1976).
28. A. S. Kende and Y. G. Tsay, *J.C.S. Chem. Commun.* p. 140 (1977).
29. F. Fariña and J. C. Vega, *Tetrahedron Lett.* No. 17, 1655 (1972).
30. T. R. Kelly, J. W. Gillard, and R. N. Goerner, Jr., *Tetrahedron Lett.* No. 43, 3873 (1976).
31. M. Chandler and R. J. Stoodley, *J.C.S. Chem. Commun.* p. 997 (1978).
32. T. R. Kelly, R. N. Goerner, Jr., J. W. Gillard, and B. K. Prazak, *Tetrahedron Lett.* No. 43, 3869 (1976).
33. R. B. Garland, J. R. Palmer, J. A. Schulz, P. B. Sollman, and R. Pappo, *Tetrahedron Lett.* No. 39, 3669 (1978).
34. F. A. J. Kerdesky and M. P. Cava, *J. Am. Chem. Soc.* **100**, 3635 (1978).
35. T. R. Kelly, J. W. Gillard, R. N. Goerner, Jr., and J. M. Lyding, *J. Am. Chem. Soc.* **99**, 5513 (1977).
36. K. Krohn and A. Rösner, *Tetrahedron Lett.* No. 4, 353 (1978).
37. K. Krohn and L. Tolkiehn, *Tetrahedron Lett.* No. 42, 4023 (1978).
38. A. S. Kende, D. P. Curran, Y. G. Tsay, and J. E. Mills, *Tetrahedron Lett.* No. 40, 3537 (1977)
39. T. Kametani, M. Takeshita, H. Nemoto, and K. Fukumoto, *Chem. Pharm. Bull.* **26**, 556 (1978).
40. T. Kametani, M. Chihiro, M. Takeshita, K. Takanashi, K. Fukumoto, and S. Takano, *Chem. Pharm. Bull.* **26**, 3820 (1978).
41. M. E. Jung and J. A. Lowe, *J. Org. Chem.* **42**, 2371 (1977).
42. M. E. Jung and J. A. Lowe, *J.C.S. Chem. Commun.* p. 95 (1978).

43. A. S. Kende, J. Rizzi, and J. Riemer, *Tetrahedron Lett.* No. 14, 1201 (1979).

44. C. D. Snyder and H. Rapoport, *J. Am. Chem. Soc.* **94**, 227 (1972).

45. K. A. Parker and J. L. Kallmerten, *Tetrahedron Lett.* No. 14, 1197 (1979).

46. C. J. Sih, D. Massuda, P. Corey, R. D. Gleim, and F. Suzuki, *Tetrahedron Lett.* No. 15, 1285 (1979).

47. S. U. O'Connor and W. Rosen, *Tetrahedron Lett.* No. 7, 601 (1979).

48. J. P. Marsh, Jr., C. W. Mosher, E. M. Acton, and L. Goodman, *Chem. Commun.* p. 973 (1967).

49. D. Horton and W. Weckerle, *Carbohydr. Res.* **44**, 227 (1975).

50. S. Hanessian, *Carbohydr. Res.* **2**, 86 (1966).

51. T. Yamaguchi and M. Kojima, *Carbohydr. Res.* **59**, 343 (1977).

52. J. K. Christensen and L. Goodman, *J. Am. Chem. Soc.* **83**, 3827 (1961).

53. C. M. Wong, T.-L. Ho, and W. P. Niemczura, *Can. J. Chem.* **53**, 3144 (1975).

54. I. Dyong and R. Wiemann, *Angew. Chem.* **90**, 728 (1978).

55. F. Arcamone, G. Cassinelli, G. Franceschi, R. Mondelli, P. Orezzi, and S. Penco, *Gazz. Chim. Ital.* **100**, 949 (1970).

56. A. Vigevani, B. Gioia, and G. Cassinelli, *Carbohydr. Res.* **32**, 321 (1974).

57. E. M. Acton, A. N. Fujiwara, and D. W. Henry, *J. Med. Chem.* **17**, 659 (1974).

58. F. Arcamone, S. Penco, and A. Vigevani, *Cancer Chemother. Rep. Part 3* **6**, 123 (1975).

59. C. R. Chen, M. Tan Fong, A. N. Fujiwara, D. W. Henry, M. A. Leaffer, W. W. Lee, and T. H. Smith, *J. Labelled Compd.* **14**, 111 (1978).

60. G. Cassinelli; Fr. Patent 2,183,710 (Dec. 21, 1972).

61. F. Arcamone and G. Cassinelli, U.S. Patent 4,020,270 (Apr. 26, 1977).

62. F. Arcamone, A. Bargiotti, A. Di Marco, and S. Penco, Ger. Patent 2,618,822 (Nov. 11, 1976); *C.A.* **86**, 140416 (1977).

63. F. Arcamone, S. Penco, S. Redaelli, and S. Hanessian, *J. Med. Chem.* **19**, 1424 (1976).

64. T. H. Smith, A. N. Fujiwara, W. W. Lee, H. Y. Wu, and D. W. Henry, *J. Org. Chem.* **42**, 3653 (1977).

3

Molecular Interactions

X-RAY DIFFRACTION STUDIES

The determination of crystal structure of pharmacologic agents is currently considered an important source of information as regards the molecular requirements for action and the understanding of drug–receptor interactions. Such views are based on the consideration that the conformation preferred in the solid state represents a significantly stable conformation of the molecule which is likely to be also favored in solution.

The results of different studies, dealing with the conformation of antitumor anthracyclines in the solid state, are now available. The first was concerned with the X-ray analysis of N-bromoacetyldaunorubicin (1). This study afforded a confirmation of the stereochemistry attributed to daunorubicin and gave indications concerning the conformation of the molecule in the solid state. The cyclohexene ring was in the "half chair" conformation, as already shown by the PMR spectra of different daunorubicin derivatives, and the sugar moiety appeared to be nearly perpendicular to the plane of the chromophore. The distance between O-5 and O-6 (2.45 Å) was found to be much lower than that between O-11 and O-12 (2.67 Å), indicating a different distribution of electronic charges within the quinonic chromophore. The relevance of this structural property for antitumor activity remains to be established. Similarly, the X-ray crystallographic analysis of carminomycin I hydrochloride allowed definitive evidence for the structure and stereochemistry of the antibiotic, the conformational features being in substantial agreement with those described above ($2,3$). The crystal structure of daunorubicin hydrochloride has been determined by Neidle and Taylor (4) for the monohydrate pyridine solvate and by Courseille et al. (5) for the butanol complex. Notwithstanding the different crystal environments and the different molecular structures, the fundamental topological parameters do not change substantially, indicating the high stability of the observed conformation (Fig. 1). These studies also reveal the importance of hydrogen bonding as a determinant of both molecular conformation and crystal structure of the anthracycline antibiotics. An increased stability to the half-chair conformation of ring A is considered to be given by a O-9, O-7 hydrogen bond which is deduced from the value of the distance between the two oxygen atoms (4) Alternatively, the C-9 hydroxyl may display an intramolecular hydrogen bond with the ring oxygen atom of the sugar moiety (5), the possibility existing in carminomycin of a bifurcated hydrogen bond (6). This second type of intramolecular linkage would contribute to stabilize a given orientation of the aminosugar moiety with respect to the aglycone residue in the anthracycline glycosides. On the other hand, an important feature of the crystal structure of daunorubicin hydrochloride is represented by the hydrogen bonds exhibited by the positively charged amino group and by the C-4′ hydroxyl, which act as donors towards the chloride anions and the molecules of the solvating species. These interactions clearly correspond

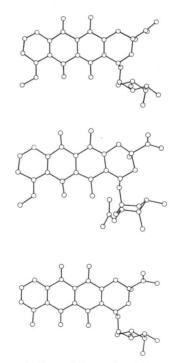

Fig. 1. Computer-drawn projections of (from above) daunorubicin, *N*-bromoacetyldaunorubicin, and carminomycin as determined by X-ray diffraction studies. Reproduced from Neidle and Taylor (4).

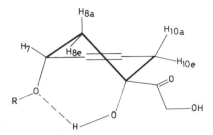

Fig. 2. The half-chair conformation of ring A in doxorubicin.

to inherent properties of the anthracycline structure contributing to stabilization of intermolecular systems and are likely to be exhibited also when the drug binds at the receptor site.

The existence of a preferred conformation of daunorubicin derivatives in solution was shown by the PMR studies (7). An important finding, in this respect, was represented by the determination of a long-range coupling between H-8 eq and H-10 eq, stereospecifically restricted only to two of the four protons at C-8 and C-10 and indicating a half-chair conformation of the A-ring (Fig. 2). As for the stabilizing effect of a 9-OH hydrogen bond, this is in agreement with the shift of the said hydroxyl proton which resonates at 4.41 δ (CDCl$_3$). The Cl conformation of the daunosamine moiety was also deduced from the PMR spectra of different derivatives including N-acetyldaunorubicin and all known daunosamine glycosides in different solvents.

ASSOCIATION AND DISSOCIATION EQUILIBRIA IN SOLUTION

Knowledge of the behavior of doxorubicin and related compounds in aqueous solution is of obvious importance for the evaluation of the biochemical interactions of these antibiotics with biologically significant macromolecules and receptors, and for the interpretation of their kinetics in biological systems. It is well known that many dyes, including compounds endowed with biological activity like the acridines, can form molecular aggregates by vertical stacking even in dilute solutions (8). This is also the case for the anthracycline glycosides, as will be shown below. On the other hand, because of the C-3' amino group and the phenolic hydroxyls, doxorubicin and its congeners can be present in aqueous media in differently charged forms, whose relative concentrations can be derived from the values of the equilibrium constants corresponding to the different protolytic reactions represented in Scheme 1. The scheme does not take account of aggregation processes and is therefore valid for dilute solutions for which the

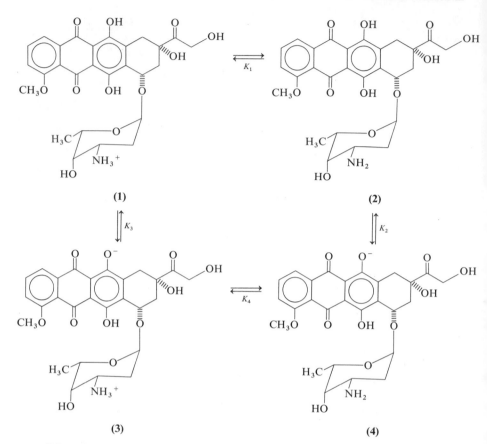

Scheme 1. Protolytic equilibria and dissociation constants of doxorubicin in aqueous solutions.

amount of aggregates can be neglected (as for instance at concentrations two orders of magnitude below the value of the dimerization constant), and it considers the two phenolic groups as equivalent.

The tendency of the anthracycline molecules to associate forming dimeric or even polymeric aggregates was revealed by X-ray diffraction (1), and by circular dichroism and PMR studies (9). The latter authors derived values of 570 M^{-1} or 700 M^{-1} for the association constant of daunorubicin dimerization. Somewhat higher value was given by Crescenzi and Quadrifoglio (10), who estimated the dimerization constant K_D of daunorubicin by spectroscopic methods as $3.0 \times 10^3 \ M^{-1}$, $1.83 \times 10^3 \ M^{-1}$, and $1.16 \times 10^3 \ M^{-1}$ at 25°C, 35°C, and 45°C, respectively (in 0.01 M, pH 7 phosphate buffer). Van't Hoff enthalpy was $\Delta H_D = -8.9$ kcal mole^{-1}, in good agreement with the result of direct microcalorimetric measurement ($\Delta H_D = -9.1$

kcal mole^{-1}), and variation of entropy was $\Delta S_D = -14.0$ eu at 25°C. For doxorubicin, the thermodynamic parameters were directly evaluated calorimetrically from heat of dilution measurements and the following results were obtained: $K_D = 1.1 \times 10^3 M^{-1}$, $\Delta H_D = -9.6$ kcal mole^{-1}, $\Delta S_D = -18.3$ eu (at 25°C). These data are similar to those obtained for other dyes and in particular an enthalpy decrease of 8–9 kcal mole^{-1} is typical for dimerization processes based on stacking interactions of planar chromophoric systems.

The spectrophotometric investigations of Sturgeon and Schulman (11) indicated that the protonated form 1 is the only species present in aqueous solution at pH below 7. However, at higher pH values, 1 can lose a proton either from the amino group to form the neutral species 2 or from a phenolic group to form the zwitterion 3. Further removal of a proton from 2 or 3 gives the singly charged anion 4 (λ_{max} 550 nm). Clearly the negative charge in 3 and 4 can be placed either at the C-11 or at the C-6 phenolic oxygen, and a dianion (λ_{max} 612 nm) is present at pH > 13. Protonation of the amino group does not substantially affect the electronic spectrum of the doxorubicin chromophore (λ_{max} 495 nm). On the other hand, a doubly charged cation, in which one of the three carbonyl groups of doxorubicin is also protonated, is present when the drug is dissolved in concentrated sulfuric acid (λ_{max} 580 nm). The following values were found for the microscopic dissociation constants: $pK_1 = 8.22$, $pK_2 = 10.10$, $pK_3 = 9.01$, $pK_4 = 9.36$. The macroscopic constants were instead given as $pK' = 8.15$ and $pK'' = 10.16$. In this study, self-aggregation of the drug was avoided by using low concentrations ($\sim 4 \times 10^{-6} M$).

Dimerization of the uncharged species DOH (where DOH stands for daunorubicin or for doxorubicin free base 2) was also evaluated by Eksborg (12) by measuring the absorbances at 480 nm and at different pH values (carbonate buffer) in the range 9.14 to 10.56 in order to exclude the presence of the protonated forms of the drugs, as well as in 0.1 M phosphoric acid (A_A) and in 0.01 M sodium hydroxide (A_B), at different concentrations (range 0.25 to 2.125 $\times 10^{-4} M$) of the drugs. The plot of the ratio $C_{DOH}/C_{DO^-} = (A_B - A)/(A - A_A)$, where $C_{DOH} = [DOH] + 2[(DOH)_2]$ and $C_{DO^-} = [H^+DO^-] + [DO^-]$, as a function of C_{DO^-} at constant pH, gave straight lines in agreement with the equation:

$$\frac{C_{DOH}}{C_{DO^-}} = \frac{a_h}{M_{OH}} + \frac{2K_D a_h^2 C_{DO^-}}{M_{OH}^2} \tag{1}$$

the function M_{OH} being defined as

$$M_{OH} = \frac{a_h([H^+DO^-] + [DO^-])}{[DOH]} = \frac{a_h C_{DO^-}}{[DOH]} \tag{2}$$

From the slopes of plots according to Eq. (1) the values 15,800 and 19,900 were found for K_D (dimerization constant) of daunorubicin and doxorubicin, respectively. It was also found that formation of the zwitterion 3 in the monomeric form was negligible and that pK_2 was equal to 9.54.

A second approach was employed by Eksborg for the evaluation of the dimerization and tetramerization constants. This was based on distribution studies using aqueous buffers and a 9:1 mixture of chloroform–1-pentanol as immiscible phases. Assuming that the drug was extracted in the organic phase in the unchanged form and that only monomeric species were present, the plot of $1/D$ (D being the distribution ratio) versus a_h when the concentrations of the drugs in the aqueous phase were in the range 10^{-7}–10^{-6} M allowed the determination of pK_1 for doxorubicin ($pK_1 = 7.20$) and for daunorubicin ($pK_1 = 6.4$). These values seem exceedingly low and the explanation offered for the difference observed between the two compounds, based on a presumed hydrogen-bond type interaction of the sugar amino group with the different side chains, is not acceptable. However, the author was able, by using higher concentrations and the already mentioned values of the dissociation constant, to evaluate the dimerization constants as 3.09×10^4 and 3.02×10^4 and the tetramerization constants as 2×10^{12} and 10^{12} for doxorubicin and daunorubicin, respectively. These constants corresponded to the association of both neutral and cationic species in the aqueous phase.

Equilibrium isoelectric focusing is a now well-established method which allows accurate determination of isoelectric pH (pI) of charged molecules of biological interest (13). A recent development is represented by two-dimensional isoelectric focusing electrophoresis technique (14), allowing direct titrations over preformed pH gradients (in the case of doxorubicin, the pH range was from 3 to 10). Isoelectric focusing of doxorubicin (15) allowed the determination of pI over a wide concentration range and its evaluation for the monomeric species on the diluted side ($C \leq 2 \mu M$). The value found was pI = 8.76. As the spectrophotometric titration of the phenolic groups indicated $pK_4 = 9.60$ for dilute solutions ($\sim 2 \mu M$), the dissociation constant $K_{NH_3^+}$ of the protonated amino group was calculated from the relationship $pI = (pK_{NH_3^+} + pK_{OH})/2$ and found to be 7.92. On the other hand, the electrophoretic titration curve of doxorubicin (Fig. 3) clearly showed anionic behavior at pH values above the isoelectric point, while below this point cationic mobility increased up to pH $\sim$ 7, where constant mobility was achieved. Mathematical treatment of this behavior indicated dissociation constants in close agreement with the values given above.

In conclusion, there is no doubt that the anthracycline glycosides form molecular aggregates in aqueous solutions. The predominant aggregate in dilute solutions is apparently a dimer and the dimerization equilibrium is

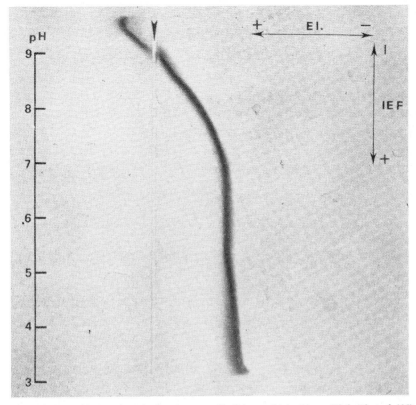

Fig. 3. Direct "electrophoretic titration curve" of doxorubicin. From Righetti *et al.* (*15*).

characterized by an association constant for which a value near 10^4 is more likely also because of comparison with other dyes showing the same type of behavior. The forces responsible for this association are not completely understood; a π–π interaction between the quinone chromophores is likely to occur, but the contribution of hydrophobic or electrostatic interactions cannot be ruled out. The aggregation of doxorubicin molecules should not be important at the biologically active concentrations ($\leq 10^{-6}$ M) of the drug, but the forces involved in this type of interaction could also operate in other cases, as in those in which the antibiotic is bound to biological macromolecules with polyelectrolyte character.

Protolysis of doxorubicin cation takes place mainly via the uncharged free base to ultimately give the phenolate anion, but the zwitterion form, although less stable than the free base in aqueous solution, could be of importance in different environments, as for instance in complexes of the drug with biological macromolecules of the polyelectrolite type. The first dissociation constant K_1 is approximately 10^{-8} (according to the spectrophotometric and electrophoretic studies mentioned above), and therefore the drug is mainly present as the cationic form in aqueous media at physiological pH values.

OXIDOREDUCTION BEHAVIOR

In both protic and aprotic solutions, quinones are reduced in two successive reversible one-electron steps, and the quinone–hydroquinone system represents one of the most thoroughly investigated organic redox complexes. Because of the likely protonation of the basic anionic radical intermediate and product, the species involved in the oxidoreduction equilibrium at physiological pH can be represented as follows:

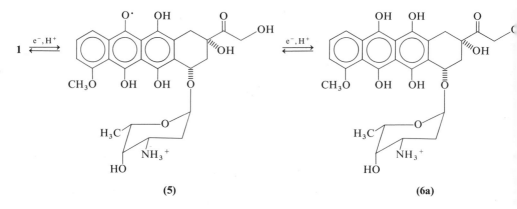

(5)   (6a)

The oxidoreduction behavior of quinones can be studied by the polarographic or other electrochemical techniques, and its detailed investigation reveals a great amount of complexity depending on the actual composition of the medium and on the structural features of the quinone itself (*16*). As already observed with daunorubicin (*17*), doxorubicin exhibits characteristic polarographic reduction waves (*18*). A more recent and a detailed electrochemical study of these two antibiotics is due to Rao *et al.* (*19*). By means of classical polarography, differential pulse polarography, chronopotentiometric studies, and cyclic voltammetry, these authors were able to identify and characterize the oxidoreduction behavior of the said anthracyclines. The main reduction process already revealed in the preceding studies was found to be distinguishable in two different quinone–hydroquinone interconversions, attributable to two distinct steps, I′ and I, whose catodic expressions I'C and IC corresponded to the reduction of **1a,b** to **6a,b** and to that of **7a,b** to **8a,b**, with the species **7a,b** arising by chemical collapse of species **6a,b** via the deglycosidated intermediate **9a,b**. To these reduction steps, exhibiting in pH 7.1 buffer peak potentials -0.62 V (IC) and -0.67 V (I'C, daunorubicin) or -0.66 V (I'C, doxorubicin) with respect to the standard calomel electrode, a single anodic counterpart was found with peak potential -0.64 V (daunorubicin) and -0.625 V (doxorubicin). These findings were in full agreement with chemical and biochemical behavior of the antitumor anthracyclines, although structure **10a,b** may also be written for a hypothetical intermediate in the conversion of reduced species **6** to the quinones **7**. Relationship of the phenomena recorded at

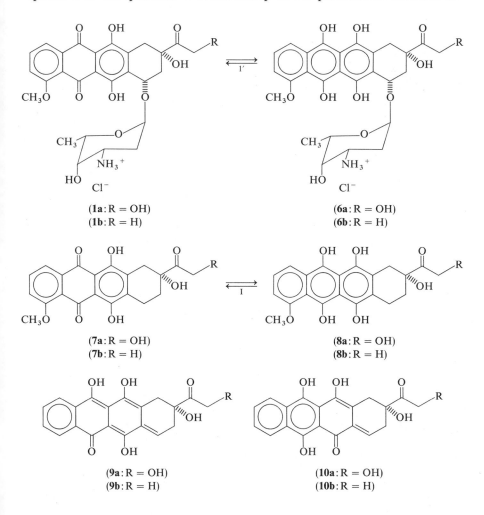

(**1a**: R = OH)
(**1b**: R = H)

(**6a**: R = OH)
(**6b**: R = H)

(**7a**: R = OH)
(**7b**: R = H)

(**8a**: R = OH)
(**8b**: R = H)

(**9a**: R = OH)
(**9b**: R = H)

(**10a**: R = OH)
(**10b**: R = H)

the dropping mercury electrode with the metabolic reactions of the anti-biotics in animal and microbial systems are clearly evident. The aglycones, daunomycinone and adriamycinone, did not exhibit the I′ process, in agreement with the deductions presented above. Reduction of the sidechain ketone could also be detected in the polarographic studies, as two other peaks, IIIC (-1.16 V) and IIC (1.34 V) of daunorubicin were attributed to two irreversible one-electron processes leading ultimately to the C-13 alcohol. Interestingly, peak IIC is shifted by approximately 70 mV more cathodic in doxorubicin, in agreement with the observed higher reaction rate in the enzymic reduction of daunorubicin in comparison to doxorubicin.

COMPLEXES WITH METAL IONS

Aluminum, iron, copper, and magnesium ions profoundly altered the electronic absorption spectrum of daunorubicin [and of its *N*-acetyl derivative; Calendi *et al.* (17)]. The copper complex was found to be a thermodynamically weak metal–ligand system (20). The property of the anthracyclines to form complexes with metal cations has also been reported by Yesair and McNitt (21). Formation of metal ion complexes has been suggested to explain the inhibiting effect of Mg^{2+} and of Cu^{2+} on the enzymatic transformation of daunorubicin (22) and the antagonisms exhibited by Ca^{2+} ions towards the reported doxorubicin inhibition of rabbit heart Na–K ATPase (23). A ferric chelate of doxorubicin, quelamycin, has been proposed as a pharmacologically active stable form of the antibiotic, also endowed with lower toxicity and more favourable pharmacokinetic properties (24).

The changes in the visible absorption spectrum of doxorubicin in the presence of Fe^{3+}, Mg^{2+}, and Ca^{2+} were studied in the author's laboratory in order to establish the stability of the corresponding complexes and the relevance of the phenomenon of metal cation binding for the pharmacological properties of antitumor anthracyclines. The formation of the complex was monitored by the intensity of the absorption maximum typical of the said chelates, in the region 550–650 nm where neither the free antibiotic nor the salts absorb (unpublished results). The chelation of doxorubicin with metal cations turned out to be a complex phenomenon needing investigation with different methodologies for adequate understanding. In the case of calcium, the absorbance curves did not reach the saturation point despite the high metal concentrations used (up to 2.25 M). It is therefore apparent that the low affinity of doxorubicin for the calcium ions in pH 7 buffer does not support the attribution of pharmacological importance to this particular interaction.

The *in vitro* adsorption of doxorubicin on insoluble calcium phosphate has been investigated by Sturgeon *et al.* (*25*). This study was aimed to obtain information about the mechanism of bone tissue staining following prolonged treatment with the drug. According to these authors, doxorubicin does not interact appreciably with calcium ions in solution at pH lower than 10, even in the presence of large excess of the said ions. When instead tribasic calcium phosphate was added to solutions of doxorubicin in pH 7.4 buffer, a substantial fraction of the antibiotic was adsorbed on the surface of the insoluble salt. However, the forces involved in the adsorption process were considered to be weaker than those typical of coordination–covalent bonding as shown by the easy of removal of the drug from the solid surface by physical methods such as gentle heating and sonication. From the Langmuir adsorption isotherm, the maximum adsorption capacity of calcium phosphate was estimated to be 1.60 mg of doxorubicin per gram of calcium phosphate in the suspension.

THE DNA INTERCALATION COMPLEX

The anthracycline glycosides form complexes with deoxyribonucleic acid (DNA) with stability constant in the range 10^5 to 10^6 M^{-1}. Because the main biochemical effects of the antitumor anthracyclines are concerned with nucleic acid synthesis and function, this type of molecular association has been studied in detail. On the basis of the physicochemical properties of the complex, including changes in the spectroscopic and polarographic properties of the antibiotics induced by native DNA (*17,26*), as well as changes in DNA sedimentation rate, viscosity, or denaturation profile induced by the antibiotics (*17,27*), an intercalative mode of association was proposed (Fig. 4).

The intercalation complex is a type of noncovalent binding of small molecules to double-helical DNA, originally suggested by Lerman (*28*) for explaining the molecular association of acridine dyes and DNA, and subsequently accepted as the mode of interaction of a wide range of different drugs with a DNA receptor (*29*). According to the model, a planar molecule is intercalated between two adjacent base pairs of the biopolymer, the distance between the same base pairs becoming 6.8 Å, in order to allow normal Van der Waals contact with the intercalating molecule. In the case of doxorubicin, as well as of the related anthracycline glycosides, stabilization of the complex was ascribed to the following factors. Because of the close contact of the electron-deficient quinone chromophore with the electron-rich purine and pyrimidine bases, insured by the intercalation, the conditions

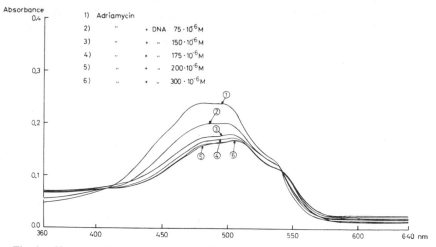

Fig. 4.   Changes in the visible spectrum of doxorubicin (25×10^{-6} M) at increasing DNA concentrations. From Di Marco and Arcamone (*32*).

for the formation of a DNA complex should be fulfilled. Such an electron donor–acceptor complex is typical of the quinones, and its wave function receives a major contribution from a term representing the so-called Van der Waals forces, the contribution of the electron transfer structure being minimal in the ground state [for an interesting review describing quinone complexes, see Foster and Foreman (*30*)]. The results of X-ray diffraction measurements (*31*) indicated that the DNA complex of daunorubicin had a conformation very similar to that of B-DNA and that its structure was in strong agreement with the intercalation model. According to the authors, the aminosugar moiety of daunorubicin is in the large groove of the DNA double helix, and the hydrophobic faces of the base pairs and of the drug overlap extensively. The charged amino group is very close to the second DNA phosphate anion away from the intercalation site, and a hydrogen bond between the C-9 hydroxyl of the antibiotic and the first phosphate is also possible. In fact, molecular requirements for complex formation strongly indicated the importance of the presence of the free amino group and of the structure and stereochemistry of the sugar moiety associated with the planar quinone chromophore for the stabilization of the complex (*32*). The local increase of the distances between base pairs would also afford a diminished repulsion between the negatively charged phosphate groups of the polynucleotide chain. Additional stabilization would be afforded by the electrostatic interaction between the protonated amino group of the sugar residue and the ionized phosphate groups. The contribution of hydrogen bonds is also possible, as can be deduced from the dissociation of the complex induced by formamide and urea.

Different methods for the study of the DNA complexation reaction were employed in the early investigations. The interaction of the anthracycline glycosides with DNA can be monitored spectrophotometrically or by equilibrium dialysis (33). A fluorometric method, based on the quenching of the typical anthracycline fluorescence by DNA, has also been developed (34). Other useful informations can be obtained by circular dichroism spectroscopy (35,36), calorimetric measurements (37), thermal denaturation of DNA, and viscosimetric determinations (33). An additional promising technique for the study of anthracycline interactions with biological macromolecules or with metal ions is offered by Raman spectroscopy, a method allowing the detection of chromophore-related absorptions in the range 300 to 1600 cm^{-1}, upon excitation of 0.02–0.04 M aqueous solutions of the drugs. This method needs, however, technical improvements due to the intense doxorubicin fluorescence (38). A strongly diagnostic test for intercalation is represented by the ability to unwind the DNA double helix in supercoiled closed circular DNA (39).

A direct consequence of DNA complexation is the inhibition exerted by daunorubicin and its congeners on the template activity of DNA *in vitro*. The detailed mechanism of this inhibition remains to be established: both prevention of separation of the DNA strands or hindrance to the attachment of the polymerase due to distortion of the DNA structure have been proposed as possible causes (32).

Taking account of the DNA intercalation model as the most widely accepted candidate for the representation of the main drug–receptor complex, a number of structural and configurational features of the antitumor glycoside have to be considered as necessary conditions for complex formation and therefore for the exhibition of biological activity. Among these, the planar, electron-withdrawing quinone chromophore should be taken as an obvious requirement (it could be noted here, however, that the ability to form intercalation complexes is shared by different structural types of compounds (29)). The relationship between the ability of forming intercalation complexes and the pharmacologic activity is not clear, because of the different biological effects of the intercalating agents. As a matter of fact, however, the most common pharmacological activities of intercalating drugs are concerned with the inhibition of growth or with cellular damage.

The results of the drug–DNA binding studies have been summarized and discussed by Neidle (40). An excellent description of current views concerning the daunorubicin–DNA intercalation model is provided by this author in (40) and in a subsequent review (41), together with suggestive graphic representations of the binding model itself. The mean value of $3.8 \times 10^6 \ M^{-1}$ was deduced for the apparent association constant k_{app} of daunorubicin and DNA from the measurements reported by different laboratories. The ranges of k_{app} values (1.3 to 9.3 × 10^6 M^{-1}) and of the number of binding sites n (0.16 to 0.20) per nucleotide were, however, quite large, reflecting differences in experimental condictions as well as in Scatchard plot treatment of results. For doxorubicin, the following values of k_{app} were recorded: 2.3 × 10^6 M^{-1} and 2.8 × 10^6 M^{-1} (33), 2.7 × 10^6 M^{-1} (42), 4.2 × 10^6 M^{-1} (35). These values indicate that no difference seems to exist between the affinities of the two drugs for DNA. Definitively lower values (4.5 × 10^5 M^{-1} for daunorubicin and 3.7 × 10^5 M^{-1} for doxorubicin) of the association constants were found in the author's laboratory using the equilibrium dialysis method at a fixed concentration (1.04 × 10^{-3} M as P) of DNA, while the drug concentration was varied from 5.2 × 10^{-4} M to 5.2 × 10^{-3} M and the buffer was pH 7, 0.1 M Tris containing 0.15 M NaCl (43), and using the Scatchard linearization procedure for the evaluation of experimental measurements.

A critical review of the methods employed for the determination of the binding parameters has been published by Plumbridge et al. (44), who consider as inappropriate any method, including the Scatchard plot, that does not fulfill the conditions for use of linear regression analysis. More correctly, the said parameters should be derived directly from the binding isotherm, by the use of nonlinear regression methods. The binding of daunorubicin to calf thymus DNA was studied spectrophotometrically by measuring the absorbance at 480 nm of a buffered 5.833 × 10^{-5} M solution of the drug containing 0.3 M NaCl (in order to avoid external binding to the double helix) to which sequential additions of DNA were made, the fraction α of drug bound after each addition of DNA being calculated using the equation of Peacocke and Skerret (45). The parameters k and n were calculated by linear regression of r/c versus r (Scatchard plot), by nonlinear regression of r versus c (one site and two site models), and by nonlinear regression of α versus x (the cumulative volume of DNA added, the true independent variable), and by a noncooperative binding model. The best fit was obtained for the two site (α versus x) model. The following values were found: $K_1 = 1.329 \times 10^6$; $n_1 = 0.143$; $K_2 = 611$; $n_2 = 0.749$. Standard Scatchard evaluation gave $K = 1.734 \times 10^6$ and $n = 0.153$.

Byrn and Dolch (46) have analyzed in detail the spectrophotometric method for the study of binding of daunorubicin and doxorubicin to DNA. The experimental conditions found optimal for the determination of the association constants were the use of 480 nm reading for absorbance measurements, 10-cm absorption cells, and drug concentrations below 7.5 × 10^{-6} M, the difference spectroscopic method, and the computerized curve-fitting program of Fletcher et al. (47), for the nonlinear equation: $r = nKc/(1 + Kc)$.

The binding constants found by the authors were 1.27×10^6 M^{-1} and 2.04×10^6 M^{-1} for daunorubicin and doxorubicin respectively.

The above-mentioned studies were based on spectrophotometric, spectro-fluorometric, or equilibrium dialysis procedures for the measurements of bound in the presence of free antibiotic. The other techniques have, however, provided confirmatory evidence and additional information.

Molinier-Jumel et al. (48) have determined the binding isotherms of some anthracycline derivatives with sonicated calf thymus DNA by voltammetry and AC polarography. The method was based on the linearity of the dependence of the height of the so-called peak 1 (corresponding to a two protons–two electrons reversible oxidoreduction reaction of the quinone) with concentration between 10^{-5} and 10^{-7} M of the drug and on the lower diffusion coefficient of the DNA complex (10^{-7} to 10^{-8} cm^{2}s^{-1}) in comparison with the diffusion coefficient of the free compound. The Scatchard plot of experimental data for daunorubicin was in agreement with the presence of a more stable intercalation complex and of a less stable ionic salt, the latter becoming evident only at higher values of the ratio of concentration of bound drug over concentration of the macromolecule. The values of the thermodynamic constant were found to be independent of the molecular weight of DNA and of DNA concentration up to 30 μg/ml. The evaluation of the binding parameters of daunorubicin gave $k_{app} = 6 \times 10^5$ M^{-1}, $n = 0.13$.

The interaction of daunorubicin with calf thymus DNA with the aid of calorimetric measurements in conjunction with spectroscopic techniques was studied by Quadrifoglio and Crescenzi (49). The results of calorimetric experiments indicated that the binding of the drug to DNA was an exothermic process for which, at low stoichiometric ratios (lower than 0.13) between the molar concentration of antibiotic and that of DNA-P an "enthalpy of intercalation," ΔH_I, of -6.5 kcal/mole was determined. Taking for the equilibrium binding constant a value of 3×10^6 M^{-1}, the entropy of daunomycin intercalation was found to be approximately $+7.7$ eu. The authors remarked that the value ΔH_I was identical to that found for the intercalation of proflavine and ethidium bromide into DNA. Finally, they found that saturation of daunorubicin strong binding sites with DNA from Micrococcus lysodeicticus (GC content 72%) occurred at the same stoichiometric ratio, thus disproving any preference of the antibiotic for dA–dT base pairs. This latter question has also been the subject of recent investigations, as will be shown below. The thermodynamics of the interaction of daunorubicin with calf thymus DNA were also investigated by Huang and Phillips (50) using the ^{3}H-labeled antibiotic in conventional equilibrium dialysis cells. The use of the radioactive compound enabled measurements of free daunorubicin concentrations down to 10^{-7} M, thereby allowing more reliable extrapolation of the data for $r \to 0$ (r was the moles of drug bound per nucleotide) from

Scatchard plots of r/c versus r. As the measurements were carried out at different temperatures, the Van't Hoff plot of the apparent association constants afforded the determination of enthalpy and entropy changes in close agreement with those given above. The value of k_{app} in 0.15 M NaCl at 25°C was found to be 2.1×10^6 M^{-1} and was insensitive to variations of ionic strength, this latter finding however in contrast with the marked decrease observed with increasing ionic strength detected for other charged intercalating agents such as the acridines (51) and for the antitumor anthracyclines by others (43). On the other hand, the apparent number of binding sites decreased with increasing ionic strength from 0.40 for $\mu = 0.05$ to 0.18 for $\mu = 0.15$.

In conclusion, there is no doubt that doxorubicin binds to DNA by intercalation and that the complex is endowed with remarkable stability, the apparent association constant being about 10^6 M^{-1}. The values of the equilibrium parameters are, however, still too approximately known, as noticeable differences appear in the results reported in the literature. This can be certainly ascribed in part to differences in techniques, concentrations used, ionic strength, methods of data treatment, etc., but it is likely that most of these discrepancies are related to the fact that the binding reaction cannot be represented with the simple equation of the mass action law, the latter being an oversimplification of the model. More detailed studies, aimed at a better understanding of the intercalation process, are clearly needed. It should also be mentioned here that other different suggestions concerning the DNA complexation process have been put forward. A recent one is that of Mikelens and Levinson (52), who demonstrated that daunomycinone was able to bind to [^{3}H]polyriboadenylate in the presence of Cu^{2+}, Ni^{2+}, and Co^{2+}, but not of Fe^{2+} or in the absence of metal ions, by a filter retention method. On the contrary, daunorubicin and doxorubicin were found to bind DNA and poly(rA) in the absence of purposefully added metal ions. However, the authors concluded that a contaminant metal ion was involved in the latter interaction as the preaddition of excess EDTA (concentrations used were 5 μM drug, 20 μM EDTA, and 480 ng/ml DNA) prevented filter retention of the labeled biopolymer by daunorubicin. The addition of $CuSO_4$ partially restored the binding. The contaminant metal ion was not identified and its presence was not otherwise demonstrated. Similar interference from ETDA on the binding reaction was recorded using a centrifugation assay. The conclusion is not very convincing, as the EDTA interference could have different explanation also in consideration of the fact that the methodology employed emphasized the ionic type of binding of the drugs to the nucleic acid which is formed at the high drug-to-DNA ratio used in the study and is measured by the assay systems used. On the other hand, the suggestion also pointed out that the ionic binding may be of relevance in the *in vitro* inhibition assay of *E. coli* DNA polymerase I is acceptable, as the exact mechanism of inactivation of template activity due to the anthracyclines remains to be established.

The intercalative mode of binding appears to be a distinctive property of nucleic acids possessing the B conformation, as is the case for double-helical DNA. Nucleic acids existing in the A conformation, such as doublestranded RNA, do not intercalate daunorubicin (53). This conclusion was confirmed by Plumbridge and Brown (54) by means of spectrophotometric and fluorescence polarization studies of the binding of the drug to calf thymus DNA and to poly(1·C), the latter being known to exist in the A conformation in the experimental conditions used.

High-resolution proton NMR allowed Patel and Canuel (55) to investigate the temperature-dependent structural transitions of the daunorubicin–poly(dA–dT) complex in 1 M NaCl, 10 mM cacodylate buffer, by monitoring the resonances of significant protons both in the anthracycline molecule and in the nucleic acid backbone. The authors concluded *inter alia* that either ring B and/or C of the daunorubicin chromophore overlaps with the nucleic acid base pairs in the intercalation complex.

The question of the existence of a selectivity in the binding of antitumor anthracyclines to different DNA base sequences is still unresolved, although the available evidence seems to be in favour of its absence. Earlier studies [for previous reviews, see Di Marco *et al.* (32,56)] showed no dependence of daunorubicin binding on the base composition of DNA when the phenomenon was analyzed by circular dichroism spectroscopy and other techniques (57) or by the degree of inhibition of DNA-directed RNA polymerase reaction using different DNA primers (58,59). On the other hand, noticeable template-specific inhibition of DNA polymerase from RNA tumor viruses by daunorubicin and doxorubicin indicated a preference for the adenine–thymine base pairs (60). Differential inhibition of DNA-dependent reactions related to base composition or nucleotide sequence of DNA was also recorded by Zunino *et al.* (61,62). Subsequently, Gray and Phillips (63) did not find significant differences between either the number of binding sites or the apparent association constant for normal and leukemic leukocyte DNA of human origin.

The interaction of daunorubicin with different synthetic polydeoxynucleotides has been investigated by Phillips *et al.* (64), also with the aim of establishing a correlation between binding ability and inhibition of the polymerization reactions catalysed by *E. coli* DNA polymerase I and rat liver DNA polymerase α. The polydeoxynucleotides used in this study were the alternating copolymers poly(dA–dT)·poly(dA–dT), poly(dG–dC)·poly-(dG–dC), and their sequence isomers poly(dA)·poly(dT), poly(dG)·poly-(dC), containing all the purine residues on one strand and all pyrimidine residues on the other. Thermal stability of each of the various polymers was differently affected by the drug. In the presence of 0.10 moles of daunorubicin per nucleotide, Δtm for the above-mentioned polymers was respectively 29.5°, 12.0°, 20.4°, and 1.6°C. Binding measurements according to the method of Blake and Peacocke (65), analyzed by the graphical Scatchard procedure, indicated, however, little difference in the k_{app} values, the association constants being in the range 4.3 to 9.6 × 10^6 M^{-1}. In contrast, the apparent number of binding sites varied and was, for the four synthetic DNA analogues, 0.18, 0.105, 0.07, and 0.115, the different behavior of poly(dA–dT) · poly(dA–dT) and poly(dA)·poly(dT) being particularly striking. The inhibition of E. coli DNA polymerase I reaction closely paralleled the value of $n_{app}k_{app}$ (binding affinity), suggesting that the differential inhibition of DNA synthesis is due to its differential binding ability. The binding and inhibition results would indicate a different type of interaction with the drug, depending on the conformations of the polymers in solution, but the molecular aspects of the binding process remain obscure.

Daunorubicin has been used to produce bright orange-red fluorescent banding of human chromosomes. This effect was related to the lower quenching of drug fluorescence taking place when the latter is bound to A–T rich sequences, as in the alternating synthetic polymer poly-d(A–T)· poly-d(A–T), with respect to the practically complete quenching arising as a consequence of binding with natural DNA and with the synthetic polymer poly-d(G–C)·poly-d(G–C). The different behavior was shown to be due to marked differences in quantum yields of daunorubicin fluorescence when bound to DNA of variable sequence arrangement, as the absence of significant difference in the affinities for particular base pairs or DNA sequences was confirmed by gel filtration studies and thermal stability measurements of the corresponding drug–DNA complexes (66). Patel and Canuel (55) have investigated the temperature-dependent helix-to-coil transition of poly(dA–dT) in the presence of daunorubicin by 360 MHz PMR spectrometry in 1 M salt solution. Biphasic transitions were observed at P/drug ratios from 50 to 8, nucleic acid [dT(H-6); dA(H-8), (H-1′); dT(CH$_3$-5)] and antibiotic (ring D aromatic protons, anomeric H-1′ and CH$_3$-5′) resonances being independently monitored through the transitions. The lower temperature 260-nm cooperative transition corresponded to the opening of antibiotic–free base regions, while the higher temperature 260-nm cooperative transition corresponded to the opening of base-pair regions containing intercalated daunomycin. By comparison with the large 0.6–0.8 ppm upfield shift shown by the four proflavine ring protons on complex formation with poly(dA–dT), due to the extensive overlap of the three aromatic rings of the intercalating mutagen and adjacent base pairs in the complex (67), the small upfield shift (0.1–0.25 ppm) of daunorubicin ring D protons upon formation of the complex indicated that these protons "project on to the periphery of the 0.34 nm shielding contours of the nucleic acid bases" (*68*). The authors concluded that "ring D does not overlap with nearest neighbor bases but that either ring B and/or C of the anthracycline chromophore overlap with the nucleic acid base pairs in the intercalation complex of daunorubicin with synthetic DNA in high salt solution." Other information deduced from this study includes the relationship of chemical shift changes of double-helical poly(dA–dT) resonances upon complexation with changes in the glycosidic torsion angles in the DNA backbone, an expected consequence of intercalation, and the decreased binding affinity of daunorubicin derivatives such as N-(N-dimethylglycyl)daunorubicin. The similar behavior exhibited when poly(dA–br^{5}dU) and poly(dA–i^{5}dU) were used in the place of poly(dA–dT) allowed no conclusion concerning the binding of the antibiotic to the major or to the minor groove of the double helix.

In studying the interaction of doxorubicin with bacteriophage T_4 DNA polymerase *in vitro*, Goodman *et al.* (*69*) recorded the presence of two modes of template-mediated inhibition, one for low doxorubicin-to-DNA-P ratios and the other values of the said ratio greater than 1:15. The first mode was uncompetitive, as it could not be reversed by the later addition of an excess of template DNA, and it was thought to involve binding of the enzyme to the template, initiation of DNA synthesis, and subsequent irreversible block at the drug intercalation sites. The second mode was competitive, as an excess of DNA reversed the inhibition, suggesting a prevention of polymerase binding to the template because of externally bonded drug, with consequent presence of free enzyme retaining the ability to initiate synthesis on a newly added DNA molecule. Binding to the DNA template, affecting viral polymerases more effectively than normal cell, has been related to the selectivity of action of the drugs (*70*). A comparative study of the relative effects of doxorubicin, daunorubicin, and rubidazone (daunorubicin benzoylhydrazone) on hepatectomized rat liver DNA polymerase α (the enzyme presumably catalyzing the DNA replicative process) and on unoperated rat liver DNA polymerase α (the presumed repair enzyme) has been published recently (*71*). The relative inhibition of the incorporation of [^{3}H]TTP in the reaction product using K_m amounts of "activated" calf-thymus DNA as the template was in the order doxorubicin > daunorubicin > rubidazone, although the differences were quite small. The compounds ranked in the same order when their effect on the melting temperature of the same DNA was determined. When the effects on the two enzyme preparations were compared directly using the same DNA concentration in all reaction mixtures while also assuring maximal reaction rate for both enzymes, the results indicated a preferential inhibition of the α-polymerase at all drug concentrations tested. These finding were confirmed using different preparations of isolated intact liver nuclei. The authors conclude that the preferential α-polymerase inhibition is in agreement with the classification of the antitumor anthracyclines as "cycle specific" cytotoxic agents, i.e., compounds acting selectively on cells with high levels of mitotic activity.

Sabeur et al. (72) have investigated the interaction between daunorubicin and a chromatin preparation from Ehrlich ascites tumor cells by measuring the quenching of drug fluorescence upon addition of increasing amounts of nucleoprotein. Scatchard plots of the data indicated a lower number of high-affinity binding sites for the chromatin ($n = 0.08$) than for ascites DNA ($n = 0.17$), whereas the apparent association constant for the same sites was only slightly changed in the case of chromatin ($k_{app} = 5 \times 10^6 \ M^{-1}$) with respect to DNA ($k_{app} = 7 \times 10^6 \ M^{-1}$). Interestingly, no difference between the values of n or k_{app} was found using chromatin from sensitive or resistant tumor cell lines. The reduced number of intercalating binding sites in chromatin was explained by a lower accessibility of the protein-bound DNA by the drug

The possibility that doxorubicin may exert inhibition of RNA synthesis by a mechanism other than DNA intercalation has been recently suggested by Chuang and Chuang (73). This conclusion was based on the observation that the antibiotic was a powerful inhibitor of chicken myeloblastosis cells RNA polymerase II in vitro when single-stranded DNA, which was shown to bind much less doxorubicin than double-stranded calf thymus DNA, was used as a template. Incidentally, daunorubicin was a less potent inhibitor than doxorubicin, in agreement with the greater therapeutic properties of the latter.

PROTEIN BINDING

Plasma protein binding of doxorubicin was taken into consideration by Harris and Gross (74) as one of the disposition parameters utilized in the building of a pharmacokinetic model for the drug in the rabbit and its use as a predictive model in human patients. The determination of doxorubicin concentrations in the supernatant fractions of different protein solutions after ultracentrifugation indicated that doxorubicin was bound to rabbit and human plasma proteins to an extent of 50 to 90%. Complex binding relationships were recorded using an equilibrium dialysis method (nonlinear behavior on the Scatchard plot), interpretation of the data being not feasible because of the high fraction of the drug bound to the cellulose dialysis bag. Other evidence concerning the ability of the antitumor anthracyclines to give rise to molecular associations with proteins has been presented. The nonhistone protein fraction isolated from rat liver chromatine displayed remarkable affinity for daunorubicin, as shown by equilibrium dialysis experiments (75). No evaluation of equilibrium parameters was attempted, but an interference due to aggregation of the proteins was noticed. When a solution containing 0.079 mg of protein per ml was dialyzed against 10^{-6} M daunorubicin, the extent of binding was 4.45 nmole/mg protein, indicating a remarkable affinity. Other proteins, such as histones, phosvitin, casein, catalase, and fibrinogen, displayed lower binding capacity. Protein-binding ability of the antitumor anthracyclines seems by no means restricted to the nuclear proteins, thus enlarging the spectrum of the possible receptor sites of these drugs. Spectrin, a protein present in the erythrocyte membrane, was found to bind doxorubicin extensively (equilibrium dialysis experiments indicated that about 100 molecules of doxorubicin were bound per molecule of the protein) with an affinity constant of 8.7×10^3 M^{-1}. The binding properties of native erythrocyte ghosts were even higher, the difference being attributed to a loss of binding sites due to the spectrin extraction procedure (76). While the binding to spectrin is of interest in view of the identification of membrane receptor sites for doxorubicin, the work of Na and Timasheff (77) is concerned with the interaction of daunorubicin with tubulin, a protein directly involved in spindle fiber formation, and therefore in the mitotic process. In this study, the quenching of tubulin fluorescence was chosen to monitor the association constant and stoichiometry. By the method of continuous variation, it was found that each tubulin dimer has two daunorubicin binding sites. The association constant of the daunorubicin–tubulin interaction, and the temperature dependence of the binding were studied by spectrofluorometric titration. The binding free energy was -20.0×10^3 J/mole, the binding constant at 37°C being 2.2×10^3 M^{-1} the enthalpy change -4.9 kcal/mole, and the entropy change assentially zero. Evidence was provided that the association was not hydrophobic in nature, but mainly based on hydrogen bonding or, more likely, on electrostatic interactions involving ionization of the chromophore phenolic groups in the molecular environment resulting from complex formation. It was also found on the basis of sedimentation studies and turbidity measurements that daunorubicin, at concentrations above 2.5×10^{-5} M, inhibited the Mg^{2+}-induced tubulin association and microtubule assembly.

The heavy meromyosin Mg^{2+}–ATPase and acto-heavy meromyosin Mg^{2+}–ATPase reactions were inhibited by daunorubicin and doxorubicin. The antibiotics also induced polymerization of G-actin, to which doxorubicin was found to bind with $K_{ass} = 7.2 \times 10^4$ M^{-1} by equilibrium dialysis studies. The binding constant of heavy meromyosin and doxorubicin was 1.2×10^4 M^{-1}, both proteins exhibiting a single binding site for the drug (78).

It can be deduced, from the above-cited studies, that different proteins are able to bind the anthracycline antibiotics, but the low values of the affinity constants do not allow to consider them as primary receptors of the said drugs in the animal body. However, the corresponding interactions could be an additional factor involved in the expression of the powerful antitumor effects of the anthracyclines, the possibility remaining that other proteins may be able to show higher affinity for the drugs. Among the latter class we may include the enzymes catalyzing the metabolic transformations of the anthracyclines. As will be seen below, the most studied of these enzymes, daunorubicin reductase, displays outstanding selectivity as regards the affinity for the different anthracyclines, allowing the speculation that, were such differences present also in other proteins involved in transport processes or in the mitotic process, they would afford an explanation for the varied pharmacological behavior of the different anthracyclines.

PHOSPHOLIPIDS

Solvent partition studies have allowed Duarte-Karim *et al.* (*79*) to estimate, qualitatively, the affinity of doxorubicin for different phospholipids. The anionic compounds of this class, namely diphosphatidylinositol and phosphatidic acid, did show ability to bind the drug, an observation of potential pharmacologic interest as cardiolipin is an important known component of heart mitochondrial membrane. The association of the antitumor anthracyclines with cardiolipin in aqueous solution of low ionic strength, free of phosphate, was studied also by Schwartz *et al.* (*80*). Spectrophotometric analysis based on the alteration of the anthracycline chromophore induced by the phospholipid indicated a remarkable affinity ($K_{diss} = 10^{-5}$ M). In the same paper, the binding of antitumor anthracyclines to cell membranes was suggested as a possible explanation of selectivity of action within this class of drugs. Daunorubicin affected membrane stability of mouse erythrocytes as it protected the cells from hypotonic lysis at low concentrations but was lytic at high (50 μg/ml) concentrations, the response being, however, variable, as a number of factors inducing individual and strain variability appeared to be involved. The authors related membrane binding of anthracyclines to phospholipid constituents, and advanced the hypothesis that the corresponding complex might exhibit steric features (e.g., preferred orientations of the planar quinone chromophore inside the hydrophobic region of the membrane) and specific electrostatic interactions (ionic and hydrogen bonds), similar to the complex with the receptor DNA.

An investigation of the interaction of the antitumor anthracyclines with phospholipids as a determinant of the inhibition of calcium ion transport in Ehrlich ascites carcinoma cells is due to Anghileri (*81*). Both daunorubicin and doxorubicin inhibited Ca^{2+} binding to individual phospholipids and to total phospholipids of microsomal or mitochondrial origin. This effect was related to the affinity of the drugs for the phospholipids as measured by solvent partition studies of the drugs in the presence of different concentrations of the phospholipids, and to the decreased incorporation rate of $^{45}Ca^{2+}$ into isolated mitochondria after 10 min incubation in a medium containing the antibiotics.

Tritton *et al.* (*82*) have determined the effect of doxorubicin on the thermal transition from the solid to fluid state of sonicated liposomes of different composition (as models of the membrane phospholipid bilayers) by turbidity measurements. Lecithin liposomes containing cardiolipin exhibited a higher transition temperature in the presence ($T_m = 35.4°C$) than in the absence ($T_m = 3.3°C$) of doxorubicin, while for other liposomes the T_m was slightly lowered by the drug. As fluorescence titrations indicated a similar affinity of doxorubicin ($K = 6 \times 10^3 \ M^{-1}$) for both dimyristoyl lecithin liposomes and for the same containing cardiolipin, the lower fluidity induced by the antibiotic with the latter was ascribed to altered membrane organization. The authors concluded by suggesting that the known presence of cardiolipin in cellular membranes of many tumor cells could give an explanation of the selectivity of the cytotoxic action of doxorubicin on normal and neoplastic cells, as this phospholipid would represent a specific site of interaction at the level of the surface membrane. The same consideration would apply to the exhibition of specific side effects (e.g., cardiotoxicity).

MUCOPOLYSACCHARIDES

The interaction of doxorubicin with sulfated mucopolysaccharides is of interest for more than one reason. These macromolecules are widely distributed in animal tissues in association with proteins, especially in the cartilage. Larger amounts of these substances have been found in tumors than in the corresponding normal tissues (*83*). Heparin or heparin-like substances are often administered to cancer patients concurrently with chemotherapic agents. The only published study at this regards is the one carried out in the author's laboratory (*84*), concerning a spectrophotometric analysis of the complexes of doxorubicin with heparin and with chondroitin sulfate (Fig. 5). Although the value of the association constant could not be determined, the binding curves indicated a remarkable stability of the complex, the number of binding sites of the biopolymers corresponding to that of the sulfonic and uronic acid residues as for the complexes with phospholipids. The pharmacological relevance of the association of the antitumor anthracyclines with mucopolysaccharides remains uncertain, and more studies on this subject are obviously needed.

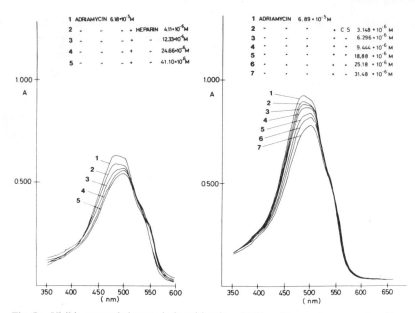

Fig. 5. Visible spectral changes induced by the addition of increasing amounts of heparin and of chondroitin sulfate to doxorubicin in pH 7.3 phosphate buffer. Concentration of mucopolysaccharides are expressed as moles/liter of hexosamine residue. Reproduced from Menozzi and Arcamone (*84*).

EFFECT ON RESPIRATORY PROCESSES
IN SUBCELLULAR PREPARATIONS

It was found in Karl Folkers's laboratory that the antitumor anthracyclines acted as inhibitors of the coenzyme Q_{10} enzymes, succinoxidase and NADH-oxidase, in mitochondria prepared from beef heart (*85*). Doxorubicin reduced by 50% succinoxidase activity when 1475 nmoles of the drug were present in the reaction mixture per nmole of mitochondrial CoQ_{10}, and NADH-oxidase activity when 772 nmoles were present per mole of the coenzyme. These figures are not particularly impressive if compared with the corresponding values for the standard CoQ_{10} inhibitor 6-ω-cyclohexylpentyl-5-hydroxy-2,3-dimethoxy-1,4-benzoquinone, which are, respectively, 5 and 20 per nm. Similar to the synthetic analogues of CoQ_{10}, doxorubicin also inhibited *in vitro* the biosynthesis of the coenzyme, as determined by measuring the conversion rate of $[^{14}C]p$-hydroxybenzoic acid to $[^{14}C]$coenzyme Q_{10} in beef heart mitochondria preparations (*86*). The inhibition due to the antibiotic ranged from 38 to 64% using concentrations of 0.3–20 mM of the drug. The mechanism of doxorubicin inhibition was not ascertained, but the fact that the antibiotic affected the activity of individual CoQ_{10} enzymes made plausible to the authors that the overall inhibition by doxorubicin of the biosynthesis of the coenzyme could include inhibition of one or more of the quinonoid precursors.

The possibility that toxicity of the antitumor anthracyclines be due to an action of the drugs on the respiratory chain has been considered (87). Doxorubicin and daunorubicin were found able to inhibit nearly 100% of respiration of isolated pigeon heart mitochondria at 10^{-3} molar concentration, the relative potencies of these drugs and of other anticancer agents on the respiration of isolated Ehrlich ascites cells being in good correlation with the corresponding relative effects in the isolated mitochondria system. The two anthracyclines considerably inhibited state 3 respiration in rat liver mitochondria at concentrations between 300 and 500 μM, but little or no effect on state 4 respiration and on oxidative phosphorilation (ADP: O ratios) was detected. When the effects on the respiration of isolated rat heart and rat liver mitochondria where compared, no significant difference in sensitivity was observed between the two types of mithochondria, a result not favoring the hypothesis of a selective sensitivity of the former towards the drugs. On the other hand, doxorubicin showed no significant reduction of respiration of Ehrlich ascites tumor cells extracted from mice 6 days after transplantation and 4 hr after treatment with the drug, even at 28 times the chemotherapeutic dose level. It was concluded that the effects exhibited by the antitumor anthracyclines on the respiratory chain could be of a relatively non-specific type and that, although specific binding sites at Site I and Site II could be involved, membrane occupancy by the anticancer agents would contribute to the inhibitory effects.

INTERFERENCE WITH REDOX REACTIONS
AND FORMATION OF RADICALS

As has been mentioned, the quinone function can be reduced by two one-electron steps to the hydroquinone form and the latter reoxidized to the quinone also by two one-electron steps, in both cases with the intermediary formation of the semiquinone radical **5**. Therefore, interference with redox processes and/or reactions due to the radical intermediates have been studied. As a matter of fact, one aspect of quinone interference with the respiratory chain is related to the production of oxygen radicals and of hydrogen peroxide generated through the autoxidation of the corresponding hydroquinones, including reduced coenzyme Q_{10} itself ($88,89$). The reduced form of mitomycin C, either free or covalently bound to DNA, generated hydrogen peroxide when exposed to air in the presence of cell extracts, this phenomenon being, however, not related to the inhibitory activity in bacterial systems (90).

Electron spin resonance (ESR) spectroscopy enabled Sato et al. (91) to detect doxorubicin and daunorubicin signals at $g = 2.004$ when rat liver microsomes were added to a solution containing 1 to 5 mM NADPH and 250 to 300 μg/ml of the drugs. The rapid disappearance (10 min) of the signal was attributed to a further reduction of the semiquinone free radical to the fully reduced hydroquinone form. However, when the incubation was prolonged after the first signal had decayed considerably, the signal reappeared, probably as a consequence of the dismutation reaction between the fully reduced form and the unreacted quinone. No free radical was generated when daunorubicin–DNA complex was used in the place of the free drug.

The involvement of anthracycline semiquinone radicals in the stimulation effect exerted by doxorubicin, daunorubicin, and related compounds on oxygen consumption as measured with a Clark electrode, and NADPH oxidation in a system containing NADPH and rat liver microsomes, has been suggested by Bachur et al. (92). The detergents Triton-101 and EDTA suppressed endogenous oxygen consumption without affecting anthracycline stimulation, but p-hydroxymercuriphenylsulfonate completely inhibited both endogenous and stimulated oxygen consumption. No inhibition was instead exhibited by SKF 525-A (β-diethylaminoethyldiphenylpropyl acetate), cyanide, and carbon monoxide. The antioxidant compound, α-tocopherol, inhibited the endogenous oxygen uptake and reduced the antibiotic stimulation nearly 80%. No alteration of the anthracycline took place in aerobic conditions, and no evidence of an allosteric effect was deduced from the reaction kinetics, but a strong ESR signal was recorded in the reaction mixture in the presence (but not in the absence) of the antibiotic (Fig. 6). On the other hand, microsomal cytochrome P-450 was not involved (lack of inhibition with SKF 525-A and carbon monoxide). The conclusion was therefore drawn that the anthracycline antibiotics participate in a single-electron enzymically catalyzed transfer, allowing NADPH oxidation by molecular oxygen without the intervention of cytochrome P-450. The authors also indicated the semiquinone free radicals as direct or indirect (via the generation of secondary free radicals) cause of DNA fragmentation and cellular damage associated with anthracycline action (93).

Doxorubicin (25 to 150 μM) stimulated the formation of superoxide from NADH and oxygen catalyzed by bovine heart submitochondrial particles in the presence of rotenone (an inhibitor of electron transfer which acts

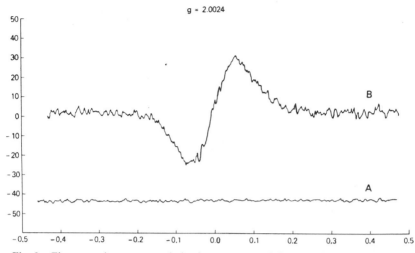

Fig. 6. Electron spin resonance derivative spectrum of daunorubicin–microsome inter-action showing the presence of a free-radical species. Reproduced from Bachur *et al.* (*92*).

after NADH dehydrogenase), as measured by the concomitant conversion of adrenalin to adrenochrome or by acetylated cytochrome *c* reduction (*94*). In the same study, oxygen uptake and hydrogen peroxide formation by the submitochondrial particles in the presence of NADH and rotenone was followed polarographically and a stimulation by doxorubicin was recorded, 50 μM being estimated as the drug concentration allowing half-maximal enhancement of oxygen uptake. Stimulation of superoxide production could be the result of an interaction of the antibiotic with a receptor present in the respiratory chain or a consequence of doxorubicin behaving as an ar-tificial electron acceptor (a 20-molar excess of NADH was found to reduce the doxorubicin chromophore in the above-mentioned system under an-aerobic conditions) giving rise to superoxide upon spontaneous reoxidation by molecular oxygen. The implications of these findings on the under-standing of cardiotoxicity induced by doxorubicin are obvious, when ac-count is taken for the low amount of catalase found in the heart in respect to other tissues. Peroxidation of polyunsaturated fatty acid residues in membrane lipids would follow with unfavorable consequences (*95*). The only doubt which still remains in this *in vitro* interpretation of heart toxi-city resides in the relatively high drug concentrations used in order to evidence the phenomenon.

Similar conclusions were reached by Goodman and Hochstein (*96*) work-ing with *P*-450 reductase or rat liver microsomes, and with NADPH as the substrate. Oxygen consumption (measured with a Clark-type electrode) in a system containing NADPH (0.8 mM) and P-450 reductase was markedly accelerated by the addition of doxorubicin (10 μM), and the addition of catalase during the incubation caused oxygen to reappear in the medium, indicating hydrogen peroxide as a reaction product. The formation of radical species was also indicated by the increase in rate of oxygen uptake from the medium when sulfite was included in the same, clearly a consequence of the presence of free radicals capable of initiating the oxidation of this substrate. On the other hand, partial inhibition of sulfite oxidation was observed after addition of superoxide dismutase, suggesting formation of superoxide anion O_2^-. No uptake of oxygen was recorded when NADH was used in place of NADPH. On the contrary, the microsomal preparation was able to catalyze oxygen consumption with both substrates, stimulation exerted by the anthracycline compound being evident and also accompanied by increased peroxidation of microsomal lipids as revealed by determination of the amount of thiobarbituric acid reactive material at the end of incubation. The latter finding and the known low levels of the enzyme superoxide dismutase in the heart allowed the authors to indicate lipid peroxidation, initiated by free radicals generated during redox cycling of the anthracyclines, as the basis of cardiotoxicity shown by these drugs.

Another enzyme involved in myocardial tissue oxygen supply processes, metmyoglobin reductase, is noncompetitively inhibited by doxorubicin (*97*). This conclusion was reached after performing measurements of the enzyme activity in a system containing either NADH or NADPH at 0.2 mM, the substrate metmyoglobin (0.05 mM), and methylene blue (2.5 μM), following the appearance of oxymyoglobin spectrophotometrically at 582 nm. Doxorubicin, at low concentration (20 μM), inhibited the NADH-dependent reaction by nearly 50%, and the NADPH-dependent reaction by 30–35%. Similar inhibitory effects were recorded when 2,6-dichlorophenolindophenol was used as the substrate. The authors also noticed that doxorubicin was able to enhance 3 to 4 times the rate of autooxidation of oxymyoglobin in the absence of enzymes. Were such effects transferred to the *in vivo* situation, one should derive the suggestion that a lower level of the reduced, oxygen-carrying form of metmyoglobin could at least in part account for the cardiotoxic effect of doxorubicin.

Doxorubicin stimulated the hexose monophosphate shunt activity in human red cells by a mechanism involving glutathione and molecular oxygen, suggesting the intermediate formation of reactive oxygen compounds such as hydrogen peroxide or hydroperoxide (*98*).

The possibility that free radical species originated during reoxidation of reduced anthracyclines could be responsible for the DNA strand breaks observed in cells exposed to the anthracycline antibiotics has been checked *in vitro* by Lown *et al.* (*99*). According to Morgan and Pulleyblank (*100*),

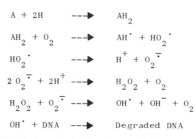

$$A + 2H \quad \dashrightarrow \quad AH_2$$

$$AH_2 + O_2 \quad \dashrightarrow \quad AH^{\cdot} + HO_2^{\cdot}$$

$$HO_2^{\cdot} \quad \dashrightarrow \quad H^+ + O_2^{-\cdot}$$

$$2\,O_2^{-\cdot} + 2H^+ \quad \dashrightarrow \quad H_2O_2 + O_2$$

$$H_2O_2 + O_2^{-\cdot} \quad \dashrightarrow \quad OH^{\cdot} + OH^- + O_2$$

$$OH^{\cdot} + DNA \quad \dashrightarrow \quad Degraded\ DNA$$

Fig. 7. Mechanism of DNA degradation by doxorubicin, as suggested by Lown *et al.* (*99*).

the conversion of PM 2 covalently closed circular DNA (PM 2-CCC-DNA) to nicked circular DNA in the presence of the intercalating agent ethidium bromide gives rise to a 30% increase in fluorescence in the assay solution but a 100% loss of fluorescence after heat-induced strand separation. Using this technique, Lown and his co-workers were able to detect single-strand scission of PM 2-CCC-DNA exposed to doxorubicin or daunorubicin and sodium borohydride or to the borohydride-prereduced antibiotics. The enzymes catalase and superoxide dismutase or the hydroxyl radical scavenger sodium benzoate inhibited the reaction. The mechanism presented in Fig. 7 was proposed for the nicking reaction, and it was also shown that the prereduced aglycones, daunomycinone and adriamycinone, also gave positive results in the test, albeit affording a distinctly lower degradation of the DNA. In the same study, the intercalation of the anthracyclines was examined by the ability to relax supercoiled PM 2-CCC-DNA as described by Pulleyblank and Morgan (*101*), and it was found that the sodium borohydride-reduced forms of doxorubicin or daunorubicin bound to DNA equally as well as the parent antibiotics.

INHIBITION OF (Na$^+$ + K$^+$)ATPase AND OF ION TRANSPORT IN SUBCELLULAR PREPARATIONS

The (Na$^+$ + K$^+$)ATPase, a Mg^{2+}, Na$^+$ and K$^+$ dependent adenosinetriphosphatase, intimately concerned with the coupled transport of Na$^+$ and K$^+$ (the Na$^+$–K$^+$ pump widely distributed in animal cells), is a glycoprotein enzyme located in plasma membranes in close association with phospholipid components which are essential to the expression of enzymatic activity. In a preliminary report (*102*), it was claimed that doxorubicin was a potent inhibitor of the (Na$^+$ + K$^+$)ATPase extracted with NaI and detergents from microsomes of various rabbit and rat tissues. The inhibition was discernible at drug concentrations as low as 10^{-15} M. An inhibition of Na^+ and K^+ transport in slices of rabbit kidney in the absence of calcium ions was also reported (although at 10^{-3} M concentrations of doxorubicin) and related with a direct action of the drug on the $(Na^+ + K^+)$ATPase (103). However, in a more recent report (104), the effect of doxorubicin on the enzyme was investigated using a shark salt-gland microsomal fraction and was found to be not easily reproducible. In a search for the requirements for expression of doxorubicin action, the authors identified the presence of a specific Fe^{3+} and Ca^{2+} dependent respiration, with ascorbate as substrate, with concomitant ATP synthesis as requirements for the inhibition exerted by the antibiotic (reproducibility was not completely reached also in this case, however). The conclusion of the authors was that the inhibition of $(Na^+ + K^+)$ATPase were an indirect effect related to an impairment of respiratory multienzymatic complexes whose coupling with the ATPase would be necessary to ensure the transporting function of the enzyme itself. The inhibiting effects of doxorubicin on $(Na^+ + K^+)$ATPase of an isolated rabbit heart microsomal preparation were lost upon treatment of the same preparations with deoxycholate or NaJ, or in the presence of Ca^{2+} ions (105). The latter result cannot be explained, as suggested by the authors, with the formation of a Ca^{2+}–doxorubicin inactive complex, because doxorubicin is a very weak chelator of this cation (see p. 102). Inhibition of glutamate and pyruvate–malate dependent oxidative phosphorylation and uncoupling effects were displayed by a relatively high concentration (50–100 nmole/mg protein) of doxorubicin in bovine heart mitochondria (20).

A significant inhibition of Ca^{2+} incorporation by Ehrlich ascites tumor mitochondria was exerted by doxorubicin and by daunorubicin (81). Energy-dependent $^{45}Ca^{2+}$ uptake by rat myocardial mitochondria *in vitro* was inhibited at the lowest doxorubicin concentration tested (10 μM), and this effect was not due to a promotion of passive efflux of calcium from mitochondria. This phenomenon was also observed when liver mitochondrial calcium uptake was tested in the presence of the drug, but not with heart or liver microsomal preparations, although the latter are known to take up calcium by an energy-dependent process (106).

REFERENCES

1. R. Angiuli, E. Foresti, L. Riva di Sanseverino, N. W. Isaacs, O. Kennard, W. D. S. Motherwell, D. L. Wampler, and F. Arcamone, *Nature (London), New Biol.* **234**, 78 (1971).
2. M. C. Wani, H. L. Taylor, M. E. Wall, A. T. McPhail, and K. D. Onan, *J. Am. Chem. Soc.* **97**, 5955 (1975).
3. G. R. Pettit, J. J. Einck, C. L. Herald, R. H. Ode, R. B. Von Dreele, P. Brown, M. C. Brazhnikova, and G. F. Gause, *J. Am. Chem. Soc.* **97**, 7387 (1975).
4. S. Neidle and G. Taylor, *Biochim. Biophys. Acta* **479**, 450 (1977).

5. C. Courseille, B. Busetta, S. Geoffre, and M. Hospital, *Acta Crystallogr. B* **35**, 364 (1979).
6. M. Damak and G. Riche, *Acta Crystallogr. Sect. B* **33**, 3415 (1977).
7. F. Arcamone, G. Cassinelli, G. Franceschi, R. Mondelli, P. Orezzi, and S. Penco, *Gazz. Chim. Ital.* **100**, 949 (1970).
8. R. W. Chambers, T. Kajwara, and D. R. Kearns, *J. Phys. Chem.* **78**, 380 (1974).
9. V. Barthelemy-Clavey, J. C. Maurizot, J. L. Dimicoli, and P. Sicard, *FEBS Lett.* **46**, 5 (1974)
10. V. Crescenzi and F. Quadrifoglio, *in* "Polyelectrolytes and Their Applications" (A. Rembaum and E. Sélégny, eds.), p. 217. Reidel Publ., Dordrecht Netherlands, 1975.
11. R. J. Sturgeon and S. G. Schulman, *J. Pharm. Sci.* **66**, 958 (1977).
12. S. Eksborg, *J. Pharm. Sci.* **67**, 782 (1978).
13. P. G. Righetti and E. Giannazza, *Biochim. Biophys. Acta* **532**, 137 (1978).
14. P. G. Righetti, R. Krishnamoorthy, E. Giannazza, and D. Labie, *J. Chromatogr.* **166**, 455 (1978).
15. P. G. Righetti, M. Menozzi, E. Giannazza, and L. Valentini, *FEBS Lett.* **101**, 51 (1979).
16. J. A. Chambers, *in* "The Chemistry of the Quinoid Compounds" (S. Patai, ed.), p. 737. Wiley, New York, 1974.
17. E. Calendi, A. Di Marco, M. Reggiani, M. B. Scarpinato, and L. Valentini, *Biochim. Biophys. Acta* **103**, 25 (1965).
18. F. Arcamone, G. Cassinelli, G. Franceschi, S. Penco, C. Pol, S. Redaelli, and A. Selva, *in* "International Symposium on Adriamycin" (S. K. Carter, Di Marco, M. Ghione, I. H. Krakoff, and G. Mathé, eds.), p. 9. Springer-Verlag, Berlin and New York, 1972.
19. G. M. Rao, J. W. Lown, and J. A. Plambeck, *J. Electrochem. Soc.* **125**, 540 (1978).
20. K. Mailer and D. H. Petering, *Biochem. Pharmacol.* **25**, 2085 (1976).
21. D. W. Yesair and S. McNitt, *Hoppe-Seyler's Z. Physiol, Chem.* **357**, 1066 (1976).
22. D. W. Yesair, L. Bittman, and E. Schwartzbach, *Proc. Am. Assoc. Cancer Res.* **15**, 72 (1974)
23. G. D. V. Van Rossum and M. Gosalvez, *Fed. Proc. Fed. Am. Soc. Exp. Biol.* **35**, 3201 (1976).
24. M. Gosalvez, M. F. Blanco, C. Vivero, and F. Valles, *Eur. J. Cancer* **14**, 1185 (1978).
25. R. J. Sturgeon, C. Flanagan, D. V. Naik, and S. G. Schulman, *J. Pharm. Sci.* **66**, 1346 (1977)
26. H. Berg and K. Eckardt, *Z. Naturforsch. Teil B* **25**, 362 (1970).
27. W. Kersten, H. Kersten, and W. Szybalski, *Biochemistry* **5**, 236 (1966).
28. L. S. Lerman, *J. Mol. Biol.* **3**, 18 (1961).
29. M. J. Waring, *Nature (London)* **219**, 1320 (1968).
30. R. Foster and M. I. Foreman, *in* "The Chemistry of Quinonoid Compounds" (S. Patai, ed.), p. 257. Wiley, New York, 1974.
31. W. J. Pigram, W. Fuller, and L. D. Hamilton, *Nature (London), New Biol.* **235**, 17 (1972).
32. A. Di Marco and F. Arcamone, *Arzneim-Forsch.* **25**, 368 (1975).
33. F. Zunino, R. Gambetta, A. Di Marco, and A. Zaccara, *Biochim. Biophys. Acta* **277**, 489 (1972).
34. F. Zunino, R. Gambetta, A. Di Marco, G. Luoni, and A. Zaccara, *Biochim. Biophys. Res. Commun.* **69**, 744 (1976).
35. V. Barthelemy-Clavey, J. C. Maurizot, and P. J. Sicard, *Biochimie* **55**, 859 (1973).
36. D. G. Dalgleish, G. Fey, and W. Kersten, *Biopolymers* **13**, 1757 (1974).
37. F. Quadrifoglio and V. Crescenzi, *Biophys. Chem.* **2**, 64 (1974).
38. K. W. Hillig and M. D. Morris, *Biochem, Biophys. Res. Commun.* **71**, 1228 (1976).
39. M. Waring, *J. Mol. Biol.* **54**, 247 (1970).
40. S. Neidle, *in* "Topics in Antibiotic Chemistry" (P. Sammes, ed.), Vol. 2, 1978. Part D, p. 240. Ellis Horwood, Chichester, England, 1978.
41. S. Neidle, *Prog. Med. Chem.* **16**, 196 (1979).
42. K. C. Tsou and K. F. Yip, *Cancer Res.* **36**, 3367 (1976).
43. E. Arlandini, A. Vigevani, and F. Arcamone, *Farmaco, Ed. Sci.* **32**, 315 (1977).

44. T. W. Plumbridge, L. J. Aarons, and J. R. Brown, *J. Pharm. Pharmacol.* **30**, 69 (1978).
45. A. R. Peacocke and J. H. N. Skerret, *Trans. Faraday Soc.* **67**, 261 (1956).
46. S. R. Byrn and G. D. Dolch, *J. Pharm. Sci.* **67**, 688 (1978).
47. J. E. Fletcher, A. A. Spector, and J. D. Ashbrook, *Biochemistry* **9**, 4580 (1970).
48. C. Molinier-Jumel, B. Malfoy, J. A. Reynaud, and G. Aubel-Sadron, *Biochem. Biophys. Res. Commun.* **84**, 441 (1978).
49. F. Quadrifoglio, V. Crescenzi, and V. Giancotti, *Biophys. Chem.* **1**, 319 (1974).
50. Y. M. Huang and D. R. Phillips, *Biophys. Chem.* **6**, 363 (1977).
51. J. Chambron, M. Daune, and C. L. Sadron, *Biochim. Biophys. Acta* **123**, 306 (1966).
52. P. Mikelens and W. Levinson, *Bioinor. Chem.* **9**, 441 (1978).
53. J. Doskočil and I. Fric, *FEBS Lett.* **37**, 55 (1973).
54. T. A. Plumbridge and J. R. Brown, *Biochim. Biophys. Acta* **479**, 441 (1977).
55. D. J. Patel and L. L. Canuel, *Eur. J. Biochem.* **90**, 247 (1978).
56. A. Di Marco, F. Arcamone, and F. Zunino, *in* "Antibiotics" (J. W. Corcoran and F. E. Hahn, eds.), Vol. 3, p. 101. Springer-Verlag, Berlin and New York, 1974.
57. W. Kersten, *Oncol. Proc. Int. Cancer Congr., 1970* p. 755 (1971).
58. D. C. Ward, E. Reich, and I. H. Goldberg, *Science* **149**, 1259 (1965).
59. K. O. Honikel and R. E. Santo, *Biochim. Biophys. Acta* **269**, 354 (1972).
60. P. Chandra, F. Zunino, A. Gotz, D. Gericke, and R. Thorbeck, *FEBS Lett.* **21**, 264 (1972).
61. F. Zunino, A. Di Marco, A. Zaccara, and G. Luoni, *Chem. Biol. Interact.* **9**, 25 (1974).
62. F. Zunino, R. Gambetta, and A. Di Marco, *Biochem. Pharmacol.* **24**, 309 (1975).
63. P. J. Gray and D. R. Phillips, *Eur. J. Cancer* **12**, 237 (1976).
64. D. R. Phillips, A. Di Marco, and F. Zunino, *Eur. J. Biochem.* **85**, 487 (1978).
65. A. Blake and A. R. Peacocke, *Biopolymers* **6**, 1225 (1968).
66. F. P. Johnston, K. F. Jorgenson, C. C. Lin, and J. H. Van de Sande, *Chromosoma* **68**, 115 (1978).
67. D. J. Patel, *Biopolymers* **16**, 2739 (1977).
68. C. Giessner-prettre and B. Pullman, *Biochem. Biophys. Res. Commun.* **70**, 578 (1976).
69. M. F. Goodman, G. M. Lee, and N. R. Bachur, *J. Biol. Chem.* **252**, 2670 (1977).
70. F. Zunino, R. Gambetta, A. Colombo, G. Luoni, and A. Zaccara, *Eur. J. Biochem.* **60**, 495 (1975).
71. G. P. Sartiano, W. E. Lynch, and W. D. Bullington, *J. Antibiot.* **32**, 1038 (1979).
72. G. Sabeur, D. Genest, and G. Aubel-Sadron, *Biochem. Biophys. Res. Commun.* **88**, 722 (1979).
73. R. Y. Chuang and L. F. Chuang, *Biochemistry* **18**, 2069 (1979).
74. P. A. Harris and J. F. Gross, *Cancer Chemother. Rep.* **59**, 819 (1975).
75. H. Kikuchi and S. Sato, *Biochim. Biophys. Acta* **434**, 509 (1976).
76. R. B. Nikkelsen, P. S. Lin, and D. F. H. Wallach, *J. Mol. Med.* **2**, 33 (1977).
77. C. Na and S. N. Timasheff, *Arch, Biochem. Biophys.* **182**, 147 (1977).
78. A. Someya, T. Akiyama, M. Misumi, and N. Tanaka, *Biochem. Biophys. Res. Commun.* **85**, 1542 (1978).
79. M. Duarte-Karim, J. M. Ruysschaert, and J. Hildebrand, *Biochem. Biophys. Res. Commun.* **71**, 658 (1976).
80. H. S. Schwartz, G. Schioppacassi, and P. M. Kanter, *Antibiot. Chemother. (Basel)* **23**, 247 (1978).
81. L. J. Anghileri, *Arzneim.-Forsch.* **27**, 1177 (1977).
82. T. R. Tritton, S. A. Murphree, and A. C. Sartorelli, *Biochem. Biophys. Res. Commun.* **84**, 802 (1978).
83. C. P. Dietrich, L. O. Sampaio, O. M. S. Toledo, and C. M. F. Cassaro, *Biochem. Biophys. Res. Commun.* **75**, 329 (1977).

84. M. Menozzi and F. Arcamone, *Biochem. Biophys. Res. Commun.* **80**, 313 (1978).
85. Y. Iwamoto, I. L. Hansen, T. H. Porter, and K. Folkers, *Biochem. Biophys. Res. Commun.* **58**, 633 (1974).
86. K. Folkers, M. Liu, T. Watanabe, and T. H. Porter, *Biochem. Biophys. Res. Commun.* **77**, 1536 (1977).
87. M. Gosalvez, M. Blanco, J. Hunter, M. Miko, and B. Chance, *Eur. J. Cancer* **10**, 567 (1974).
88. H. P. Misra and I. Fridovich, *J. Biol. Chem.* **244**, 6049 (1969).
89. A. Boveris, E. Martino, and A. O. M. Stoppani, *Anal. Biochem.* **80**, 145 (1977).
90. M. Tomasz, *Chem. Biol. Interact.* **13**, 89 (1976).
91. S. Sato, M. Iwaizumi, K. Handa, and Y. Tamura, *Gann* **68**, 603 (1977).
92. N. R. Bachur, S. L. Gordon, and M. V. Gee, *Mol. Pharmacol.* **13**, 901 (1977).
93. N. R. Bachur, S. L. Gordon, and M. V. Gee, *Cancer Res.* **38**, 1745 (1978).
94. W. S. Thayer, *Chem. Biol. Interact.* **19**, 265 (1977).
95. C. E. Myers, W. P. McGuire, R. H. Liss, I. Ifrim, K. Grotzinger, and R. C. Young, *Science* **197**, 165 (1977).
96. J. Goodman and P. Hochstein, *Biochem. Biophys. Res. Commun.* **77**, 797 (1977).
97. D. Taylor and P. Hochstein, *Biochem. Pharmacol.* **27**, 2079 (1978).
98. C. A. Henderson, E. N. Metz, S. P. Balcerzak, and A. L. Sagone, Jr., *Clin. Res.* **25**, 615A (1977).
99. J. W. Lown, S. Sim, K. C. Majumdar, and R. Chang, *Biochem. Biophys. Res. Commun.* **76**, 705 (1977).
100. A. R. Morgan and D. E. Pulleyblank, *Biochem. Biophys. Res. Commun.* **61**, 396 (1974).
101. E. Pulleyblank and A. R. Morgan, *Biochemistry* **14**, 5205 (1975).
102. M. Gosalvez and M. Blanco, *Int. Biophys. Congr., 5th, Copenhagen*, 1975.
103. G. D. V. Van Rossum and M. Gosalvez, *Fed. Proc., Fed. Am. Soc. Exp. Biol.* **3**, Abstr. 3201 (1976).
104. M. Gosalvez and M. F. Blanco, *Biochem. Soc. Trans.* **6**, 945 (1978).
105. M. Gosalvez, G. D. V. Van Rossum, and M. F. Blanco, *Cancer Res.* **39**, 257 (1979).
106. L. Moore, E. J. Landon, and D. A. Cooney, *Biochem. Med.* **18**, 131 (1977).

4

Studies with Living Systems

The number of studies concerning the effects of doxorubicin and of the parent compound, daunorubicin, in different biological systems is now indeed very large. Such studies are aimed at obtaining information on the mode of action of these clinically useful antibiotics and toward the objective of optimization of their use, which is hampered by serious unfavorable side effects. The results of these investigations are also of interest as potential sources of a rationalized development of new analogues of the antitumor anthracyclines, hopefully endowed with a wider spectrum of activity and with reduced toxicity for the host. Along this line, a minimal objective would be the understanding of the different effects exhibited by structurally related compounds and to what extent the differences can be ascribed only to differences in metabolism or pharmacokinetics of the active drug. However, a detailed account of the literature covering this field is deemed to be out of the scope of this book, and therefore only those studies showing clear correlations with phenomena at least partially understood at the molecular level will be dealt with here.

UPTAKE AND DISTRIBUTION IN
CULTURED SENSITIVE CELLS

Investigations carried out in Di Marco's laboratory had shown that daunorubicin and doxorubicin were rapidly taken up from the medium by cultured mammalian cells and that within a few minutes localization in the nuclear structure, especially in the perinuclear chromatin, was evident (1–3). A partial saturation kinetics was observed in hepatoma (4) and in Ehrlich ascites tumor cells (5). The latter author also showed that the presence of the metabolic inhibitor 2-deoxyglucose had the effect of increasing the amount of daunorubicin taken up at the steady state, a result explained by the active outward transport mechanism with which the cells counteract the influx of the drug, the latter taking place apparently by simple diffusion or carrier-mediated transport under the chemical potential gradient of the drug at the two sides of the cell membrane (6). Daunorubicin and doxorubicin are accumulated by mouse L 1210 cells, the rate of uptake of the former being distinctly higher than that of the latter (7,8). According to Cherwinsky and Wang (9), the uptake of daunorubicin by L 1210 cells exposed *in vitro* to 5 μg/ml of the drug reached a maximum (2.5 μg/10^7 cells) within 20 min, while the intracellular level of doxorubicin in similar conditions was 0.4 μg/10^7 cells but continued to rise over a 2-hr period. The uptake was dependent on temperature but was not affected by metabolic inhibitors such as 2,4-dinitrophenol, iodoacetic acid, N-ethylmaleimide, and ouabain. Both drugs appeared to be strongly bound to intracellular receptors, and no difference in doxorubicin uptake was found in sensitive and doxorubicin-resistant cells.

A detailed study on membrane transport and intracellular binding of the antitumor anthracyclines in Ehrlich ascites tumor cells is due to Skovsgaard (10). When the drugs were added to the cell suspension at 10 μg/ml, spectrophotometric determination of the drug remaining in the medium indicated that for daunorubicin a steady state corresponding to approximately 8 μg/10 μl of packed cells was reached within 30 min, while with doxorubicin the cell content was increasing during the whole period of incubation. A pronounced intracellular accumulation took place as, for instance, the cell-to-medium concentration ratio for doxorubicin was 380. The uptake was considerably influenced by pH in the medium, as lowering of the pH in the range 7.4 to 5.8 decreased the rate of uptake and the steady-state level. It is currently accepted that the anthracyclines, after penetration through the cell membrane to the cell interior, bind mainly to DNA in the nucleus. This was confirmed as nuclear binding at pH 7.45, when isolated nuclei were suspended in a medium containing 10 μg/ml of daunorubicin, was 5.33 μg in nuclei corresponding to 10μl packed cells (for doxorubicin the value was 6.43), and was influenced by changes in pH of the medium in the range 8.7 to 6.4. Experiments with cell homogenates showed that the nuclear binding accounted for about 70% of the total cellular binding. In addition, it was found that an uptake of 8 μg/10 μl "packed cells" in the homogenate equilibrated with 1.2 μg/ml in the medium, the latter being an approximate measure of the drug concentration at the cytoplasmic side of the cell membrane for the said uptake values. When sodium azide, an uncoupler of oxidative phosphorilation, was added to the cellular suspensions, a significant enhancement of net uptake was recorded in agreement with the presence of an energy-dependent active efflux process. When cells preloaded with the anthracyclines were resuspended in a drug-free medium, biphasic curves were obtained with an initial rapid loss, after which the rate of release became essentially constant for at least 10 min (the release of doxorubicin in this linear phase of the efflux was 0.7% per minute). Similar experiments performed using isolated nuclei showed that the release from the nuclei was the rate-limiting process.

A carrier-mediated transport of the antitumor anthracyclines in Ehrlich ascites tumor cells *in vitro* has been suggested in a subsequent paper of Skovsgaard (*11*). The initial rate of uptake of doxorubicin and of daunorubicin benzoylhydrazone (rubidazone) was considerably slower than that of daunorubicin, and the influx rate was not correlated to the lipophilic characteristics of the drugs. The process of uptake followed simple saturation kinetics, the values of K_m being 35.0, 5.72, 29.5 μg/ml and those of V_{max} 12.7, 0.64, 2.64 (μg/10 μl packed cells/min) for daunorubicin, doxorubicin, and rubidazone respectively. Although daunorubicin competitively inhibited the influx of [^{3}H] daunorubicin in agreement with the values of the kinetic constants, this was not the case with doxorubicin and rubidazone, whose effect on [^{3}H] daunorubicin rate of uptake indicated a lower efficiency in comparison with that expected from the above-mentioned constants. This could be explained by assuming that the total number of sites that can bind the two latter drugs do not correspond to the number of sites that can translocate these drugs. Alternatively, more than one carrier could be involved. On the other hand, the enhancement of initial cellular uptake of daunorubicin induced by sodium azide supported previous results concerning the active efflux of antitumor anthracyclines in the Ehrlich ascites tumor cells (*10*). A considerable proportion of the initial uptake was accounted for as strongly bound drug associated with sites on the surface of the membrane, and an involvement of phospholipids in the binding was suggested.

Subcellular localization of daunorubicin and doxorubicin in cultured rat embryo fibroblasts was investigated by Noël *et al*. (*12*). When the cells were incubated with 17.5 μM concentrations of the drugs, steady state conditions were obtained after 6 to 10 hr, the uptake of daunorubicin (35 nmoles/mg cell protein) being higher than that of doxorubicin (12 nmoles/mg cell protein). This corresponded to a cell-to-medium concentration ratio of 800 and 150 respectively. Fractionation studies indicated that at the end of the incubation period, 80% of accumulated daunorubicin was found in the lysosomes and 20% in the nucleus. The corresponding figures for doxorubicin were 40 and 60% respectively; that is, the nuclear concentrations of the two drugs were equal, 7 nmoles/mg cell protein. The saturation of the nuclei was about 10 nmole/mg cell protein, corresponding to a binding capacity of 0.1 drug molecule per DNA mononucleotide (*13*). Similar results concerning doxorubicin uptake by normal human fibroblasts had been obtained by Lie and Lie (*14*), who also found that the uptake was markedly increased as the pH of the incubation medium was increased in the range from 6.2 to 8.0.

In conclusion, the available albeit not conclusive evidence indicates that the affinity of doxorubicin to DNA is the main driving force ensuring the accumulation of the drug into the sensitive cells. Because of the binding to the DNA, the concentration of the antibiotic and therefore its electrochemical potential in the cytoplasm remains low enough to allow the uptake against an apparent concentration gradient by a passive diffusion or a facilitated (carrier-mediated) mechanism not dependent on the energy supply from the cell. The presence of an active extrusion process should also be accepted, and this aspect will be considered in more detail later, as it has been more clearly demonstrated in investigations concerning the problem of resistance. The overall picture of cellular kinetics of the anthracyclines remains, however, still undefined. This is also because some findings, such as the strong increase in the uptake observed in the presence of an excess of potassium ions (6) or of the calcium-ion sequestering agent EDTA, (15) are not completely understood. The available information is not sufficient to evaluate the relative importance of the nonionized free base form of the drug versus the protonated form in the inward and outward processes. The pH-dependent behavior would indicate the former species to be involved in the uptake process, while presence in the cell membrane of potential receptor sites represented by mucopolysaccharides, proteins, and phospholipids should bring in cause electrostatic interactions involving the ionized form of the drug. Certainly, additional studies are needed and the investigation of structural analogues of daunorubicin and doxorubicin will be of help in this respect.

EFFECTS ON DNA-RELATED CELL FUNCTIONS *IN VITRO*

Similarly to daunorubicin, doxorubicin displays a strong inhibiting effect on the growth of cultured cells (Table I). This effect has been related to the property of the anthracyclines to bind to chromosomal DNA (16–18). Different studies based on cell fluorescence and on radioisotopic techniques have shown that the largest fraction of the drug that enters into the cells is associated with the nucleus (16). As a matter of fact, a great number of observations have indicated the inhibition of the template function of DNA and of the mitotic process as the most likely causes of the lethal effect of the anthracyclines in cultured mammalian cells.

The older studies concerning the inhibition of the incorporation of radioactive precursors into cell nucleic acid and its relationship to an inhibition of

Table I

ID$_{50}$ Values (μg/ml) of Daunorubicin and Doxorubicin on the Viability of Cultured Mammalian Cells After 24-hr Exposure to the Drug[a]

Cell line	Daunorubicin	Doxorubicin
HeLa	0.025	0.025
3 T 3	0.4	0.09
3 T 12	0.082	0.04
SVT 2	0.068	0.08
MS-2	0.04	0.03
MS-T	0.01	0.07

[a] From Di Marco and Arcamone (19).

the DNA-dependent RNA and DNA polymerase as a consequence of the binding of the drug (daunorubicin) to the DNA receptor have been summarized in the above-mentioned review papers in which the reader will find the relevant references. Inhibition of [^{3}H]uridine incorporation into RNA in HeLa cell cultures was recorded for the lowest concentration of daunorubicin tested (5×10^{-7} M), the ID$_{50}$ being attained when one molecule of the antibiotic was bound per 62 to 100 DNA nucleotide residues (corresponding to approximately 5×10^{-6} M in the medium), in comparison to a ratio of 1:5 observed for the RNA polymerase *in vitro* (19). Incorporation into nucleolar RNA appeared more sensitive than extranucleolar RNA, in agreement with different observations indicating a preferential inhibition of ribosomal RNA synthesis, similarly to what was found for other DNA-interacting antitumor antibiotics. A marked alteration of the nucleoli was evidenced by electron microscopy after 2 hr of incubation of HeLa cells with 1 μg/ml of daunorubicin. No significant difference was found in the relative inhibition of the incorporation rate of precursor into RNA and into DNA (the latter measured from the uptake of [^{3}H]thymidine) in the presence of similar concentrations of daunorubicin in the medium (Fig. 1). In summarizing the older studies already discussed by Di Marco *et al.* (16), mention should be made of the work of Kim *et al.* (20), who reported that the lethal effect produced by daunorubicin in a synchronously dividing population of HeLa cells was most pronounced when the cells were treated during the S phase of growth (corresponding to the period of DNA replication), suggesting a higher accessibility of DNA in chromosomal structure during this phase of the cell cycle, and of the work of Silvestrini *et al.* (21), who, analyzing the incorporation rate of labeled precursors after treatment of synchronized cultures of rat fibroblasts with daunorubicin during different phases of the cell cycle, concluded that the most sensitive processes were the DNA synthesis occurring in the late S

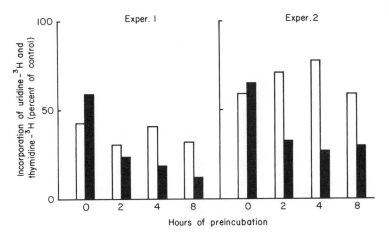

Fig. 1. Effect of daunorubicin (1 μg/ml as the hydrochloride) on the incorporation of [^{3}H]uridine (clear bars) or [^{3}H]thymidine (dark bars) into cultured HeLa cells. Labeled precursors were added 0, 2, 4, or 8 hr after drug addition to medium, and incubation was carried out for 60 min. From Rusconi and Di Marco (2).

phase and the RNA synthesis occurring in the middle of G_1 and in the G_2 phase just before the mitotic peak. Maximal inhibition of DNA synthesis was recorded when the cells were treated in the middle of the G_1 phase, when the peak of RNA synthesis occurred in the control cells. Evidence of a G_2 inhibition caused by doxorubicin and daunorubicin in HeLa cells (Fig. 2) was provided by Wheatley (22). Using cell cultures treated with hydroxyurea (which restricts progression to mitosis of G_2 cells), a distinct fall in the number of mitotic cells was recorded at drug concentrations as low as 50 ng/ml.

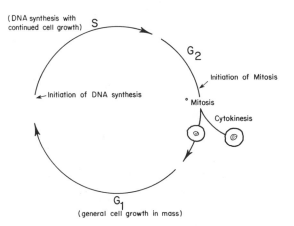

Fig. 2. Schematic representation of cell cycle. From Wheatley (22).

The two compounds showed comparable effects and, although no reduction of the rate of protein synthesis could be demonstrated, an inhibition of RNA synthesis accompanied the antimitotic activity. The author suggested that interaction of the drugs with DNA prevented both transcription and chromosome condensation. Another major observation of Silvestrini *et al.* (*21*) was, however, that concerning the presence of an antimitotic activity apparently unrelated with the inhibition of nucleic acid synthesis.

A detailed study on survival and cell kinetic effects of doxorubicin on chinese hamster ovary cells growing *in vitro* has been reported by Barranco (*23*). According to this author, the antibiotic affected by 50% survival of 99% of a population of asynchronously growing cells exposed to a concentration of 0.2 μg/ml for one hour, the remaining more resistant group of cells being inhibited by 50% at 9.4 μg/ml. Interestingly, significant activity (albeit lower than for dividing cells) was recorded in nondividing cells. In synchronized cell cultures, mitotic cells appeared more sensitive than G_1-phase ones, and cells treated in early S phase exhibited a more marked reduction in survival than those treated in late S. Doxorubicin caused progression delay in all phases of the cycle except mitosis, in agreement with the known inhibition of RNA synthesis in G_1 and of DNA polymerase activity in S phase. The effect of treatment of G_2 cells (prevention from progressing into mitosis), already observed previously in other cell types, was ascribed to an interference with transcriptional reactions, thereby affecting the synthesis of proteins necessary for the start of the division process.

Doxorubicin has been found to inhibit the incorporation rate of labeled precursors into DNA and RNA of cultured hamster fibrosarcoma cells to about the same extent (40% inhibition at 5 μg/ml after 1 hr incubation), this result being not in agreement with the higher inhibition recorded for the DNA-dependent DNA polymerase reaction in comparison with the DNA-dependent RNA polymerase reaction *in vitro* using purified enzymes prepared from calf thymus or isolated fibrosarcoma cell nuclei (*24*). Unless a chemical modification of the drug in intact cells be called in cause, these observations suggest that the purified enzymes may not represent correct models for those involved in the replication and transcription processes affected *in vivo* by doxorubicin.

The effect of doxorubicin on nucleic acid synthesis of serum-stimulated mouse embryo fibroblasts has been investigated by Supino *et al.* (*25*). [³H]Thymidine incorporation rate into DNA at 24 hr after stimulation was maximally inhibited when the cells were exposed to the antibiotic (0.05–0.5 μg/ml) during the first 8-hr period, before the start of DNA synthesis. Remarkable inhibition of [³H]uridine incorporation into RNA already at 30 min after cell stimulation was recorded. Doxorubicin was more effective than daunorubicin at the same concentrations levels. Exposure of the cells for 24 hr to 0.02 μg/ml of each antibiotic (the dose causing approximately 50% inhibition of DNA synthesis) completely suppressed stimulated cell growth as measured at 36 hr after the start of the experiments.

In a study concerning the effects of known chemical carcinogens on DNA replication in HeLa cells, Painter (*26*) found that doxorubicin showed a small but significant inhibition of replicon initiation and a more marked effect on the rate of chain elongation, as determined by the alkaline sucrose gradient profile of ^{3}H-labeled nascent DNA from the said cells after 30 min incubation with μM concentrations of the drug. The behavior shown by doxorubicin was therefore clearly different from that shown by 4-nitroquinoline 1-oxide, specifically inhibiting the initiation reaction, and by ethyleneimine, a radiomimetic agent effective on both above-mentioned processes. The effect of doxorubicin on replicon initiation was tentatively ascribed to an alteration of the DNA supercoiled conformation, probably required for initiation of DNA replication, as a result of the intercalating properties of the drug.

Daunorubicin induced formation of alkali-labile regions and strand breaks in DNA from P-388 lymphocyte cells in culture was investigated by Schwartz (*27*). Two hours exposure of cells to 25×10^{-8} M daunorubicin resulted in about 80% inhibition of growth and partial inhibition of [2-^{14}C]-thymidine incorporation rate into DNA, while a marked decrease of the sedimentation rate in an alkaline sucrose gradient of prelabeled DNA from cells treated with this drug concentration was observed after 30 min exposure. Using a neutral formamide sucrose gradient, the decrease of the sedimentation rate was observed after treatment of 120 min. It appeared that DNA fragmentation was a primary effect of the antibiotic in this system, occurring even at concentration levels or at times of exposure showing little, if any, effect on thymidine incorporation or on subsequent growth. Extensive fragmentation of prelabeled DNA in L 1210 cells exposed for 2 hr to 10 μg/ml of doxorubicin (a dose exhibiting significant inhibition of DNA synthesis) was demonstrated by Lee and Byfield (*28*) by sedimentation analysis of the cell DNA after treatment. As no effect was found when purified DNA was incubated with doxorubicin *in vitro*, it was assumed that the DNA breaks were the product of the action of cell nucleases spontaneously activated in the presence of the antibiotic. The authors also suggested that such mechanism could be responsible for the damage to nondividing cells (as the cardiac cells), although the operation of other mechanisms in doxorubicin cardiotoxicity could not be excluded.

An interesting finding has stemmed out from the investigations of Ross *et al.* (*29*), who examined the effect of doxorubicin and of the other intercalating agent, ellipticine, on mouse leukemia L 1210 cell DNA. After treatment of the cell suspension for 1 hr with the drugs, the cells were collected on a millipore filter, washed and lysed on the filter. An alkaline solution was then used for the elution of DNA, with or without a preliminary enzymatic deproteinization of the lysed cell material. As DNA single-strand breaks result in decreased retention of DNA on the filter but cross-linking and tight protein binding increase retention, the alkaline elution kinetics (followed radiochemically as cell DNA was labeled with [^{14}C]thymidine before the treatment) allowed deductions about the effects of drugs. The results indicated the existence of single-strand breaks with concomitant tight protein binding (DNA–protein cross-links), the possibility being considered that the protein(a repair enzyme?) introduced a nick in order to relieve the distortion due to intercalation and remained tightly bound to the nick site. This finding, allowing the speculation that the function of the protein was a response of the cell to the injury of intercalation, would offer an explanation of DNA breaks formation following doxorubicin treatment as an alternative to the free-radical hypothesis, the latter being based only on circumstantial evidence obtained in artificial conditions. The independence of the formation of the DNA breaks recorded by the authors from the formation of semiquinone radicals would be supported by the similar behavior shown by ellipticine. Further evidence has been presented by the same authors more recently (30). Firstly, the behavior shown by doxorubicin and by ellipticine was found to be shared by a range of other intercalators including actinomycin D, daunorubicin, ethidium bromide, and lucanthone, but not by other nonintercalative DNA binders such as anthramycin and chromomycin A_3, or other inhibitors of nucleic acid synthesis such as cordycepin, cytosine arabinoside, and streptonigrin. Secondly, the dependence of strand breaks and protein cross-link frequencies on drug concentration was studied, and the presence of approximately one DNA–protein cross-link per break was demonstrated. The authors suggested that the intercalating molecules would alter the conformation of the topologically constrained cell chromatin DNA, causing the intervention of a nuclease (which might be a repair enzyme or an enzyme of the nicking–closing type), and considered the possibility that the enzyme itself was the protein covalently linked to the terminus of each break. The mechanism of DNA degradation was different from that shown by *trans*-dichlorodiamineplatinum(II), the latter exhibiting a "random" relationship between DNA breaks and DNA–protein cross-links. However, the lesions recorded here were not considered by the authors to be directly responsible for the cytotoxicity of doxorubicin, as it was also found that, for a given extent of protein-associated DNA break production, doxorubicin was much more cytotoxic than ellipticine.

In agreement with the above-mentioned effects on cell DNA synthesis, structure, and function, chromosomal damage is a well-documented consequence of anthracycline action on cultured cells. Chromosomal fragmentations and mitotic aberrations in cultured mammalian cells treated with daunorubicin were first described by Di Marco *et al.* (*31*). A detailed review concerning the effects of the antitumor anthracyclines on chromosomes in cultured cells is that of Vig (*32*), which summarizes a long list of contributions to the genetic toxicology of these drugs. Chromosome aberrations induced by doxorubicin were first observed by Massimo *et al.* (*33*) and by Vig (*34*), who reported a high percentage (more than 70%) of abnormal cells in cultured human lymphocytes after exposure to low (0.02–0.05 μg/ml) concentrations of the drug. Chromatic damage was observed in murine cells treated with doxorubicin for 2 hr (then washed three times in growth medium before resuspending in regular growth medium) at 24 hr (corresponding to almost two generation periods) after treatment (*35*). The cell damage was clearly related to drug molecules remaining in the DNA or in the cytoplasma of the affected cells. A general consideration made by the authors is cited here in their own words:

> This situation should be the same for both cells *in vitro* and cells *in vivo* of patients receiving such cancer chemotherapeutic agents as doxorubicin. Actively proliferating tissues, e.g. bone marrow and intestinal mucose, would probably recover faster than nonproliferating tissues because the initial drug concentration in each cell would be sufficiently diluted by several cycles of cell division. Non proliferating cells, however, retain in their chromatin the drug molecules which may interfere with normal cellular activities for long periods of time.

Newsome and Littlefield (*36*) observed a decrease of mitotic index and noticeable cytogenetic alterations in human fibroblasts exposed for 1 hr to concentrations of doxorubicin as low as 10 ng/ml. In chinese hamster cells, a 30-min treatment with 0.1–0.5 μg/ml of doxorubicin delayed progression of G_2 cells into mitosis in a dose-dependent manner, the greatest delay, together with the more extensive chromosome damage, being shown by cells treated in the S phase (*37*). The authors have used mitosis labeling and premature chromosome condensation techniques and concluded that genetic cell damage induced by the antibiotic was the result of the formation of chromosomal aberrations with concomitant inhibition of repair processes, a property which could play a role also in the cumulative dose-related cardiotoxicity of the drug. Bempong and Brooks (*38*) reported on the effect of doxorubicin on nuclear division, cell survival, and induced anomalous changes in cultered human leukocytes. These authors stressed the dependence of mitotic behavior, frequency of chromosome aberrations, and cytotoxicity observed in the lymphocytes, exposed to 0.005–0.1 μg/ml of the antibiotic, on the time of exposure. They concluded that the drug was most effective in producing chromosome anomalies at late G_1 and S phase of the cell cycle, and that breakage–reunion and incomplete exchange were the underlying causes of the types and frequency of doxorubicin-induced fragments (mostly chromosome fragments) and exchanges (mostly chromatid exchanges).

In a recent study, it was found that doxorubicin induced an increased frequency of sister chromatid exchanges at concentrations as low as 1 ng/ml in human peripheral whole blood lymphocyte cultures, but at concentrations of 60 ng/ml and over chromosomal aberrations were also observed. An increase in the frequency of the said alterations in cancer patients treated with the drug was also recorded 10 min after injection, the control values being reached 1 month after treatment (39).

Mutagenicity and induction of malignant transformation properties of the antitumor anthracyclines have been studied in cell culture. Definite mutagenic activity was shown by these antibiotics in a bacterial system (40), and the transforming potential of doxorubicin had been stressed by Price et al. (41). Marquardt et al. (42) have used a clone of mouse fibroblasts susceptible for chemical transformation for the assay of malignant transformation, the latter being based on the observation of morphologically transformed cells 56 days after treatment, and a model using change from 8-azaguanine susceptibility to resistance in chinese hamster cells as a marker for mutagenesis. Doxorubicin (and daunorubicin) caused a high rate of transformation in mouse fibroblasts at concentrations as low as $0.001-0.01$ μg/ml (cells were exposed to the drug for 24 hr). Anthracycline-transformed cells were also shown to give rise to tumors in mice. In the mutagenicity test, major dose-dependent changes in mutation rate were recorded upon exposure of the cells to 0.01 and 0.1 μg/ml of the drugs. On the other hand, the DNA binding compound actinomycin D appeared minimally effective in the said tests. A direct specific carcinogenic action of the anthracyclines, apparently related to their ability to interfere with DNA, seems therefore to be established, but the mechanism underlying these important biological effects remains unknown. However, doxorubicin ranked second only to daunorubicin in a comparative assay of eight antineoplastic agents for their mutagenic potency in *Salmonella typhimurium* strains, and only to vincristine in a mouse lymphoma assay (43).

OTHER STUDIES IN CULTURED CELLS

Intracellular sodium concentration increased significantly in HeLa cells treated with doxorubicin at 10^{-7} M concentrations for 3 hr, while potassium content of the cells was not altered, leading to a decrease of the K^+/Na^+ ratio from 5.53 (untreated cells) to 3.42 (treated cells) (44). The same authors also found an increase of calcium ion influx into the cells, due to an enhanced rate of the slow component of the biphasic uptake process of calcium, as well as a net increase of the intracellular exchangeable pool of this ion. These results are in agreement with those of Solie and Yuncker (45), who found that doxorubicin stimulated the net transport of sodium ions across frog skin epithelium exposed to sodium Ringer's solution, as deduced from short-circuit current measurements. Stimulation was obtained at $4 \times 10^{-5} M$ drug concentration, was not affected by excess calcium ions, amiloride, ouabain, and vasopressin, and was related with an increase in passive transport across the membrane. Transfer of this information at the cell level would suggest an increase of intracellular sodium as a result of doxorubicin action, inducing a constant and abnormal demand of energy for the necessary compensation by the active extrusion processes. This hypothesis is in agreement with the observations concerning myocardial mitochondrial damages in the absence of effect on respiration or on ADP/oxygen ratios in mitochondria from rabbits treated with doxorubicin (46).

Taking account of previous results indicating mitotic inhibition by doxorubicin and daunorubicin under conditions in which nucleic acid synthesis is apparently not modified, Murphree et al. (47) have investigated the implication of cell surface phenomena in the growth inhibitory properties of the former on the basis of the alterations induced by the antibiotic of the concanavalin A mediated agglutination of sarcoma 180 ascites cells. In fact, exposure of the cells for 24 hr to $10^{-7} M$ doxorubicin (a concentration already showing growth-inhibitory properties) resulted in a significant increase of the rate of agglutination without modification of the number of concanavalin A binding sites or of the rate of their occupancy. The authors concluded that doxorubicin might cause an acceleration of the clustering of the concanavalin A occupied receptors, as a consequence of a direct action at the membrane level, suggesting a possible role of changes in cell surface in the antitumor effects of the drug. More recently, Gosalvez et al. (48) have reported a morphological alteration (inhibition of capping) of surface immunoglobulins induced by incredibly low ($10^{-20} M$ and above) concentrations of doxorubicin (and of compound ICRF-159 and tetrodotoxin as well) in mouse lymphocytes. The phenomenon was explained as involving a cell-to-cell propagation by direct contact through membrane microfilaments of primary changes induced by single doxorubicin molecules in a limited portion of the cell population present in the sample.

STUDIES WITH RESISTANT CELLS

Development of resistance to daunorubicin in hamster cells by *in vitro* culture methods gave rise to cells showing an ED_{50} up to 883 times that of the original cell line (49,50). The cells were also cross-resistant to actinomycin D, vincristine, and doxorubicin (and cells resistant to actinomycin D were found cross-resistant to daunorubicin). Development of resistance was ascribed to reduced permeability of the cell membrane on the basis of uptake studies with labeled drugs.

Using murine L 1210 ascites leukemia cells (51) and Ehrlich ascites tumor cells (52) with resistance to daunorubicin developed *in vivo* (and cross-resistant to doxorubicin), it was found that daunorubicin inhibited the incorporation of [^{3}H]thymidine and [^{3}H]uridine less in resistant than in wide-type cells, in the case of Ehrlich ascites tumor cells for both the DNA synthesis and the RNA synthesis about five times as much drug being required in order to give the same inhibition in resistant and in sensitive cells. Danø et al. (52) also investigated the sensitivity of the different RNA species to daunorubicin in the two types of cells and found that the preferential inhibition of ribosomal RNA was less pronounced in the resistant cells in comparison to the sensitive ones. In addition, resistant cells showed also a reduced uptake of daunorubicin. Therefore, more than one factor is operating in the expression of resistance, as is shown also by the observation that the same degree of inhibition of nucleic acid synthesis was obtained exposing resistant and sensitive cells to respectively 10 μg/ml and 2 μg/ml, whereas the intracellular concentrations of the drug in the resistant cells were about twice that in sensitive cells. The authors concluded indicating other possible factors, in addition to decreased uptake of the antibiotic, namely a reduced sensitivity of the RNA and DNA synthesizing systems, a different intracellular distribution, and an altered intracellular metabolism of daunorubicin. A reduced uptake of daunorubicin in resistant L 1210 cells was reported by Cherwinsky and Wang (53); however, the most detailed investigations on the mechanism of the cellular uptake in cultured resistant cells have been carried out with the Ehrlich ascites tumor cells resistant to daunorubicin [see Danø (6), for an outstanding review of this topic]. The presence of an active outward transport of the antibiotic in the resistant cells was suggested by Danø (5). This hypothesis was based on a number of observations, such as the higher uptake of daunorubicin at steady state in isolated nuclei prepared from resistant cells than that in the intact cells, the strong increase in the amount of the antibiotic which was taken up in the steady state in resistant cells treated with inhibitors of energy metabolism (2-deoxyglucose, iodoacetate), and the increased accumulation of daunorubicin in resistant cells induced by its structural analogues N-acetyldaunorubicin and daunorubicinol. The presence of an active transport mechanism, which pumps daunorubicin out of the resistant cells against an electrochemical potential gradient and which at the steady state is balanced by a passive, or carrier-mediated, inward transport, was in agreement with the kinetics of uptake and with the lower concentration of the drug in the cytoplasma of the resistant cells in comparison with that of the free drug in the surrounding medium. In addition, a common uptake mechanism for daunorubicin and doxorubicin in resistant lines of Ehrlich ascites tumor cells was demonstrated. The observation of Kessel *et al.* (*54*) that uptake *in vitro* of different murine ascites tumors did not correlate with the retention of daunorubicin *in vivo* by the same tumors (and therefore with the antitumor response) was considered not conclusive because of the inadequacy of the experimental conditions used (*6*). The details of the assumed mechanism of extrusion are, however, unknown. It appears not to be associated with active transport of sodium out of the cells, as the pretreatment of the latter with ouabain displayed no effect on daunorubicin uptake (*6*). A number of points of general importance also remain to be clarified: the form in which the drug is transported through the membrane (protonated or free base), the effect of the incubation temperature, the presence of a common mechanism of extrusion for the anthracycline and the vinca alkaloids, the structural requirements of the same anthracyclines as regards the active transport process, and finally evaluation of the rate-limiting process in the elution of the drug from the cells (whether it is the release of the compound from the binding in the nuclei or the transport across the cell membrane) (*6*).

Using L 1210 cell lines in which resistance to doxorubicin or to daunorubicin was developed *in vivo*, Cherwinsky and Wang (*9*) found no difference in the *in vivo* uptake of both antibiotics between the cells sensitive and resistant to doxorubicin, but a consistently lower uptake of both antibiotics in the daunorubicin-resistant cells, when compared with the sensitive ones, was recorded.

Londos-Gagliardi *et al.* (*55*) have measured the uptake of daunorubicin in sensitive and resistant Ehrlich ascites tumor cells by spectrofluorimetry or by the use of tritium-labeled drug. *In vitro* accumulation of daunorubicin was lower in the resistant cells than in the sensitive cells and was in the ratio of 2 to 3, using different concentrations of the drug and after incubation times ranging from 30 min to 7 hr. The difference was mainly related to a decrease of daunorubicin uptake by the nuclei.

The results of a series of investigations using doxorubicin- and daunorubicin-resistant (and nonresistant to other antitumor agents including actinomycin D) sublines of P 388 leukemia have elucidated some important aspects of drug resistance in these sublines (*56–59*). Resistance indices *in vitro* (ratio of LD_{99} values) for daunorubicin were 18 and 56 for the doxorubicin- and daunorubicin-resistant sublines respectively, and approximately 800 for doxorubicin in both sublines. Labeled thymidine

incorporation rate into DNA was inhibited by 50% when sensitive, daunorubicin-resistant, and doxorubicin-resistant cells were exposed to 2.5, 8.3,
and 27 μg/ml of doxorubicin or to 0.8, 2.2, and 5.3 μg/ml of daunorubicin
respectively, indicating that the degree of inhibition of DNA synthesis could
not account for the differences between the drugs or for the degree of
resistance with respect to cytotoxic activity. Rate of uptake of the two drugs
in resistant cells was lower than in the sensitive cells, being decreased,
however, to a similar extent for both drugs. This observation, coupled with
the small difference in the rate of uptake of actinomycin D between the
resistant and sensitive cells, allowed the deduction that the decreased rate
of uptake was not the basis of resistance. Resistance to the cytotoxic effects
of the anthracyclines was most closely related to the much lower retention of
the drugs by the sublines. The sensitive cells took up less doxorubicin than
daunorubicin, 80% of the former being however retained, in comparison
with 55% for daunorubicin after 1 hr of exposure to drug-free medium. On
the other hand, the levels of doxorubicin retained in resistant cells were
below the background (the amount bound to the cells after exposure to the
drug for 10 sec, then to drug-free medium for 1 hr) at all drug concentrations
tested. In addition, increasing the pH of the medium from 7.4 to up to 8.0
or the presence of 0.1% of the surfactant Tween 80 in the medium did
enhance the uptake of doxorubicin in the resistant cells, but the decreased
retention, and therefore the resistance to the cytotoxic effects, were not
affected. The difference in the binding to isolated nuclei from the different
cells was small in comparison with that observed in the intact cells. The
conclusion of these studies was that the decreased retention of the drugs
in the resistant P 388 sublines suggested the presence of an active efflux
mechanism which was enhanced in the resistant cells, as already proposed
for Ehrlich ascites tumor cells. Similarly, the cross resistance of the anthra-
cycline-resistant sublines to actinomycin D and to the protein-synthesis
inhibitor emetine were explained by the decreased capability to retain inhibitory concentrations of the drugs.

Other observations are available that can possibly throw some light in
the physicochemical changes of the cell membranes associated with the
development of resistance to the anthracyclines. For instance, cells exposed
to heat developed considerable resistance to doxorubicin, suggesting that
prolonged heat exposure modified the cell membrane permeability to the
antibiotic (60). It has been recently demonstrated that ethanol also induced
cellular resistance to doxorubicin, the qualitative patterns of heat- or
ethanol-induced tolerance being quite similar. The effect was probably related to permeability changes involving increased fluidity of the membranes
(61). According to Nishimura et al. (62), both decreased uptake and retention

of the drug are the cause of resistance to doxorubicin in a subline of mouse lymphoblastoma cells.

STUDIES WITH CULTURED HEART CELLS

Doxorubicin (0.1–0.5 μg/ml) reduced the beating rate of mouse myocardial cells *in vitro* (*63*). Electron microscopy showed a hypertrophy and swelling of the sarcoplasmic reticulum and a marked increase in the number and extension of gap junction between the cells as major ultrastructural consequences of drug treatment. No alteration of mitochondrial and of contractile components were observed after this type of acute *in vitro* treatment (*64*). Ouabain restored the doxorubicin-induced reduction of beating rate, and pretreatment with ouabain prevented the effects of the antibiotic, suggesting for doxorubicin an interaction with sites on the cellular membrane (*65*).

Doxorubicin inhibited growth of newborn rat cardiac cells in culture and induced alteration of the frequency and rhythm of the cell contractions, but apparently not of the energy metabolism of the cells. Nonmyocardial cells were the most sensitive to drug-induced growth inhibition (*66*).

METABOLISM

Doxorubicin and its parent compound daunorubicin are extensively metabolized in mammals, and available evidence indicates that two main reactions take place in animal tissues, namely the reduction of the side chain carbonyl group to a secondary alcoholic group, the products being doxorubicinol (**1a**) and daunorubicinol (**1b**) respectively, and a reductive deglycosidation giving rise to the 7-deoxyaglycones **2a**, **2b**, **3a**, and **3b**.

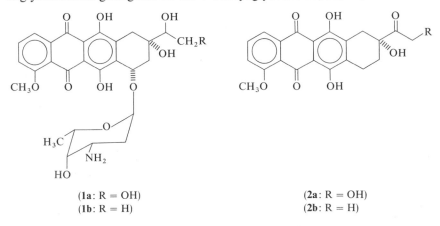

(**1a**: R = OH)
(**1b**: R = H)

(**2a**: R = OH)
(**2b**: R = H)

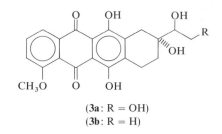

(3a: R = OH)
(3b: R = H)

The former reaction is catalyzed by widely distributed enzymes, the cytoplasmic aldo–keto reductases. The ability to convert daunorubicin to daunorubicinol was detected in different rat tissue preparations, the enzyme involved being constitutive and requiring reduced triphosphopyridine nucleotide (NADPH) as cofactor (*67,68*). Daunorubicinol was isolated from the urines of patients treated with daunorubicin in amounts sufficient to allow the determination of its structure (*69*). Daunorubicin reductase was isolated and purified from rat liver and showed a molecular weight approaching 40,000 (*70,71*). A range of carbonyl compounds, mainly aldehydes, were reduced in the presence of the enzyme and cofactor. Doxorubicin was reduced 20 times less efficiently than daunorubicin. A physiological role of daunorubicin reductase was also suggested (*72*).

In a recent publication, Ahmed *et al.* (*73*) reported the pH activity profile of rabbit, human, rat, and mouse liver daunorubicin reductase as determined on dialyzed ammonium sulfate preparations obtained from supernatants of tissue extracts (Fig. 3). In contrast to mouse and rat, whose preparations gave optimal activity only at pH 8.5, rabbit and human liver crude enzyme preparations exhibited maximum activity at pH 6.0 together with a second peak at pH 8.5. Gel filtration chromatography of the rabbit and human dialyzed fractions allowed the recovery of the two daunorubicin reductase activities as separate eluting peaks, while the pH 8.5 and 6.0 doxorubicin reductase activities were eluted in a single peak nearly coincident to that containing the pH 6.0 daunorubicin reductase. Molecular weights corresponding to the gel filtration chromatographic fractions, as determined by comparison with protein standards, were in the range 32,300 to 38,700. Analysis of the dialyzed ammonium sulfate fractions by DEAE-cellulose chromatography or by isoelectric focusing afforded evidence of further heterogeneity within each type of enzyme. These results are consistent with the higher metabolism of anthracyclines shown by the rabbit and man in comparison to rat and mouse.

Metabolic conversion of daunorubicin to aglycone-like products was recorded in different studies (*67,68,74–77*), **2a**, **3a** and **2b**, **3b** being the main products of respectively doxorubicin and daunorubicin metabolism by liver

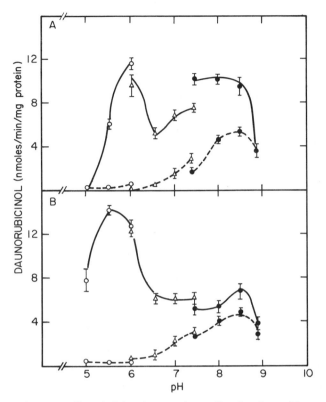

Fig. 3. Activity pH profiles of dialyzed ammonium sulfate fractions of human (A, ——), rat (A, ---), rabbit (B, ——), and mouse (B, ---) liver daunorubicin reductase in citrate phosphate (○), potassium phosphate (△), and Tris-HCl (●) buffer. Figure reproduced from Ahmed *et al.* (*73*).

homogenates of rat and hamster (*78,79*). Bachur and Gee (*80*) demonstrated that the enzyme catalyzing the reductive splitting of the aminosugar moiety was associated with the microsomal fraction of rat liver, was inhibited by oxygen (partial pressures of oxygen in the system greater than 15% inhibited the reaction more than 90%), required NADPH as cofactor, was induced by phenobarbital pretreatment of the animals, was not affected by inhibitors of microsomal enzyme such as carbon monoxide and β-diethylaminoethyldiphenylpropyl acetate (SKF 525 A) or by Mg^{2+}, Mn^{2+}, Fe^{2+}, or Ni^{2+}, but was inhibited by Cu^{2+} and Zn^{2+}.

The isolation and identification of 13-dihydroadriamycinone (**4**), 4-demethyl-7-deoxy-13-dihydroadriamycinone (**5**), 4-demethyl-7-deoxy-13-dihydroadriamycinone 4-*O*-sulfate (**6**), and 4-*O*-β-D-glucuronide (**7**), in

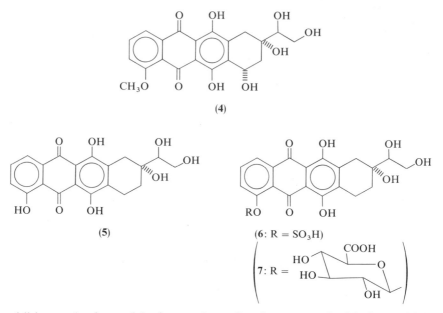

(4)

(5)

(6: R = SO₃H)

7: R =

addition to **1a**, **2a**, and **3a** from urines of patients treated with doxorubicin afforded a clear picture of the metabolism of the drug (*81*), which was similar to that of daunorubicin (*82*). In these studies, metabolites were extracted from pooled urinary samples by adsorption on XAD-2 Amberlite resin followed by methanolic elution. Other studies, concerning the metabolism of doxorubicin and daunorubicin in clinical patients, were reported by Huffman *et al*. (*83*), Huffman and Bachur (*84*), and Benjamin *et al*. (*85,86*). A GLC–mass spectral analysis of doxorubicin metabolites has been proposed (*87,87a*).

The comparison of doxorubicin and daunorubicin metabolism in human and animal systems has been reported by Loveless *et al*. (*88*). Tissue samples were obtained from mice, rats, hamsters, rabbits, dogs, and from adult human males dying of accidental death not associated with drug usage. Reductase activities were determined on ultracentrifugation supernatants of cytoplasmic extracts and on ammonium sulphate fractions of the same. Glycosidase activities were determined using microsomes isolated from tissue homogenates. In both cases, quantitative spectrophotometric determination of the reaction products after a thin-layer chromatographic separation was used for the evaluation of enzymatic activity. Results indicated that reductase activity was highest in the kidney of rat, mouse, and rabbit, but in humans and dogs liver showed activity equal or greater than that of kidney. Heart and skeletal muscle showed low activity, with the exception of rat heart. In all species examined, doxorubicin and daunorubicin displayed similar affinity (as measured from the K_m values) for the reductase of liver and kidney, but the ability to reduce the C-9 side chain (measured from the V_{max} values) was distinctly greater for the latter. However, rabbit liver and kidney enzymes displayed K_m values for doxorubicin clearly lower than that shown by daunorubicin and also than the values shown by daunorubicin and doxorubicin reductases from all other species. Microsomes from liver, kidney, and heart of all species exhibited glycosidase activity, the enzyme generally preferring daunorubicin over doxorubicin as the substrate. Doxorubicin seemed therefore to be more slowly metabolized than the parent drug, daunorubicin, and this property was related with the higher therapeutic effects of the former.

PHARMACOKINETICS

The pattern of distribution of [^{3}H]doxorubicin in mice was similar to that observed with [^{3}H]daunorubicin, but the latter compound was more rapidly excreted, no difference being found between normal and S-180 tumor-bearing animals (77). In mice bearing spontaneous mammary carcinoma, labeled doxorubicin gave higher tissue levels of radioactivity than did labeled daunorubicin (89). In the same study, significant levels of tritium, equivalent to 1 μg of antibiotic/g of fresh tissue, were still detected in the tumor 1 week after treatment with three 2.5 mg/kg doses at 12-hr intervals of [^{3}H]doxorubicin. In humans, [^{3}H]doxorubicin was rapidly fixed in body tissues, with the exception of brain. Urinary excretion of tritium for the first 7 days after treatment with a single iv dose of 0.5 mg/kg was 22.7% of the dose administered, and faecal excretion was 45% of dose for the same period (90). The decay curve of radioactivity in plasma and tissues of rats treated with [^{3}H]doxorubicin was in agreement with a two-compartment model (91). The organs showing the highest uptake of tritium were liver, lungs, and spleen; very low concentrations were found in bone and brain. In the same study, plasma and urinary drug concentrations of patients with advanced malignant disease treated with a single dose of doxorubicin were determined by the total fluorescence method used for daunorubicin by Bachur et al. (92) and by Alberts et al. (93). The half-life of the first exponential component of plasmatic decay of fluorescence was 7 min and that of the second exponential component was 31 hr; the corresponding values in the rat were 20 min and 61 hr. Urinary excretion in patients was 12.6% of dose during the first 48 hr, mainly constituted by unchanged drug. The initial rapid decay was ascribed to redistribution in the tissues, the amounts of doxorubicin measured in rat tissues being in agreement with the proposed model. The TLC–fluorometric method allowed Bachur et al. (94) to evaluate the behavior of daunorubicin and doxorubicin in the rabbit. Both drugs were cleared from plasma at apparent first-order rate for 2 hr, after which the disappearance rate decreased. Using a procedure involving extraction followed by acid hydrolysis and TLC–fluorometric determination of the aglycones, Benjamin *et al.* (*85*) found that, in cancer patients, doxorubicin showed a biphasic decay in plasma, the short half-life being 1.1 hr, the long half-life 16.7 hr, and total urinary excretion in 5 days 5.5% of administered dose. Other studies in laboratory animals and in patients based on different recovery procedures of the drug and of its metabolites were reported by Dusonchet *et al.* (*95*), Mhatre *et al.* (*96*), Bachur *et al.* (*97*), Chan and Harris (*98*), and Schwartz (*99*). Pharmacokinetic investigations of doxorubicin in clinical patients with normal or impaired hepatic function were discussed by Benjamin (*100*), who pointed out, *inter alia*, that the detailed analysis of plasmatic decay of chromatographically isolated doxorubicin revealed three phases with half-lives of approximately 30 min, 8 hr, and 28 hr respectively, instead of the biphasic pattern displayed by total plasma fluorescence. A recovery of 40% of administered fluorescent material was obtained in the bile over a 1 week period (*101*). The main species present in the bile was doxorubicin, the next most prominent being doxorubicinol. The total fluorescent chromatographic species were, however, approximately 10 and included conjugate compounds and different aglycone-type compounds, the latter being present in smaller amounts.

A physiologic pharmacokinetic model of doxorubicin disposition has been developed from rabbit drug distribution data (*102*), and its validity to predict drug plasma concentrations in cancer patients was evaluated by Chan *et al.* (*103*). The model depicted the body as being composed of 10 compartments and considered hepatic clearance combining hepatic metabolism and biliary excretion. Tissue uptake in surgery patients was also measured. The method used for the analysis of doxorubicin and its metabolites in plasma and tissue samples was based on a thin-layer chromatographic fluorescence scanning technique (*104*) affording a lower limit of sensitivity of 2 ng/ml. A triexponential decay curve for doxorubicin was expressed by

$$C = \sum_{i=1}^{3} A_i \varepsilon^{\alpha} i^t$$

Model predictions generated using a digital computer program and comparison between predicted and observed doxorubicin concentrations indicated reasonable agreements in the majority of patients who did not have clinical evidence of impaired liver or kidney function, the poor agreement found in some of these cases being related to particularly high doxorubicinol plasma concentrations and rapid doxorubicin clearance. The model did not fully account for individual differences in metabolic rate and profile, nor for variability in the terminal log-linear halflives. Patients with impaired liver function showed higher plasma concentrations and prolonged plasma half-life than predicted by the model. The authors concluded that the model could be further improved considering metabolism and clearance separately, including a tumor compartment and reducing the number of compartments by the combination of those which appeared not to be patient-specific. The development of radioimmunoassay (RIA) procedures, although unable to differentiate among the different glycosidated species, allowed rapid detection of amounts as low as 1 ng/ml of the drug (*105*). Bachur *et al.* (*106*), using both the RIA and the fluorescence procedure, were able to confirm the three-phase plasma disappearance curve for total doxorubicin mentioned above (Fig. 4). These authors also found that the fluorescence assay detected material escaping detection by the antisera. The possibility that these fluorescent species were constituted by aglycone-like compounds was considered, although higher readings observed especially at later times where drug levels were low could also be ascribed to other drug unrelated compounds, scattering fluorescence in the region of doxorubicin emission wavelengths. The high-pressure liquid chromatographic (HPLC) technique has been proved to be the method of choice for the quantitative separation of doxorubicin and its metabolites in extracts of urines and plasma. The RIA method was used for the quantitation of the individual HPLC fractions (*107*). According to this methodology, doxorubicin and doxorubicinol were proved to be the major components in urines of patients. A limit of sensitivity of approximately 10 ng/ml was obtained by Hulhoven and Desager (*108*) using HPLC and visible spectrophotometric detection of the components in the plasma of rabbits treated with daunorubicin. Other applications of HPLC methods for metabolic studies have also been reported (*108a–c*).

The availability of $[^{14}C]$doxorubicin and of $[^{14}C]$daunorubicin has allowed a quantitative balance of distribution and excretion of these antibiotics in experimental animals. An accumulation experiment in rats has been reported by Liss *et al.* (*109*). After initial dosing with $[^{14}C]$doxorubicin (51.3 μCi/kg, 4 mg/kg), the animals were given single intravenous doses of cold doxorubicin (4 mg/kg) at 24-hr intervals through 96 hr. Whole-body radioautograms indicated a rapid distribution of the drug in the tissues, with the exception of the central nervous system. Doxorubicin was present in gastric and biliary secretions, and its distribution via thoracic lymphatic channels was observed. The amount accumulated in cardiac muscle was always greater than that observed in skeletal muscle. At 96 hr, cumulative excretion was 7.5% in the urines, 65% in the feces, and 6.75% in expired CO_2, and the highest fractions of retained radioactivity were found in

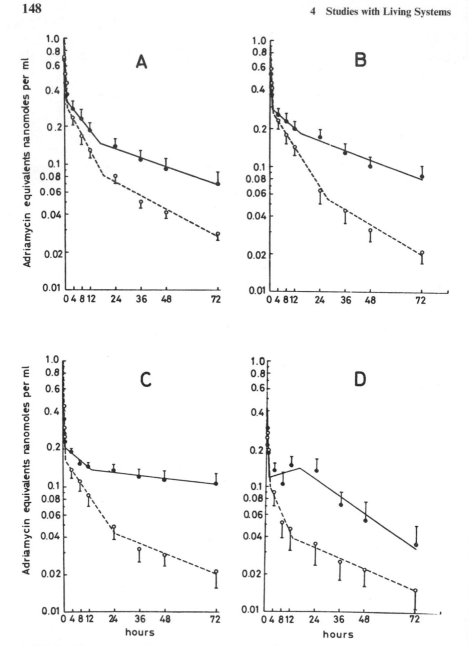

Fig. 4.   Plasma doxorubicin determined by fluorescence (●) or radioimmunoassay (○) in four treatment groups: A, 60 mg/m²; B, 45 mg/m²; C, 30 mg/m²; D, 15 mg/m². Number of patients was 16 in group A, 8 in B, 10 in C and 4 in D. Reproduced from Bachur *et al.* (*106*).

liver, skeletal muscle, lymphatic and glandular tissues, gastrointestinal contents, and renal tubules. Distribution experiments carried out with [^{14}C]doxorubicin (2.3 mCi/mM, single iv dose of 0.5 mg/kg) in mice indicated that during 4 hr after administration 20–30% of dose was accumulated in the liver (in agreement with a preferential elimination in the bile), and the level of radioactivity in the heart was higher than that in the skeletal muscle and 0.75 times that in the lung [this ratio was 0.5 for [^{14}C]daunorubicin (*110*)].

Pharmacokinetics of doxorubicin have also been investigated in laboratory animals with presumable alterations of metabolism or distribution. Plasma fluorescence due to the drug and metabolites was lower and disappeared at a faster rate in phenobarbital pretreated mice than in control mice, suggesting an accelerated disposition of doxorubicin as a consequence of microsomal enzyme induction. Phenobarbital pretreatment caused lower similar rates in L 1210 leukemia bearing animals treated with the antibiotic (*111*).

Tritium-labeled doxorubicin was rapidly taken up by tumor cells of sarcoma 180 ascites bearing mice and showed a half-life of 12 hr in this tissue (daunorubicin 4 hr) (*112*). Mice bearing ascitic L 1210 showed intracellular levels of 0.5 and 2.0 μg/10^7 tumor cells 1 hr after the ip injection of respectively doxorubicin or daunorubicin at a 10 mg/kg dosage. However, doxorubicin was retained for a longer time than daunorubicin, as after 24 hr the concentration of the former was 78% of that after 1 hr, whereas the concentration of daunorubicin was 40% of the 1-hr value (*9*).

Pharmacokinetic parameters in mice bearing the intramuscular Lewis lung carcinoma and treated with single intravenous doses of the drugs were determined by Martini *et al.* (*113*). *Inter alia*, a higher and more prolonged accumulation of doxorubicin in comparison with daunorubicin was detected in the neoplastic tissue, in agreement with the higher therapeutic effectiveness of the former antibiotic.

PHARMACOLOGICAL PROPERTIES
IN WHOLE MAMMALIAN SYSTEMS

Although a discussion of the pharmacological properties of the antitumor anthracyclines does not fall within the scope of this book, a summarized presentation of the studies concerned with the mode of action and the toxic side-effects of doxorubicin in experimental animals and in human patients will be given. Current views of the subject are reported in a recent review entitled "Clinical Correlations of Adriamycin Pharmacology," in which the author (*114*) states that

> Adriamycin should be considered a milestone in cancer chemotherapy because of its
> wide spectrum of activity: However . . . adriamycin induces toxic effects in those normal
> tissues which have a high rate of cell turnover. Damage of the blood-forming elements
> and mucous membranes therefore limits the dose of adriamycin that can be given to
> patients during each course of therapy. About 75–90 mg/m^2 is the upper limit for the
> dose that can be given at one time. . . . A severe, cumulative dose-dependent cardio-
> myopathy which may be fatal, limits the use of the drug to induction or consolidation
> therapy rather than long-term maintenance.

It is therefore not surprising that, in addition to investigations aimed to
relate the therapeutic effects of the drug with the properties already recognized at the molecular or cellular level, several studies have been carried
out in order to throw some light on the mechanism of the cardiotoxicity
which appears to be a major drawback of doxorubicin therapy. Both lines
of investigations are of relevance not only for the optimization of doxorubicin use in human chemotherapy, but also for the development of new more
selective analogue compounds once the different biological actions were
related with determined structural features of the parent drug.

Studies on the Mechanism of Antitumor Activity

In patients with acute leukemia, the therapeutic treatment with daunorubicin or doxorubicin induced an initial increase of DNA polymerase and
thymidine kinase activity in peripheral leukocytes followed, after a few days,
by a distinct decrease of the enzyme activities preceding the fall of the
leukocyte count (*115*). Massimo *et al.* (*116*) had observed statistically higher
chromosome abnormalities after doxorubicin treatment in lymphocytes
from blood of children suffering from tumor diseases than before treatment.
Both groups of investigators related these effects to those observed in lymphocytes cultured *in vitro*. Schwartz (*117*) reported that doxorubicin and
daunorubicin produced extensive fragmentation of tumor cell DNA in mice
bearing ascitic P 388 lymphocytic leukemia. *In vivo* degradation of DNA
in murine L 1210 leukemia cells was also reported by Lee and Byfield (*28*),
and it was assumed by these authors that the presence of the antibiotic led
to spontaneous activation of cell nucleases. Depression of [^{3}H]thymidine
incorporation into Morris tumor hepatoma cell DNA after doxorubicin
treatment has been recorded (*117a*).

Comparative studies showed that high doses of daunorubicin and doxorubicin inhibited to the same extent nucleic acid synthesis in leukemia
L 1210 cells *in vivo* (*51*). In mice bearing sarcoma 180 ascites, the halflives
of daunorubicin and doxorubicin in the tumor cells after a single ip injection
were 4 and 12 hr, respectively. The incorporation of labeled thymidine into

DNA of tumor cells was similar for the two drugs, but doxorubicin inhibited labeled uridine incorporation into RNA more markedly than daunorubicin. A higher antitumor effect was displayed by doxorubicin when treatment schedules allowing similar intracellular levels of the two antibiotics were used, suggesting that mechanisms other than higher drug retention (as for instance the different inhibition of RNA synthesis) might be involved in the different antiproliferative activity of the drugs.

Changes in the distribution of nucleolar ribonucleoproteins produced by doxorubicin in Novikoff hepatoma cells *in vivo* were studied by Smetana *et al.* (*118*). The investigators used the toluidine staining procedure on the unfixed, smeared tumor cells removed from rats bearing a 6-day-old Novikoff hepatoma ascites tumor 1 hr after treatment with doses of doxorubicin hydrochloride ranging from 0.15 to 10.0 mg/kg. Treatment with the drug caused a dose-dependent increase in the percentage of altered nucleole forms as those which are known to be associated with treatment of inhibitors of RNA synthesis.

The first study in which the behavior of doxorubicin in respect to the immunological reactions of the host was taken in consideration as a determinant of the selective cytotoxicity of the drug in tumor-bearing animals is that of Schwartz and Grindey (*119*). According to these investigators the much higher response of mice bearing P 388 lymphocytic leukemia to doxorubicin in comparison with daunorubicin was no more evident (and made equal for the two drugs) when the animals were pretreated with immunosuppressive doses of X radiation or after splenectomy. This and other evidence, including the higher accumulation of daunorubicin in the spleen of normal and tumor bearing mice, suggested that selective differences between the two drugs might be due to a greater cytotoxicity exhibited by daunorubicin than by doxorubicin towards spleen lymphoid cells (*120*).

The importance of effects exhibited by the anthracycline antibiotics on the immune response of the host as regards to the antitumor activity was also outlined by Casazza *et al.* (*121*). The authors approached the subject by comparing daunorubicin with doxorubicin in a variety of immunological systems. The first system was the Murine Sarcoma Virus-Moloney (MSV-M) induced tumor in mice, which is known to undergo spontaneous regression due to immunological mechanisms, the latter being inhibited by immuno-depressant treatments. When tested in this system, daunorubicin displayed a partial inhibition of tumor growth, while recurrence of the tumor was also observed. On the other hand, doxorubicin exhibited a higher inhibition of tumor growth while the effect on spontaneous tumor regression was less marked or even absent, depending from the treatment schedule. In the same study, it was reported that both daunorubicin and doxorubicin induced a strong reduction of virus-neutralizing antibodies in the serum of treated mice as well as of serum antibodies arising in mice after injection of sheep red blood cells. On the other hand, doxorubicin appeared to be clearly less effective than daunorubicin, at equitoxic doses, in the inhibition of cell-mediated immune responses, as shown in the skin allograft test, in the graft versus host reaction, and in delayed-type hypersensitivity tests in mice. Differential effects of both drugs as regards different immunological responses in mouse systems have been reported. A selective effect on spleen cell populations leading to a greater cytotoxic immune response *in vitro* with spleen cells derived from treated animals than with those from untreated ones were demonstrated [Orsini *et al.* (*122*), and references cited therein].

Resistance of Ehrlich ascites tumor cells to daunorubicin was obtained upon treatment with the drug in partially growth-inhibiting doses daily for 5 days during 16 weekly passages in mice. Resistant tumor exhibited karyotypic alteration with respect to the sensitive one. Tetraploid cells containing approximately 81 chromosomes prevailed in the latter, while cells of the resistant subline appeared mostly as hyperdiploid in character and exhibited chromosome numbers around 46. Discontinuation of treatment induced loss of resistance together with a resumption of the initial karyotype, likely as a consequence of abundant growth of sensitive cells present in the resistant tumor (*123*). Similarly, Danø (*124*) obtained doxorubicin-resistant Ehrlich ascites tumor cells *in vivo*, by treatment with the drug for 5 days a week at 2.1 mg/kg body weight during 25 weekly passages of the tumor in mice. The resistant tumor was cross-resistant to daunorubicin and vincristine and was characterized by a slower growth rate as, 7 days after an inoculum of 15×10^6 tumor cells, the established resistant subline yielded 40×10^6 cells per mouse, while the wild tumor under identical conditions grew to 493×10^6 cells per mouse. A reduced uptake of doxorubicin was found in a resistant Ehrlich ascites tumor of the mouse in comparison with the nonresistant one. Treatment of the resistant tumor bearing animals with liposome-entrapped doxorubicin or with a solution of the drug in Tween 80 partially restored both drug uptake in tumor tissue and drug antitumor effect (*125*).

A subline of P 388 leukemia resistant to doxorubicin and daunorubicin *in vivo* was found to be cross-resistant to 19 anthracycline analogues, both semisynthetic and biosynthetic, and to other unrelated antitumor agents including a variety of DNA intercalators, mitotic spindle poisons, and inhibitors of protein synthesis. No cross resistance was shown by antimetabolites, alkylating agents, camptothecin, and neocarcinostatin (*126*). The resistance was ascribed to reduced uptake and enhanced efflux of the drugs in resistant cells, the interesting hypothesis being put forward of a common efflux mechanism for a large number of cytostatic compounds belonging to different chemical families.

Enhancement of the antitumor activity of doxorubicin in experimental animal systems has been reported by Casazza et al. (127). A higher increase of lifespan in mice bearing Gross leukemia when the animals were treated iv with the drug dissolved in water containing from 1 to 20% of the nonionic surfactant Tween 80 than in water alone was recorded. Similarly, doxorubicin dissolved in 10% aqueous Tween 80 showed a more marked antitumor activity than the same drug dissolved in water, without increase of toxicity. However, this effect was only present when the drug was administered intravenously, as after intraperitoneal administration Tween 80 increased the toxicity but not the activity of the antibiotic. Similar observations were made in mice bearing transplanted MLV leukemia and MS-2 sarcoma, the effect of the surfactant appearing to be dose- or schedule-dependent. Tween 80 was also shown to increase drug concentration in spleen, lung, and kidney, but not in other tissues, including liver, heart and tumor. Different possible explanations of the above-mentioned effects were considered by the authors: (a) formation of molecular aggregates between the drug and the surfactant with properties similar to those of artificial liposomes; (b) a modification exerted by the surfactant of the cell-surface structures and therefore an enhanced uptake in tumor resistant cells, as already observed in another system (125); and (c) the known immunostimulating activity of Tween 80 would accelerate tumor growth and bring a higher number of tumor cells into cycle, thus making then more sensitive to the action of the drug.

Studies Related to Toxic Side-Effects

The clear relationships between the pattern of toxic manifestations consequent to doxorubicin treatment in experimental animals and the inhibiting action of the drug on actively proliferating cells, together with the observation of the presence of noticeable species differences in the sensitivity to the antibiotic, were established in the original toxicological evaluation of the compound [Bertazzoli et al., (128,129), and referencies cited therein].

A delayed cardiomyopathy, showing morphological alterations remarkably similar to those observed in cancer patients following prolonged chemotherapy with daunorubicin and doxorubicin, was demonstrated in rabbits receiving chronic treatment with the drugs (130). This experimental model, originally studied by Maral et al. (131) for daunorubicin, has also been used by Bertazzoli et al. (132) as an experimental model for the evaluation of cardiotoxicity of doxorubicin. Ballerini et al. (133) reported a chronic model in the rat allowing development of a severe doxorubicin-induced cardiomyopathy showing the same histologic patterns as those observed in human patients and in rabbits. The usefulness of subacute models in the rat for the evaluation of anthracycline antibiotic cardiotoxicity was stressed by Zbinden and Brändle (*134*) Bachmann *et al.* (*135*), and by Olson and Capen (*136*). According to the former authors, the cardiotoxicity could be monitored following the ECG changes induced by repeated daily doses of doxorubicin. Cardiovascular effects of doxorubicin treatment in the dog have also been studied (*137,138*). Myocyte damage was found in rabbits chronically treated with doxorubicin, and the lesions were enhanced when the animals also received X radiation in the cardiac area (*139*).

The various aspects of doxorubicin toxicity in experimental systems have been reviewed and discussed in a number of papers, among them those of Philips *et al.* (*140*) and of Young (*141*). The former authors stressed the fact that, in addition to its capacity to damage the cell-renewal system, doxorubicin exhibits unique toxic effects on the kidneys and on the heart. Renal lesions have been documented in rats and rabbits as a long-term event following prolonged treatment schedules. Similarly, myocardial damage appeared as a slowly evolving process progressing steadily in rabbits even after cessation of treatment with the drug, although severe pathologic changes of the myocardium were also evident in animals receiving high single doses shortly after treatment. The tumorigenicity of doxorubicin was also discussed. In the other article, 78 references were cited out of which half were concerned with the experimental evaluation of cardiovascular toxic effects as those appearing to be of major concern in human patients. The author reported in detail the morphological alterations of the myocardium induced by the anthracyclines, pointing out that in his own rabbit studies the most severe changes occurred as extensive perivascular fibrosis in close proximity to coronary arterial branches and arterioles, although other areas were also severely affected. Ultrastructural observations of affected myocardium collected by different investigators indicated myofibrillar degeneration, mitochondrial damage, and nuclear alterations. The following possible mechanism of doxorubicin cardiotoxicity were mentioned: (a) inhibition of DNA-directed RNA synthesis (and therefore of synthesis of protein necessary for the myocardial function and integrity); (b) interference with mitochondrial function (and consequent impairment of the energetic machinary of the cells); (c) alteration of membrane permeability to inorganic ions and other electrolytes, enzymes; and (d) alteration of the neurovascular function.

Reduction of DNA synthesis in cardiac tissues of mice treated with toxic doses (10–20 mg/kg) of doxorubicin had been found to be more marked and more long-lasting than the alteration in DNA synthesis observed in bone marrow and gastrointestinal tissues (*142*). Although significance of DNA synthesis in cardiac muscle of adult animals is not yet clear, as it may monitor different events such as continuous repair processes, mitochondrial DNA synthesis, metabolic DNA, or DNA synthesis in reproducing cardiac cells such as endothelial and interstitial cells, the authors underlined the temporal relationship of the said effect with fatal toxicity.

The inhibition of DNA synthesis in mouse heart, liver, and small intestine following treatment with toxic doses (10–20 mg/kg body weight) was also demonstrated by Formelli et al. (143) following the incorporation rate of [methyl-^{3}H]thymidine into the DNA. Inhibition values up to 70–80% were recorded, DNA synthesis reverting to normal values after a week in the liver and the intestine, while in the heart an overshoot was observed at 2 weeks, lasting as late as 4 weeks after treatment. These effects were, however, not specific nor necessarily correlated to cardiotoxicity, as actinomycin D and ara-C were found to exhibit similar effects although they were not known to give rise to the cardiomyopathy typical of the anthracyclines, and, on the other hand, duration of inhibition could be partially ascribed as an indirect consequence of intoxication. In addition, the overshoot effects monitored in this study were tentatively related to regenerative proliferation of endothelial or other interstitial cells by analogy with similar observations made after X radiation. The authors (139) conclude that "It must be considered that the myocardial fibrosis caused by adriamycin is in all likelihood a direct effect on the myocytes and it remains nuclear why the effect develops long after treatment has ended."

The careful electron microscopy study of Lambertenghi-Deliliers et al. (144) related interesting ultrastructural consequences of doxorubicin treatment in myocardial ventricular cells of mice. The early marked disorganization of nucleolar structure following treatment was no more evident after 14 hr but was followed by the start and progressive increase of the sarcoplasmic alterations. These are related by the authors, on the basis of the ultrastructural findings and of the available biochemical information, to a block of RNA and protein synthesis affecting either the removal of cytoplasmic proteins which control the functional integrity of the myocardial cell or the selective permeability of cell membranes. A reduction in the turnover of myofibrillar proteins which, under normal conditions, have a half-life of approximately 8 to 10 days was also considered, as 5 days following treatment extensive lysis of contractile components were observed.

The relationship of doxorubicin-induced cardiomyopathy with an effect on energy metabolism and myocardial mitochondrial function in the heart has been investigated, as ultrastructural observations (145,146) showed that various stages of mitochondrial degenerations were associated with the development of anthracycline induced human cardiomyopathy. Mitochondria isolated from the hearts of rats treated with cardiotoxic doses of daunorubicin exhibited no difference in P/O ratios, respiration rates, or ATPase activity when compared with similar preparations from untreated animals (147). In contrast with an intermittent treatment schedule, a continuous daily treatment of rabbits with doxorubicin induced reversible alterations of respiration, oxidative phosphorylation, and membrane permeability to NADH of isolated heart mitochondria (148). On the other hand, Bier and Jaenke (46) failed to demonstrate functional changes in heart mitochondria during the genesis of the myocardial lesion in the same species. In the working isolated rat heart, no changes in the concentrations of ATP and phosphocreatine were associated with the loss of contractile force and cessation of work caused by addition of daunorubicin to the perfusing fluid (149). It was reported by Iwamoto et al. (150) that doxorubicin exerted an inhibition of coenzyme Q_{10} enzymes in isolated mitochondria, and by Bertazzoli et al. (151) that CoQ_{10} was able to counteract the cardiotoxic properties of doxorubicin in chronically treated rabbits. Enhanced deficiency in the activity of the succinate dehydrogenase–coenzyme Q_{10} reductase in rabbits treated with doxorubicin in comparison with untreated animals was also found (132). Pretreatment with coenzyme Q_{10} decreased the acute toxicity of adriamycin in mice. The mechanism of this effect was tentatively ascribed to a prevention of the inhibition caused by the antibiotic to coenzyme Q_{10}-dependent enzymes in cardiac and other tissues (152). A protection against doxorubicin cardiotoxicity in rats pretreated with CoQ_{10} but not with CoQ_7 was also recorded by Zbinden et al. (153). A curative effect of CoQ_{10} on the cardiotoxicity induced in rats by doxorubicin has been described by Folkers et al. (154). Evidence of the presence of tissue damage related to lipid peroxidation, presumably a consequence of radical formation in vivo as already demonstrated in cultured cells, in hearts of mice treated with a single ip dose of 15 mg/kg of doxorubicin has been reported (155). Lipid peroxidation was monitored by measurement of malondialdehyde, a known product of unsaturated fatty acid peroxide degradation, in acid tissue extracts. No peroxidation was detected in tumor tissue of mice bearing P 388 ascites leukemia after treatment with the drug. These results were in agreement with the protection afforded by prior treatment with tocopherol towards the acute toxic effects of doxorubicin (156) and towards the doxorubicin-induced cardiomyopathy in mice (157).

Van Boxtel et al. (158) were able to recognise two effects of doxorubicin on myocardial contractile function in right ventricular papillary muscle preparations from rabbit heart. These were a small positive inotropic response similar to that of the cardiac glycoside and a prolongation of the duration of myocardial contraction probably related to a decreased calcium uptake due to impairment of mitochondrial function. Using isolated spontaneous beating atria of guinea pig, Villani et al. (159) have determined the ratio between the specific radioactivity in the cellular compartment and that in the medium (a measure of the amount of cellular Ca exchanged) after different periods (5–60 min) of exposure to $^{45}Ca^{2+}$ in the absence and in the presence of doxorubicin hydrochloride (10 μg/ml). The results indicated that the drug significantly reduced the amount of Ca^{2+}-exchangeable fraction and that combined administration of ouabain counteracted the doxorubicin-induced effect. Detailed analysis of the time course of calcium exchange allowed the suggestion that adriamycin exerted its negative inotropic effect on the said preparation by affecting the Ca^{2+} fast exchangeable phase, this being apparently a consequence of an enhanced stability of the membrane–calcium complex. Doxorubicin inhibited oxygen consumption by rat mitochondria *in vitro* and caused uncoupling of Ca^{2+} translocation from electron transfer reaction in the same system. Mitochondria isolated from doxorubicin-treated animals exhibited a marked reduction of oxygen consumption, the ADP/O ratio remaining, however, unchanged when compared with mitochondria isolated from untreated controls, and exhibited a fall of Ca/O ratio (*160*). The authors relate these effects to a primary action of the drug on the membranes, leading to loss of the regulation of Ca^{2+} concentration in the cardiac cell and in the case of mitochondria, and also to an impairment of electron transfer functions. Both lesions affect cardiac contractility and eventually lead to degeneration of the myocytes.

It has been reported by Bertazzoli *et al.* (*161*) that single doses of either daunorubicin or doxorubicin induced mammary tumors in rats. These results have been recently confirmed, but it was noted that tumors were obtained only with single sublethal doses much higher than those used for therapeutic purpose (*162*). Similar observations were reported by Philips *et al.* (*140*), the results being in agreement with *in vitro* studies. Induction of cataracts, abnormal dental growth, and tumors in rats repeatedly treated as infants with doxorubicin has also been recorded, the genesis of such effects being, however, not understood at the present time (*163*). Neurotoxic properties of doxorubicin associated with a selective damage of the ganglia of the peripheral nervous system have been reported (*164*).

REFERENCES

1. A. Di Marco and L. Massimo, *Minerva Med.* **59**, 3511 (1968).
2. A. Rusconi and A. Di Marco, *Cancer Res.* **29**, 1507 (1969).
3. R. Silvestrini, C. Gambarucci, and T. Dasdia, *Tumori* **56**, 137 (1970).
4. E. Calendi, A. Di Marco, M. Reggiani, M. B. Scarpinato, and L. Valentini, *Biochim. Biophys. Acta* **103**, 25 (1965).
5. K. Danø, *Biochim. Biophys. Acta* **323**, 466 (1973).
6. K. Danø, *Acta Pathol. Microbiol. Scand., Sec. A, Suppl.* No. 256 (1976).
7. W. D. Meriwether and N. Bachur, *Cancer Res.* **32**, 1137 (1972).
8. N. R. Bachur, M. Steel, W. D. Meriwether, and R. C. Hildebrand, *J. Med. Chem.* **19**, 651 (1976).

9. D. S. Cherwinsky and J. J. Wang, *J. Med.* **7**, 63 (1976).
10. T. Skovsgaard, *Biochem, Pharmacol.* **26**, 215 (1977).
11. T. Skovsgaard, *Biochem. Pharmacol.* **27**, 1221 (1978).
12. G. Noël, C. Peterson, A. Trouet, and P. Tulkens, *Eur. J. Cancer* **14**, 363 (1978).
13. C. Peterson and A. Trouet, *Cancer Res.* **38**, 4645 (1978).
14. K. K. Lie and S. O. Lie, *Proc. Congr. Nord. Soc. Cell Biol.*, *9th* p. 121 (1976); *C.A.* **89**, 16642.
15. A. Di Marco, *Antibiot. Chemother.* (*Basel*) **23**, 216 (1978).
16. A. Di Marco, F. Arcamone, and F. Zunino, *in* "Antibiotics" (J. W. Corcoran and F. E. Hahn, eds.), Vol. 3, p. 101. Springer-Verlag, Berlin and New York, 1974.
17. A. Di Marco and F. Arcamone, *Arzneim.-Forsch.* **25**, 368 (1975).
18. A. Di Marco, *Cancer Chemother. Rep.* **6**, 91 (1975).
19. A. Di Marco and F. Arcamone, *in* "Adriamycin Review" (M. Staquet *et al.*, eds.), p. 11. European Press Medikon, Ghent, 1975.
20. J. H. Kim, A. S. Gelbard, B. Djordievic, S. H. Kim, and A. G. Perez, *Cancer Res.* **28**, 2437 (1968).
21. R. Silvestrini, A. Di Marco, and T. Dasdia, *Cancer Res.* **30**, 966 (1970).
22. D. N. Wheatley, *in* "International Symposium on Adriamycin" (S. K. Carter *et al.*, eds.), p. 47. Springer-Verlag, Berlin and New York, 1972.
23. S. C. Barranco, *Cancer Chemother. Rep.* **6**, 147 (1975).
24. R. L. Momparler, M. Karon, S. E. Siegel, and F. Avila, *Cancer Res.* **36**, 2891 (1976).
25. R. Supino, A. M. Casazza, and A. Di Marco, *Tumori* **63**, 31 (1977).
26. R. B. Painter, *Cancer Res.* **38**, 4445 (1978).
27. H. S. Schwartz, *J. Med.* **7**, 33 (1976).
28. Y. C. Lee and J. E. Byfield, *J. Natl. Cancer Inst.* **57**, 221 (1976).
29. W. E. Ross, D. L. Glaubiger, and K. W. Kohn, *Biochim. Biophys. Acta* **519**, 23 (1978).
30. W. E. Ross, D. L. Glaubiger, and K. W. Kohn, *Biochim. Biophys. Acta* **562**, 41 (1979).
31. A. Di Marco, M. Gaetani, P. Orezzi, B. M. Scarpinato, R. Silvestrini, M. Soldati, T. Dasdia, and L. Valentini, *Nature* (*London*) **201**, 706 (1964).
32. B. K. Vig, *Mutat. Res.* **39**, 189 (1977).
33. L. Massimo, F. Dagna-Bricarelli, and A. Fossati-Guglielmoni, *Rev. Eur. Etud. Clin. Biol.* **15**, 793 (1970).
34. B. K. Vig, *Cancer Res.* **31**, 32 (1971).
35. T. C. Hsu, S. Pathak, and C. J. Kusyk, *Mutat. Res.* **33**, 417 (1975).
36. Y. L. Newsome and L. G. Littlefield, *J. Natl. Cancer Inst.* **55**, 1061 (1975).
37. W. Hittelman and P. N. Rao, *Cancer Res.* **35**, 3027 (1975).
38. M. A. Bempong and M. N. Brooks, *Sci. Biol. J.* **4**, 1 (1978); *C.A.* **89**, 16780c (1978).
39. N. P. Nevstad, *Mutat. Res.* **57**, 253 (1978).
40. B. Pani, C. Monti-Bragadin, and L. Samer, *Experientia* **31**, 787 (1975).
41. P. J. Price, W. A. Suk, P. C. Skeen, M. A. Chirigos, and R. J. Huebner, *Science* **187**, 1200 (1975).
42. H. Marquardt, F. S. Philips, and S. S. Sternberg, *Cancer Res.* **36**, 2065 (1976).
43. D. Matheson, D. Brusick, and R. Carraro, *Drug Chem. Toxicol.* **1**, 277 (1978).
44. T. Dasdia, A. Di Marco, M. Goffredi, A. Minghetti, and A. Necco, *Pharmacol. Res. Commun.* **11**, 19 (1979).
45. T. N. Solie and C. Yuncker, *Life Sci.* **22**, 1907 (1978).
46. C. C. Bier and R. S. Jaenke, *J. Natl. Cancer Inst.* **57**, 1091 (1976).
47. S. A. Murphree, L. S. Cunningham, K. M. Hwang, and A. C. Sartorelli, *Biochem. Pharmacol.* **25**, 1227 (1976).
48. M. Gosalvez, L. Pezzi, and C. Vivero, *Biochem. Soc. Trans.* **6**, 659 (1978).

49. J. L. Biedler and H. Riehm, *Cancer Res.* **30**, 1174 (1970).
50. H. Riehm and J. L. Biedler, *Cancer Res.* **31**, 409 (1971).
51. J. J. Wang, D. S. Chervinsky, and J. M. Rosen, *Cancer Res.* **32**, 511 (1972).
52. K. Danø, S. Frederiksen, and P. Hellung-Larsen, *Cancer Res.* **32**, 1307 (1972).
53. D. Cherwinsky and J. J. Wang, *Proc. Am. Assoc. Cancer Res.* **13**, 51 (1972).
54. D. Kessel, V. Botteril, and I. Wodinsky, *Cancer Res.* **28**, 938 (1968).
55. D. Londos-Gagliardi, C. Molinier-Jumel, and G. Aubel-Sadron, *Stud. Biophys.* **67**, 63 (1978).
56. M. Inaba and R. Johnson, *Cancer Res.* **37**, 4629 (1977).
57. M. Inaba and R. K. Johnson, *Biochem. Pharmacol.* **27**, 2123 (1978).
58. M. Inaba and R. K. Johnson, *Cancer Res.* **37**, 4629 (1977).
59. M. P. Chitnis and R. K. Johnson, *J. Natl. Cancer Inst.* **60**, 1049 (1978).
60. G. M. Hahn and D. P. Strande, *J. Natl. Cancer Inst.* **57**, 1063 (1976).
61. G. C. Li and G. M. Hahn, *Nature (London)* **274**, 699 (1978).
62. T. Nishimura, H. Suzuki, K. Muto, and N. Tanaka, *J. Antibiot.* **32**, 518 (1979).
63. A. Necco and T. Dasdia, *IRCS Med. Sci.* **2**, 1293 (1974).
64. A. Necco, T. Dasdia, S. Cozzi, and M. Ferraguti, *Tumori* **62**, 537 (1976).
65. A. Necco, T. Dasdia, D. Di Francesco, and A. Ferroni, *Pharmacol. Res. Commun.* **8**, 105 (1976).
66. M. W. Seraydarian and M. F. Goodman, *Rec. Adv. Stud. Card. Struct. Metab.* **12**, 713 (1978).
67. N. R. Bachur and J. C. Cradock, *J. Pharmacol. Exp. Ther.* **175**, 331 (1970).
68. N. R. Bachur and M. Gee, *J. Pharmacol. Exp. Ther.* **177**, 567 (1971).
69. N. R. Bachur, *J. Pharmacol. Exp. Ther.* **177**, 573 (1971).
70. N. R. Bachur and D. H. Huffman, *Br. J. Pharmacol.* **43**, 828 (1971).
71. R. L. Felsted, M. Gee, and N. R. Bachur, *J. Biol. Chem.* **249**, 3672 (1974).
72. R. L. Felsted, D. R. Richter, and N. R. Bachur, *Biochem. Pharmacol.* **26**, 1117 (1977).
73. N. K. Ahmed, R. L. Felsted, and N. R. Bachur, *Biochem, Pharmacol.* **27**, 2713 (1978).
74. A. Di Marco, G. Boretti, and A. Rusconi, *Farmaco, Ed. Sci.* **22**, 535 (1967).
75. A. Rusconi, G. Di Fronzo, and A. Di Marco, *Cancer Chemother. Rep.* **52**, 331 (1968).
76. G. Di Fronzo and R. A. Gambetta, *Rev. Eur. Etud. Clin. Biol.* **16**, 50 (1971).
77. G. Di Fronzo, R. A. Gambetta, and L. Lenaz, *Rev. Eur. Etud. Clin. Biol.* **16**, 572 (1971).
78. M. A. Asbell, E. Schwartzbach, F. J. Bullock, and D. W. Yesair, *J. Pharmacol. Exp. Ther.* **182**, 63 (1972).
79. F. J. Bullock, R. J. Bruni, and M. A. Asbell, *J. Pharmacol. Exp. Ther.* **182**, 70 (1972).
80. N. R. Bachur and M. Gee, *J. Pharmacol. Exp. Ther.* **197**, 681 (1976).
81. S. Takanashi and N. R. Bachur, *Drug Metab. Dispos.* **4**, 79 (1976).
82. S. Takanashi and N. R. Bachur, *J. Pharmacol. Exp. Ther.* **195**, 41 (1975).
83. D. H. Huffman, R. S. Benjamin, and N. R. Bachur, *Clin. Pharmacol. Ther.* **13**, 895 (1972).
84. D. H. Huffman and N. R. Bachur, *Blood* **39**, 637 (1972).
85. R. S. Benjamin, C. E. Riggs, Jr., and N. R. Bachur, *Clin. Pharmacol. Ther.* **14**, 592 (1973).
86. R. S. Benjamin, C. E. Riggs, and N. R. Bachur, *Cancer Res.* **37**, 1416 (1977).
87. E. Watson and K. K. Chan, *J. Pharm. Sci.* **67**, 1243 (1978).
87a. K. K. Chan and E. Watson, *J. Pharm. Sci.* **67**, 1748 (1978).
88. H. Loveless, E. Arena, R. L. Felsted, and N. R. Bachur, *Cancer Res.* **38**, 593 (1978).
89. L. Lenaz and G. Di Fronzo, *Tumori* **58**, 213 (1972).
90. G. Di Fronzo, L. Lenaz, and G. Bonadonna, *Biomedicine* **19**, 169 (1973).
91. P. M. Wilkinson and G. E. Mawer, *Br. J. Clin. Pharmacol.* **1**, 241 (1974).
92. N. R. Bachur, A. L. Moore, J. B. Bernstein, and A. Liu, *Cancer Chemother. Rep.* **54**, 89 (1970).

93. D. S. Alberts, N. R. Bachur, and J. L. Holtzman, *Clin. Pharmacol. Ther.* **12**, 96 (1971).
94. N. R. Bachur, R. C. Hildebrand, and R. S. Jaenke, *J. Pharmacol. Exp. Ther.* **191**, 331 (1974).
95. L. Dusonchet, N. Gebbia, and F. Gerbasi, *Pharmacol. Res. Commun.* **3**, 55 (1971).
96. R. M. Mhatre, E. H. Herman, V. S. Waravdekar, and I. P. Lee, *Biochem. Med.* **6**, 445 (1972).
97. N. R. Bachur, M. J. Egorin, and R. C. Hildebrand, *Biochem. Med.* **8**, 353 (1973).
98. K. K. Chan and P. A. Harris, *Res. Commun. Chem. Pharmacol.* **6**, 447 (1973).
99. H. S. Schwartz, *Biochem. Med.* **7**, 396 (1973).
100. R. S. Benjamin, *Cancer Chemother. Rep.* **6**, 183 (1975).
101. R. S. Benjamin, C. E. Riggs, Jr., A. A. Serpick, and N. R. Bachur, *Proc. Annu. Meet. Am. Assoc. Cancer Res., 65th*; *Proc. Annu. Meet. Am. Soc. Clin. Oncol. 10th* **15**, No. 301 (1974).
102. P. A. Harris and J. F. Gross, *Cancer Chemother. Rep.* **59**, 819 (1975).
103. K. K. Chan, J. L. Cohen, J. F. Gross, K. J. Himmelstein, J. R. Bateman, Y. Tsu-Lee, and A. S. Marlis, *Cancer Treat. Rep.* **62**, 1161 (1978).
104. E. Watson and K. K. Chan, *Cancer Treat. Rep.* **60**, 1611 (1976).
105. H. Van Vunakis, J. J. Langone, L. J. Riceberg, and L. Levine, *Cancer Res.* **34**, 2546 (1974).
106. N. R. Bachur, C. E. Riggs, M. R. Green, J. J. Langone, H. Van Vunakis, and L. Levine, *Clin. Pharmacol. Ther.* **21**, 70 (1977).
107. J. J. Langone, H. Van Vunakis, and N. Bachur, *Biochem. Med.* **12**, 283 (1975).
108. R. Hulhoven and J. P. Desager, *J. Chromatogr.* **125**, 369 (1976).
108a. M. Israel, W. J. Pegg, P. M. Wilkinson, and M. B. Garmick, *J. Liq. Chromatogr.* **1**, 795 (1978).
108b. R. N. Pierce and P. I. Jetlow, *J. Chromatogr.* **64**, 471 (1979).
108c. S. Eksborg, H. Ehrsson, and I. Andersson, *J. Chromatogr.* **164**, 479 (1979).
109. R. H. Liss, D. W. Yesair, J. P. Schepis, and I. C. Marenchic, *Acta Pharmacol. Toxicol.* **41**, Suppl. No. 1, 128 (1977).
110. K. Harrison and H. N. Wagner, Jr., *J. Nucl. Med.* **19**, 84 (1978).
111. S. D. Reich and N. R. Bachur, *Cancer Res.* **36**, 3803 (1976).
112. R. Silvestrini, L. Lenaz, G. Di Fronzo, and O. Sanfilippo, *Cancer Res.* **33**, 2954 (1973).
113. A. Martini, M. G. Donelli, A. Mantovani, M. A. Pacciarini, E. Fogar-Ottaviano, L. Morasca, S. Garattini, and F. Spreafico, *Oncology* **34**, 173 (1977).
114. S. D. Reich, *Pharmacol. Ther. (c)* **2**, 239 (1978).
115. K. Wilms and W. Wilmanns, *Klin. Wochenschr.* **50**, 866 (1972).
116. L. Massimo, F. Dagna-Bricarelli, and M. G. Cerchi, *in* "International Symposium on Adriamycin" (S. K. Carter *et al.*, eds.), p. 35. Springer-Verlag, Berlin and New York, 1972.
117. H. S. Schwartz, *Res. Commun. Chem. Pathol. Pharmacol.* **10**, 51 (1975).
117a. H. A. Hopkins, W. B. Looney, K. Teja, A. S. Hobson, and M. S. McLeod, *Br. J. Cancer* **37**, 1006 (1978).
118. K. Smetana, J. Merski, Y. Daskai, R. K. Busch, and H. Busch, *Cancer Treat. Rep.* **61**, 1253 (1977).
119. H. S. Schwartz and G. B. Grindey, *Cancer Res.* **33**, 1837 (1973).
120. H. S. Schwartz and P. M. Kanter, *Cancer Chemother. Rep.* **6**, 107 (1975).
121. A. M. Casazza, A. M. Isetta, F. Giuliani, and A. Di Marco, *in* "Adriamycin Review" (M. Staquet *et al.*, eds.), p. 123. European Press Medikon, Ghent, 1975.
122. F. Orsini, Z. Pavelic, and E. Mihich, *Cancer Res.* **37**, 1719 (1977).
123. L. Hasholt, J. Visfeldt, and K. Danø, *Acta Pathol. Microbiol. Scand., Sect. A* **79**, 665 (1971).
124. K. Danø, *Cancer Chemother. Rep., Part 1* **56**, 321 (1972).

125. S. Seeber, T. Meshkov, and C. G. Schmidt, *Int. Congr. Chemother.*, *10th, Zurich* Abstr. 498 (1977).

126. R. K. Johnson, M. P. Chitnis, W. M. Embrey, and E. B. Gregory, *Cancer Treat. Rep.* **62**, 1535 (1978).

127. A. M. Casazza, G. Pratesi, F. Giuliani, F. Formelli, and A. Di Marco, *Tumori* **64**, 115 (1978).

128. C. Bertazzoli, T. Chieli, M. Grandi, and G. Ricevuti, *Experientia* **26**, 389 (1970).

129. C. Bertazzoli, T. Chieli, G. Ferni, G. Ricevuti, and E. Solcia, *Toxicol. Appl. Pharmacol.* **21**, 287 (1972).

130. R. S. Jaenke, *Lab. Invest.* **30**, 292 (1974).

131. R. Maral, G. Bourat, J. Fournel, P. Canter, Y. de Ratuld, and G. H. Werner, *Arzneim.-Forsch.* **17**, 939 (1967).

132. C. Bertazzoli, L. Sala, L. Ballerini, W. Tatsuo, and K. Folkers, *Res. Commun. Pathol. Pharmacol.* **15**, 797 (1976).

133. L. Ballerini, E. Solcia, O. Bellini, L. Sala, and C. Bertazzoli, *IRCS Med. Sci. J.* **5**, 431 (1977).

134. G. Zbinden and E. Brändle, *Cancer Chemother. Rep.*, *Part 1* **59**, 707 (1975).

135. E. Bachmann, G. Zbinden, and E. Weber, *Proc. Eur. Soc. Toxicol.* **17**, 309 (1976).

136. H. M. Olson and C. C. Capen, *Lab. Invest.* **37**, 386 (1977).

137. R. Kehoe, D. H. Singer, A. Trapani, M. Billigham, R. Levandowski, and J. Elson, *Cancer Treat. Rep.* **62**, 963 (1978).

138. E. Herman, R. Young, and S. Krop, *Agents Actions* **8**, 551 (1978).

139. L. F. Fajardo, J. R. Eltringham, and J. R. Stewart, *Lab. Invest.* **34**, 86 (1976).

140. F. S. Philips, A. Gilladoga, H. Marquardt, S. S. Sternberg, and P. M. Vidal, *Cancer Chemother. Rep.* **6**, 177 (1975).

141. D. M. Young, *Cancer Chemother. Rep.* **6**, 159 (1975).

142. S. H. Rosenoff, E. Brooks, F. Bostick, and R. C. Young, *Biochem. Pharmacol.* **24**, 1898 (1975).

143. F. Formelli, M. S. Zedeck, S. S. Stenberg, and F. S. Philips, *Cancer Res.* **38**, 3286 (1978).

144. G. Lambertenghi-Deliliers, P. L. Zanon, E. F. Pozzoli, and O. Bellini, *Tumori* **62**, 517 (1976).

145. L. M. Buja, V. J. Ferrans, R. J. Mayer, W. C. Roberts, and E. S. Henderson, *Cancer* (*Philadelphia*) **32**, 771 (1973).

146. E. A. Lefrak, J. Pitha, S. Rosenheim, and J. A. Gottlieb, *Cancer* (*Philadelphia*) **32**, 302 (1973).

147. C. Cargil, E. Bachmann, and G. Zbinden, *J. Natl. Cancer Inst.* **53**, 481 (1974).

148. M. E. Ferrero, E. Ferrero, G. Gaja, and A. Bernelli-Zazzera, *Biochem. Pharmacol.* **25**, 125 (1976).

149. J. W. Dow and J. H. Burns, *Biochem. Soc. Trans.* **6**, 928 (1978).

150. Y. Iwamoto, I. L. Hansen, T. H. Porter, and K. Folkers, *Biochem. Biophys. Res. Commun.* **58**, 633 (1974).

151. C. Bertazzoli, L. Sala, E. Solcia, and M. Ghione, *IRCS Med. Sci. J.* **3**, 468 (1975).

152. A. B. Combs, J. Y. Choe, D. H. Truong, and K. Folkers, *Res. Commun. Chem. Pathol. Pharmacol.* **18**, 565 (1977).

153. G. Zbinden, E. Bachmann, and H. Bolliger, *in* "Biomedical and Clinical Aspects of Conzyme Q" (K. Folkers and Y. Yamamura, eds.), p. 219. Elsevier/North-Holland Biomed. Press, Amsterdam, 1977.

154. K. Folkers, J. Y. Choe, and A. B. Bombs, *Proc. Natl. Acad. Sci. U.S.A.* **75**, 5178 (1978).

155. C. E. Myers, W. P. McGuire, R. H. Liss, I. Ifrim, K. Grotzinger, and R. C. Young, *Science* **197**, 165 (1977).

156. C. E. Myers, W. P. McGuire, and R. C. Young, *Cancer Ther. Rep.* **60**, 961 (1976).

157. R. H. Liss, I. Ifrim, and C. E. Myers, *Proc. Annu. Meet. Electron. Microsc. Soc. Am.* **35**, 572 (1977); *C.A.* **88**, 99119 (1978).

158. C. J. Van Boxtel, R. D. Olson, R. C. Boerth, and J. A. Oates, *J. Pharmacol. Exp. Ther.* **207**, 277 (1978).

159. F. Villani, F. Piccinini, P. Merelli, and L. Favalli, *Biochem. Pharmacol.* **27**, 985 (1978).

160. E. Bachmann and G. Zbinden, *Toxicol. Lett.* **3**, 29 (1979).

161. C. Bertazzoli, T. Chieli, and E. Solcia, *Experientia* **27**, 1209 (1971).

162. E. Solcia, L. Ballerini, O. Bellini, L. Sala, and C. Bertazzoli, *Cancer Res.* **38**, 1444 (1978).

163. A. M. Casazza, O. Bellini, F. Formelli, F. Giuliani, L. Lenaz, and U. Magrini, *Tumori* **63**, 331 (1977).

164. E. Cho, *J. Neuropathol. Exp. Neurol.* **36**, 907 (1977).

5

Analogues Modified in Ring A Substitution

Ring A, the alicyclic moiety of the tetracyclic anthracycline chromophore, contains the site of the main intramolecular junction of the original poly-ketide precursor, according to current views on anthracyclinone biosynthesis. The site corresponds to carbon 9 which, as a consequence of the biogenetic mode of formation, bears the two-carbon-atom side chain and a tertiary hydroxyl, both characteristic features of most anthracyclines. In addition, ring A also contains the site of sugar attachment (the benzylic carbon at position 7) and therefore both asymmetric centers of the aglycone moiety of the antitumor glycosides. The formation of a hydrogen bond between the C-9 hydroxyl group and the C-7 oxygen atom apparently stabilizes the half-chair conformation of ring A as indicated in Fig. 2, Chapter 3. The importance of the said structural and conformational features as regards the pharmacological properties of the antitumor anthracyclines and the possi-bility of developing new agents by chemical modification have been exten-sively explored. The synthesis of new analogues containing different sugar moieties at C-7 will be dealt with in Chapter 6, because of the peculiar aspects of the chemistry involved and of the large number of studies concerned with such modifications.

DERIVATIZATION AT C-13 AND C-14

Many chemically modified analogues of the antitumor anthracyclines have been obtained by exploitation of the reactivity of the methyl ketone and hydroxymethyl ketone functionalities of daunorubicin and doxorubicin res-pectively. The derivatives originated by this approach may be grouped as products reduced at C-13, derivatives of the C-13 ketone function, 14-esters and thioesters, 14-ethers of doxorubicin, 14-amino derivatives and compounds obtained by oxidative degradation of the doxorubicin side chain.

Reduction of the C-13 Carbonyl Group

The 13-dihydro derivatives of daunorubicin and of carminomycin have already been mentioned as biosynthetic representatives of the anthracycline glycosides and the former, together with 13-dihydrodoxorubicin, as metabolic product of the parent antibiotic. Reduction of the C-13 carbonyl group of daunorubicin and carminomycin has also been carried out with a variety or microorganisms (1–3). The glycosides bearing the C-13 secondary hydroxyl group have, however, also been obtained upon complex borohydride treatment of the corresponding carbonyl compounds. The reaction was described for daunorubicin and doxorubicin, an 82% yield being reported for the reduction of the former with potassium borohydride (4). The regioselectivity of the reaction is guaranteed by the air reoxidation of the reduced quinone. The biological activity of 13-dihydrodaunorubicin in four different experimental tumors of mice was found to be similar to that of the parent compound, although 50% inhibition of HeLa cell proliferation *in vitro* occurred at a nearly 10 times higher concentration (5). In a more recent study (6), the optimal doses (the most effective doses showing less than 10% toxic deaths among treated mice) of 13-dihydrodaunorubicin and of 13-dihydrocarminomycin were not very different from those of the parent compounds (Table I). Although no information is available concerning the absolute stereochemistry at C-13 in these derivatives, it is reasonable to consider both the biosynthetic derivatives and the enzymatically reduced ones as being con-

Table I

Activity of 13-Dihydroderivatives on L 1210 Leukemia in Mice at Optimal Nontoxic Doses[a]

Compound	Dose (mg/kg)	T/C[b]
Daunorubicin	2.9	147
13-Dihydrodaunorubicin	4.4	138
Carminomycin	0.6	150
13-Dihydrocarminomycin	0.4	162

[a] Data from Cassinelli *et al.* (6).

[b] Average survival time of treated animals expressed as percent of untreated controls.

stituted by a single stereoisomer, while the same is not true for the chemically originated 13-dihydrodaunorubicin, as deduced also on the basis of the optical rotation shown by bisanhydro-13-dihydrodaunomycinone (**1**) when obtained from natural or from semisynthetic 13-dihydrodaunorubicin (un-

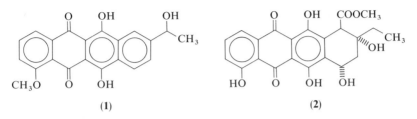

(1)   (2)

published data from the author's laboratory). However, no differences could be found in the biological behavior of the biosynthetic and the chemically derived glycoside (Di Marco, personal communication).

The synthesis of the 13-deoxo analogues of the antitumor anthracyclines was of obvious interest, also because of the presence of the ethyl C-9 side chain in the majority of naturally occurring known anthracyclines, including the less cardiotoxic aclacinomycin. This aim was pursued by Smith *et al.* (*7*). These authors first attempted, without success, the decarbomethoxylation of ε-rhodomycinone (**2**), a known abundant byproduct of the daunorubicin fermentation (*8*). On the other hand, daunomycinone tosylhydrazone (**3**), obtained in 85% yield from daunomycinone, was selectively reduced to 13-deoxodaunomycinone (18% yield) with sodium cyanoborohydride in 1:1 sulfolane and dimethylformamide at 100°C. The reaction was then performed with daunorubicin and with doxorubicin tosylhydrazones with excess reducing agent to afford the 13-deoxoanalogues **4a** and **4b** in reasonable yields.

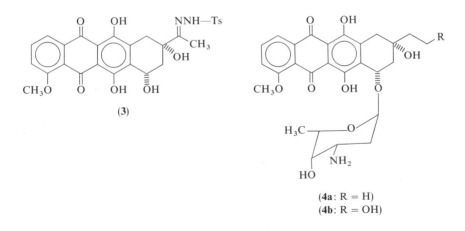

(3)

(**4a**: R = H)
(**4b**: R = OH)

The new analogues retained substantial antitumor activity on P 388 leukemia in mice, **4b** being superior to **4a** similarly to what is observed when the corresponding parent drugs were compared (*9*).

Derivatives of the Ketone Function

The easy derivatization of daunorubicin with carbonyl reagents has prompted the preparation of a number of derivatives described in the scientific (*10*) and in the patent (*11*) literature. Daunorubicin semicarbazone, thiosemicarbazone, oxime and related derivatives were less effective, both *in vitro* and *in vivo*, when compared with the parent compound (*5,10*). On the other hand, daunorubicin benzoylhydrazone (rubidazone) has been found to be endowed with similar antitumor activity on experimental tumors but with a lower toxicity than daunorubicin and doxorubicin (*12*).

Rubidazone displayed antitumor activity similar to the parent compound when equitoxic doses were administered to mice bearing the Ehrlich ascites tumor and was cross-resistant with the same as well as with doxorubicin, vincristine, and vinblastine (*13*). A subline of P 388 leukemia with acquired resistance to doxorubicin exhibited complete cross resistance to a variety of anthracycline analogues, including rubidazone (*14*). The compound formed an intercalation complex with DNA (*15*). Mechanism of uptake by cultured cells was essentially similar to that of daunorubicin (*16*). Cardiotoxicity in rats was accompanied by an uncoupling effect on heart mitochondrial oxidative phosphorylation both *in vivo* and *in vitro* (*17*). Rubidazone was found to differ considerably from doxorubicin in its effect on heart mitochondrial function (*18*), as a much weaker effect on intracellular Ca^{2+} translocation and electron transfer activity was accompanied by a potent uncoupling of oxidative phosphorylation. However, the type of lesions recorded in the heart muscle of experimental animals and in human patients at cardiotoxic doses of both compounds were similar. This is understandable as all effects considered above lead to depletion of high-energy phosphates, impairment of membrane function and, ultimately, to necrosis of the cardiac cells. Hematotoxic and cardiotoxic doses in the Zbinden's rat model were about double those giving rise to similar effects for daunorubicin (*19*).

Clinical trials suggested a superiority over daunorubicin in the treatment of acute leukemias, both in adults and children (*20*). The efficacy of the drug in adult acute leukemias has been confirmed by Benjamin *et al.* (*21*), but studies at M.D. Anderson and Wayne State Hospitals indicated inactivity in solid tumors (*22*). Cardiotoxicity of rubidazone in clinical patients was demonstrated by Benjamin *et al.* (*23*), the estimate of the cumulative cardiotoxic dose being 1500 mg/m^2, based on a single patient examination by endomyocardial biopsy. The primary plasmatic species after rubidazone treatment even during infusion of the drug was daunorubicin itself (*24*). Clinical studies in 133 patients confirm a role of this drug in the treatment of acute leukemia (25).

A series of rubidazone analogues with different phenyl substituents were prepared, their interaction with calf thymus DNA, inhibition of nucleic acid synthesis in cultured L 1210 cells, cardiotoxicity in the Zbinden's rat model, and activity against P 388 leukemia in the mouse being tested and related to the electronic character of the phenyl substituent. Within this series, substituent variation did not significantly affect the biochemical and biological properties with the exception of cardiotoxicity, no improvement in terms of therapeutic index being however evident.

Interesting antitumor characteristics have been claimed for daunorubicin and doxorubicin bishydrazone by Henry and Tong (*26*). The claim refers to compounds of structure **5a** and **5b**, where *n* is an integer having a value from 0 to 8. They were prepared by reaction of daunorubicin or doxorubicin

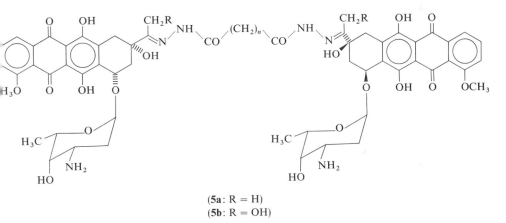

(**5a**: R = H)
(**5b**: R = OH)

with the corresponding dihydrazide in methanol. For doxorubicin, only the compound with $n = 2$ was described. Inhibition of DNA and RNA synthesis *in vitro* in L 1210 leukemia cells gave ED_{50} values in the range of $1-10 \ \mu M$, that is 5 to 10 times higher than the reference drugs, antitumor activity *in vivo* (P 388 leukemia in mice) being comparable to or even higher than that of the parents, although optimal doses were generally higher. No information is, however, available concerning the metabolic transformations of the new compounds.

Daunorubicin-13-ethylene acetal and 13-trimethylene acetals were obtained upon treatment of daunorubicin with ethylene glycol or with 1,3-dihydroxypropane in dioxane and in the presence of an acid catalyst. The compounds were claimed to be active in experimental mouse tumors (*27*).

Esters, Thioesters, and Ethers of Doxorubicin

Doxorubicin esters such as **7a–g** were obtained by reaction of **6a** with the sodium or potassium salt of the corresponding carboxylic acids (*28*). Other

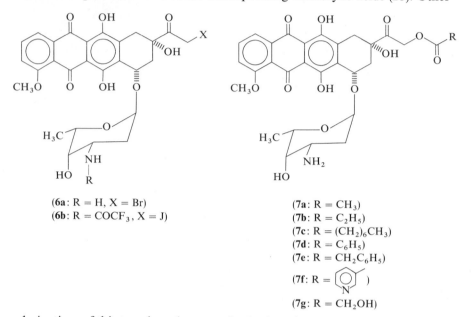

(**6a**: R = H, X = Br)
(**6b**: R = COCF$_3$, X = I)

(**7a**: R = CH$_3$)
(**7b**: R = C$_2$H$_5$)
(**7c**: R = (CH$_2$)$_6$CH$_3$)
(**7d**: R = C$_6$H$_5$)
(**7e**: R = CH$_2$C$_6$H$_5$)

(**7f**: R = ⟨⟩)

(**7g**: R = CH$_2$OH)

derivatives of this type have been synthesized, owing to the high level of anti-tumor activity retained by compounds **7a–f**. These new compounds are double esters **8a–d** (*29*) and thioesters **9a** and **9b** (*30*).

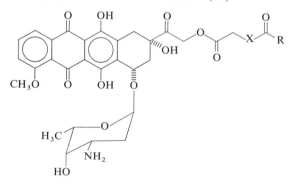

(**8a**: R = (CH$_2$)$_4$CH$_3$, X = O)
(**8b**: R = (CH$_2$)$_{10}$CH$_3$, X = O)
(**8c**: R = (CH$_2$)$_{16}$CH$_3$, X = O)
(**8d**: R = (CH$_2$)$_4$CH$_3$, X = S)

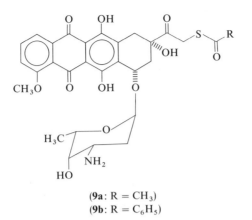

(**9a**: R = CH$_3$)
(**9b**: R = C$_6$H$_5$)

Compounds **7a–f** were found to retain substantial activity in cell cultures and in tumor-bearing animals when compared with doxorubicin itself (*28*). In the same study it was also shown, on the basis of experiments with tritium-labeled doxorubicin 14-octanoate, that esterification of the side-chain hydroxyl leads to modification of the distribution characteristics of the drug, and that a conversion of the said ester to doxorubicin takes place in mouse serum samples and homogenates from liver and from other tissues. According to the above-mentioned authors and to a subsequent report of Lenaz *et al.* (*31*), doxorubicin esters display a somewhat lower antiproliferative but higher antimitotic activity on cultured HeLa cells, when compared with adriamycin. In the animal tests the octanoate (**7c**) appeared generally the most effective, but no clear relationship existed between biological activity and partition coefficient in a 1-butanol/aqueous buffer system in this series. The activity of doxorubicin esters on Gross leukemia is presented in Table II.

Doxorubicin 14-octanoate, as well as doxorubicin 14-*O*-glycolate (**7g**), were both found able to form a complex with DNA (*32*), with stability constants respectively 1.3×10^5 and 2.2×10^5 (doxorubicin 3.7×10^5). The compound caused inhibition of phage T4 DNA polymerase even more effectively than the parent compound (*33*). On the basis of this information and of the cell culture data, it could be concluded that the esters may possess biological activity per se, but enzymic formation of doxorubicin in body fluids or intracellularly should play a predominant role in the exhibition of antitumor activity. In their report concerning the comparison of the efficacy of doxorubicin and related compounds in different experimental tumors, Goldin and Johnson (*34*) demonstrated that esters **7a–f** were not more active than the parent drug in the L 1210 and P 388 test systems. However, in view

Table II

**Activity of Doxorubicin Esters on Gross Leukemia
in Mice at Optimal Nontoxic Doses[a]**

Compound	Dose[b] (mg/kg)	T/C
Daunorubicin	3.25	176
Doxorubicin	2	187
Doxorubicin 14-acetate	2.5	168
Doxorubicin 14-propionate	4	147
Doxorubicin 14-octanoate	4.1	214
Doxorubicin 14-benzoate	2.5	138
Doxorubicin 14-phenylacetate	3.25	156
Doxorubicin nicotinate	4	227

[a] Data from Arcamone *et al.* (*28*).
[b] Treatment iv on days 3–5.

of their retention of activity with differences in solubility and potential differences in pharmacological characteristics, such compounds were considered by the authors as worthy of further investigation and possibly of clinical application. A subline of P 388 leukemia with acquired resistance to doxorubicin exhibited essentially complete cross resistance to doxorubicin 14-octanoate (*14*), but Hill and Price (*35*) have reported that doxorubicin 14-octanoate was superior to doxorubicin in reducing the viability of L 5178Y lymphoblasts resistant to methotrexate.

The behavior of daunorubicin, doxorubicin, doxorubicin 14-acetate, doxorubicin 14-octanoate, and N-trifluoroacetyldoxorubicin 14-valerate with respect to membrane models and human erythrocytes was studied by Goldman *et al.* (*36*). The interaction of these drugs with single-walled liposomes made of egg phosphatidylcholine and diethylphosphate was followed by changes in fluorescence spectrum of the drugs and found to correlate with their octanol/buffer partition coefficients. The apparent dielectric constant of the medium surrounding the anthracycline chromophores in the bound state, measured on the basis of the ratio of the emission peak intensities around 556 and 579 nm in the fluorescence spectra of the drugs in the liposome dispersions, suggested that the three 14-esters were intercalated in the upper hydrocarbon layer of the lyposomes, while daunorubicin and doxorubicin were more likely associated with the hydrocarbon–water surface. The anthracycline derivatives were also found to be free-rotating in a fluid domain on the basis of fluorescence depolarization measurements. Additionally, with the exception of doxorubicin, all compounds displayed a considerable effect on the thermotropic properties of dipalmitoyl phosphatidylcholine and phosphatidylserine as indicated by differential scanning calorimetry. The various compounds exhibited different effects on osmotic fragility and shape of human erythrocytes, the doxorubicin esters being much more effective than the parent compound in exerting detectable changes from the normal behavior of the cells.

Compounds **8a–d** exhibited antitumor activity comparable to that shown by doxorubicin although at a somewhat higher dosage (29). On the other hand, thioesters **9a** and **9b** were clearly less effective (30). Data obtained under the auspices of the National Cancer Institute are presented in Table III.

Table III

Activity of Doxorubicin Esters and Thioesters on P 388 Leukemia in Mice[a]

Compound	Dose[b] (mg/kg)	T/C
Doxorubicin[c]	1.08	215
Doxorubicin 14-octanoate	2	247
Doxorubicin 14-nicotinate	2	229
Doxorubicin 14-stearoylglycolate	3.13	202
Doxorubicin 14-hexanoylthioglycolate	3.13	201
Doxorubicin 14-thioacetate	9.4	145
Doxorubicin 14-thiobenzoate	3.13	141

[a] NCI data (screener A. D. Little).
[b] Dose affording the highest T/C value in the QD 1–9 ip treatment schedule.
[c] Average of 60 experiments.

Toxicology of doxorubicin octanoate in the rat was studied by Zbinden and Brändle (19). The compound displayed a lower general toxicity than both doxorubicin and daunomycin, hematotoxicity being of the same order as that of the former. The compound also showed a minimal cumulative cardiotoxic dose (MCCD) in the rat of 18–20 mg/kg, substantially higher than that shown by adriamycin (11–12 mg/kg). The MCCD value, which appears to be a useful screening parameter for the classification of the cardiotoxic properties of the new analogues (37), has also been determined for the nicotinate and the stearoyl glycolate esters, the value being 32 mg/kg for the former and 40 mg/kg for the latter (Zbinden, personal communication). These results are clearly indicative of the potential clinical value of the 14-O-esters of doxorubicin.

A group of new doxorubicin derivatives is represented by compounds
10a–10c. These compounds have been prepared starting from 14-bromodau-
nomycinone (*38*), which was converted to the tosylhydrazone **11a** and the
latter transformed into 14-alkoxy derivatives **11b–d** upon treatment with an
alcohol in the presence of silver trifluoromethansulphonate (silver triflate).
Refluxing of **11b–d** in acetone in the presence of *p*-toluenesulphonic acid
afforded deblocking of the C-13 ketone group. Glycosidation of the resulting substituted daunomycinones with *N,O*-ditrifluoroacetyldaunosaminyl
chloride in the presence of silver triflate followed by removal of the trifluoro-
acetyl groups gave the desired glycosides **10a–c**. In addition, 14-phenoxy-
daunorubicin was prepared by treatment of 14-bromodaunomycinone with
phenol in the presence of potassium carbonate to give 14-phenoxydaunomy-
cinone, which was converted into the daunosaminyl derivative **10d** using the
silver triflate glycosidation procedure (see Chapter 2). Compounds **10a–d**,
when tested in the P 388 system (*39*), appeared to be less effective than doxorubicin and showed responses similar to those obtained with daunorubicin
(*40*).

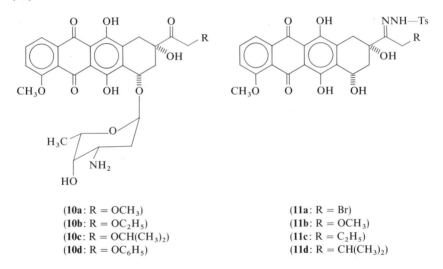

(**10a**: R = OCH₃)	(**11a**: R = Br)
(**10b**: R = OC₂H₅)	(**11b**: R = OCH₃)
(**10c**: R = OCH(CH₃)₂)	(**11c**: R = C₂H₅)
(**10d**: R = OC₆H₅)	(**11d**: R = CH(CH₃)₂)

A number of 14-esters with dialkoxy, diacyloxy, and dialkylmercapto-
acetic acid derivatives were reported in a patent (*41*). The compounds were
prepared upon reaction of the salt of a carboxylic acid with either bromodau-
norubicin or its 13-dimethylketal, the latter being an intermediate of
daunorubicin bromination in a solvent mixture of dioxane and methanol.
Among the new derivatives, 14-diethoxyacetoxydaunorubicin was studied in
comparison with daunorubicin and doxorubicin by Maral *et al.* (*42*). In

cultured K 13 cells, the compound displayed cytotoxic activity and inhibition of nucleic acid synthesis which were intermediate between the two parent drugs. The Ames test indicated for **12** mutagenic properties as for doxorubicin. Toxicity in laboratory animals and cardiotoxicity in the rat Zbinden's model resulted to be similar to those exhibited by doxorubicin. In

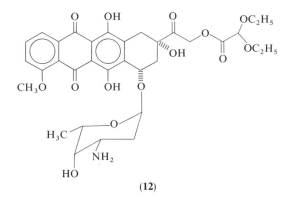

(12)

different mouse tumors, however, equitoxic doses of the new compound displayed generally a more marked antitumor effect than did the parent drugs. Clinical trials showing high response rates in acute lymphocytic leukemia and non-Hodgkin's lymphoma were reported at the 1978 NCI-EORTC Symposium (*43*).

14-Aminodaunomycins

Raction of **6a** with amines afforded the introduction of a substituted amino group at C-14. This type of substitution was of interest in connection with the anionic character of DNA and the possibility of increasing affinity for the receptor because of the presence of an additional basic function in the non-intercalating part of the drug molecule. Compounds **13a–e** were prepared and tested for biological activity in cultured cells and in tumor-bearing mice (*44*). The new compounds were 10 to 50 times less effective on the proliferation of mouse embryo fibroblasts (MEF) when compared with daunorubicin or doxorubicin, but **13a** and **13b** displayed antiviral activity on murine sarcoma (Moloney) in MEF at, respectively, sixfold and twofold higher doses than doxorubicin. *In vivo* activity on ascites sarcoma 180 was significant at optimal doses, but considerably lower than that of the parent drugs on a weight basis. Compound **13a** was found to form a DNA complex with stability constant 2.1×10^5 [daunorubicin 4.5×10^5, see Arlandini *et al.* (*32*)].

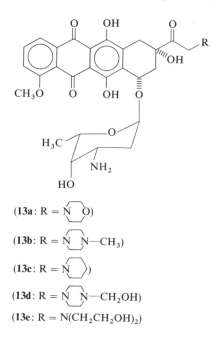

(13a: R = N   O)

(13b: R = N   N—CH₃)

(13c: R = N   )

(13d: R = N   N—CH₂OH)

(13e: R = N(CH₂CH₂OH)₂)

14-Alkyl Derivatives

The synthesis of daunorubicin analogues with novel 9-acyl substituents, representing interesting variations in antitumor anthracyclines structure, has been carried out by Smith *et al.* (*45*). The new compounds **14a** and **14b** were obtained by generating the enolate of *N*-trifluoroacetyldaunorubicin with lithium diisopropylamide in tetrahydrofurane at −78°C, followed by reac-

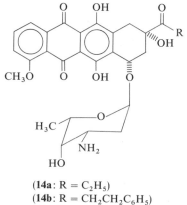

(14a: R = C₂H₅)
(14b: R = CH₂CH₂C₆H₅)
(14c: R = CH(CH₃)₂)

tion with methyl iodide or with benzylbromide respectively and alkaline de-*N*-trifluoroacetylation of the alkylation products. The two analogues **14a** and **14b** behaved almost similarly to daunorubicin as DNA complexing agents, compound **14a** showing also comparable activity *in vivo*. On the other hand, analogue **14b** exhibited a lower potency in the mouse P 388 test. The conclusion can be drawn that homologation of the antitumor anthracyclines at C-14 does not seem to be a promising approach to improved analogues of the antitumor anthracyclines. In the same paper it was also reported that compound **14c** was only marginally active in the P 388 mouse test, notwithstanding the demonstrated effect on melting temperature and on template function of DNA *in vitro*.

SIDE-CHAIN OXIDATIVE DEGRADATION

Periodate oxidation of doxorubicin hydrochloride at 0°C with an equimolar amount of sodium periodate in methanol–water gave almost quantitatively the highly insoluble amphoteric compound **15a**, easily converted to the methyl ester **15b**. Both compounds were able to complex helical DNA as shown by the modifications induced in the visible spectra when the biopolymer was added to their solutions over a nucleotide-to-drug ratio range of 1:1 to 16:1, but the free acid failed to increase the melting temperature of calf thymus DNA and was inactive as an inhibitor of nucleic acid synthesis in cultured L 1210 cells, whereas the ester afforded a $\triangle T_m$ of 12.6°C (doxorubicin 17.8°C) and was nearly as potent as doxorubicin in the cell culture system. Surprisingly, **15a** was instead more effective than **15b** in the

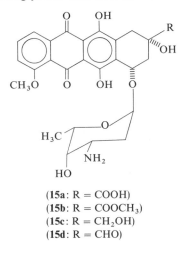

(**15a**: R = COOH)
(**15b**: R = COOCH$_3$)
(**15c**: R = CH$_2$OH)
(**15d**: R = CHO)

mouse P 388 test, although at dose levels 25 times higher than the parent compounds. No explanation of this behavior is available (*46*).

Periodate oxidation of 13-dihydrodoxorubicin *N*-trifluoroacetate, followed by reduction of the resulting C-9 formyl compound **16a** to a C-9 hydroxymethyl derivative and de-*N*-acylation gave **15c**. This compound displayed considerable affinity for native DNA, as equilibrium dialysis measurements gave $K_{app} = 3.1 \times 10^5$ [doxorubicin 4.0×10^5; see Arlandini *et al.* (*47*)] and retained substantial activity in the mouse P 388 system, the T/C values being however lower than those displayed by daunorubicin and doxorubicin (*48*). The reaction of aldehyde **16a** with diazomethane has already been mentioned in Chapter 1 as affording both *N*-trifluoroacetyl-daunorubicin and epoxide **16b**. The latter compound was formed as a major product when the reaction was carried out in methanol. Treatment of **16b** with dilute sodium hydroxide at 0°C afforded the daunorubicin isomer **17** (*49*).

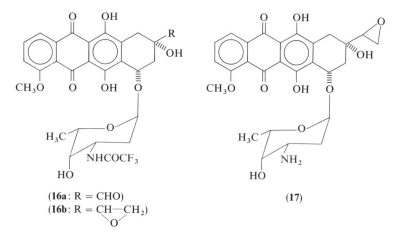

(**16a**: R = CHO)
(**16b**: R = CH—CH₂)
            \O/

(**17**)

The 9-formyl aminoglycoside **15d** has been obtained by Smith *et al.* (*45*) upon sodium metaperiodate oxidation of 13-dihydrodoxorubicin in 64% yield, and was isolated in the hydrate form, characterized by PMR and infrared analysis. The compound showed a lower affinity for native DNA as compared with the clinically useful antibiotics, as determined by its effect on the helix–coil transition of DNA and on nucleic acid synthesis in cultured L 1210 cells. Antitumor activity in mice bearing P 388 lymphocitic leukemia was intermediate between that of daunorubicin and doxorubicin, albeit at a 5–6 times higher dosage.

Oxidative degradation of 13-dihydrodaunorubicin *N*-trifluoroacetate with sodium metaperiodate afforded ketone **18**. Reduction of **18** with sodium cyanoborohydride gave the two epimeric alcohols **19a** and **20a**, the cis compound **19a** being the main product of the reaction. Glycosides **19b** and **20b** were obtained upon alkaline treatment, and the stereochemistry of the compounds was deduced on the basis of the PMR spectrum of the corresponding tetraacetylated aglycones (*50*). In the same paper, antitumor activity and DNA binding ability of **19b** and **20b** were reported. The cis compound exhibited an higher affinity of DNA as deduced from the stability constants of the drug–DNA complex (cis, 2.2×10^5; trans, 0.8×10^5) and from the greater enhancement of DNA viscosity shown by **19b** in comparison to **20b**. The two epimers also showed different efficacy in the P388 system, the cis compound giving (at optimal doses) $T/C\% = 228$ (dose 12.5 mg/kg) and the trans $C\% = 171$ (dose 6.25 mg/kg). The treatment schedule was QD 1–9. This study indicated that a higher selectivity of biological activity was associated with the 9(*S*)-cis in comparison with the 9(*R*)-trans compound, and that the effect of stereochemistry on pharmacological activity paralleled that on DNA complexing ability.

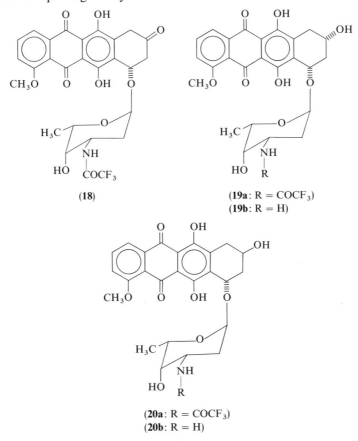

MODIFICATIONS AT C-9 AND C-10

In addition to the already mentioned 9-deacetyldaunorubicins, different analogues bearing modifications at C-9 and/or C-10 are now available. Although all known biosynthetic anthracyclines display the same substitution—that is a tertiary hydroxyl group, and the same absolute configuration at the C-9 position as a result of the ring closure by a formal aldol type condensation in the biogenetic polyketide intermediate (see p. 9)— the substitution at C-10 is variable. This carbon atom, which is present as a methylene in doxorubicin and its congeners, is instead bearing a carboxymethyl group or a hydroxyl group in other biologically active groups of anthracycline glycosides such as the rhodomycins, the pyrromycins, and the apparently more important cinerubins and aclacinomycins. Moreover, the C-9 hydroxyl has been proposed as being involved in the stabilization of the DNA complex either by forming a hydrogen bond with the DNA phosphate groups or by favoring, through a hydrogen bond with the C-7 oxygen, the half-chair conformation of ring A displayed by the antitumor anthracyclines in solution and in the currently accepted model of the DNA–drug intercalation complex. On the other hand, it seemed important to verify the possible contribution of a C-10 substituent and of the stereochemistry at the new chiral center, on the biological activity and antitumor efficacy of the antitumor anthracyclines.

9,10-Anhydro Derivatives

A suitable substrate for reactions aimed to perform variations of anthracycline substitution at C-9 and C-10 is represented by 9,10-anhydro-N-trifluoroacetyldaunorubicin (**21a**), easily obtained in almost 60% yield upon treatment of daunorubicin hydrochloride with trifluoroacetic anhydride in a dry organic base, such as collidine, at 0°C, followed by chromatographic purification of the reaction product. The free base **21b** was prepared by alkaline deblocking of **21a** at 0°C and in a nitrogen atmosphere. Similarly, the corresponding doxorubicin analogues **21c** and **21d** were synthetized starting from doxorubicin hydrochloride (*51*). As reported by Zunino *et al.* (*52*) compound **21b** increased the double-helical DNA T_m by 10.2°C at a drug to DNA-P ratio of 0.1 (daunorubicin 14.0°C). The apparent association constant with native calf thymus DNA was measured by the equilibrium dialysis method and found to be 3.4×10^5 (doxorubicin 4.0×10^5) by Arlandini *et al.* (*47*). In the same study, the effect of **21b** on the viscosity of native DNA was investigated and a distinctly lower reduction of viscosity than with the parent daunorubicin was observed. Clearly the compound was able to complex DNA, although the type of binding seems to be different

to some extent from that of daunorubicin. It is of interest to notice that
21b was devoid of antitumor activity but toxic to the host in the mouse
L 1210 test (*47*).

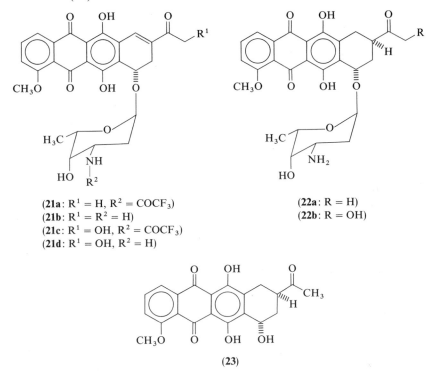

(**21a**: R¹ = H, R² = COCF₃)
(**21b**: R¹ = R² = H)
(**21c**: R¹ = OH, R² = COCF₃)
(**21d**: R¹ = OH, R² = H)

(**22a**: R = H)
(**22b**: R = OH)

(**23**)

The 9-Deoxy Analogues

Catalytic hydrogenation of **21a** in the presence of palladium on barium
sulfate, followed by mild alkaline treatment and a chromatographic separation, afforded 9-deoxydaunorubicin (**22a**) in 20% yield, the low yield being
also due to the necessity of terminating the reduction step before the starting
material was completely transformed because of the concurrent hydrogenolysis of the C-7 benzylic glycoside bond. That the isolated product possessed
the stereochemistry indicated in **22a** was demonstrated on the basis of the
PMR spectrum at 270 MHz in pyridine-d_5 solution and at 70° of the corresponding aglycone **23**. In this spectrum the axial proton at C-10 (double
doublet at 2.84 δ) displayed a vicinal coupling with $J = 11$ Hz, typical of
the interaction between two diaxial protons. This attribution was also in
agreement with the splitting of the H-8 signals at 1.74 (two *dd*, $J_{8ax,9ax} =$
13.5 Hz) and at 2.56 δ (broad *d*, $J_{8eq,9ax}$ 3 Hz) (*53*).

Table IV

Comparison of 9-Deoxy Analogue with Daunorubicin and Doxorubicin in Mice Bearing P 388 Lymphocytic Leukemia[a]

Control number	Compound	Optimal dose (mg/kg)	T/C
6280	9-Deoxydaunorubicin	25.0	136
	Daunorubicin	4.0	121
	Doxorubicin	8.0	227
6452	9-Deoxydaunorubicin	12.5	120
	Daunorubicin	2.0	136
	Doxorubicin	2.0	136
6505	9-Deoxydoxorubicin	12.5	117
	Daunorubicin	2.0	124
	Doxorubicin	8.0	171
6696	9-Deoxydoxorubicin	50.0	136
	Daunorubicin	2.0	136
	Doxorubicin	16.0	154

[a] Drugs administered ip on days 5,9,13. Experiments performed under the auspices of NCI (screener A. D. Little).

Bromination followed by sodium formate treatment afforded 9-deoxy-doxorubicin (**22b**) (*53*). Activity of analogues **22a** and **22b** in the P 388 mouse test was similar to that of daunorubicin but lower than that of doxorubicin, optimal dose values being, however, always higher than for the parents (Table IV). The results were almost in agreement with the DNA affinity constants of the analogues, which were found to be 2.6×10^5 and 2.3×10^5, respectively (doxorubicin 4.0×10^5), and with the marked effect on intrinsic viscosity of the DNA solution (*47*).

The 10-Methoxy Derivatives

The 9,10-epoxidation of 9,10-anhydro-*N*-trifluoroacetyldaunorubicin (**21a**) was an obvious route to C-10 substituted analogues (*54*). However, formation of the oxirane ring at the said position required reduction of the side-chain carbonyl with sodium cyanoborohydride to give **24**, whose treatment with *m*-chloroperbenzoic acid afforded **25** in high yield. Oxidation of the latter with the dimethyl sulfoxide–dicyclohexylcarbodiimide reagent, using pyridinium trifluoroacetate as catalyst, followed by careful work-up gave a 1:1 mixture of epimeric compounds **26a** and **26b** differing in the stereochemistry of the sugar moiety as shown by the formation of a single chloridrine **27** by reaction of **26** with dry hydrogen chloride in anhydrous acetic acid. The aglycone **28** was obtained from **27** by a mild basic treatment, and it was shown to be a single isomer with an equatorial hydrogen atom at C-10 by PMR analysis. Of relevant diagnostic value were the long range coupling $J_{8eq,10} = 0.5$ Hz already found in daunomycinone and the coupling constants $J_{7,8eq} = 4.3$ Hz; $J_{7,8ax} = 1.5$ Hz, indicating that the conformation of the A ring was the same as in the latter compound.

Two aglycones were obtained when **28** was treated with methanol in the presence of a catalytic amount of *p*-toluensulfonic acid, the predominant reaction product **29** deriving from a trans opening and the minor product **30** from the cis opening of the oxirane ring. Stereochemistry of **29** and **30** has been established on the basis of chemical and PMR spectroscopical evidence, that of **30** being in contrast with a previous assignment (*55*). Both **29** and **30** afforded 7-deoxydaunomycinone upon catalytic hydrogenolysis

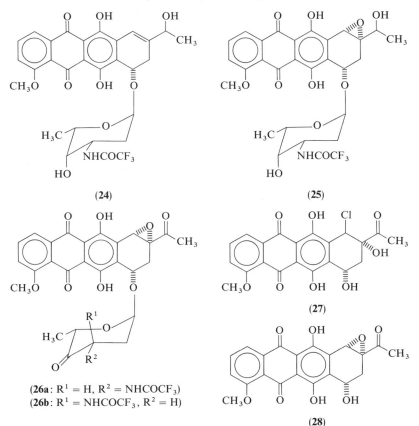

(24)

(25)

(26a: R^1 = H, R^2 = NHCOCF$_3$)
(26b: R^1 = NHCOCF$_3$, R^2 = H)

(27)

(28)

at C-7 and C-10, indicating unequivocally the absolute configuration at C-9 and that of epoxide **28**.

The long-range coupling constant between H-10 and H-8_{eq} shown by **29** and the values of the coupling constants between H-7 and H-8_{eq} and H-8_{ax}, very similar to those of daunomycinone (indicating the usual half-chair conformation), allowed the assignment of an axial orientation to the C-10 methoxyl in **29**. On the other hand, the sharp singlet corresponding to H-10

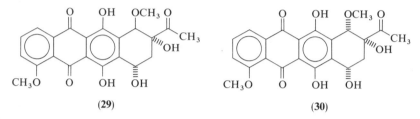

(29)   (30)

in **30** indicated that this compound was the epimer at C-10 of the former. The spectroscopic analysis also showed that the conformation of the A ring in **30** was of the half-boat type ($J_{H-7,H-8eq} = J_{H-7,H-8ax} = 6$ Hz), a consequence of the different orientation of the 10-methoxyl. The latter was apparently also the cause of the lack of formation of a 7,9-isopropylidene derivative upon treatment of **30** with dimethoxypropane and *p*-toluenesulfonic acid, this derivative being instead promptly obtained from **29**. These conclusions are, as already mentioned, in contrast to the former assignment of trans relative orientation of the C-7 and C-9 hydroxyl groups for **30**, and therefore also the deduction concerning the formation of two epoxides upon peroxidation of **24** does not hold true. Glycosidation of aglycones **29** and **30** by the silver triflate method followed by deblocking afforded glycosides **31a** and **32**, the former being also converted to the corresponding doxorubicin analogue **31b**. Biological testing has shown that **31a** and **31b** possessing the

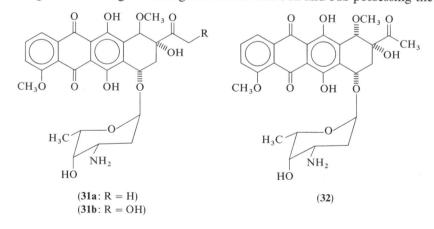

(**31a**: R = H)   (32)
(**31b**: R = OH)

Table V

Comparison of 10-Methoxy Analogues with Daunorubicin and
Doxorubicin in Mice Bearing P 388 Lymphocytic Leukemia[a]

Compound	Optimal dose (mg/kg)	T/C
10(R)-Methoxydaunorubicin	12.5	127, 133
10(R)-Methoxydoxorubicin	6.25	141
10(S)-Methoxydaunorubicin	50	no activity
Daunorubicin	2.0 to 4.0	123 to 132
Doxorubicin	8.0	166 to 173

[a] Experiments No. 6505, 6795, 6947, 7007 performed under the
auspices of NCI (screener A.D. Little). Drugs administered ip on
days 5,9,13.

same configuration at C-10 as the biosynthetic C-10 substituted anthracyclines and the same half-chair conformation as daunomycinone, were distinctly effective as antitumor agents, whereas the C-10 epimer **32** was inactive
at the highest dose tested (Table V).

Methylation Studies

Compound **18** was submitted to other reactions, owing to the potential
pharmacological interest of analogues bearing ring A modifications (55).
Treatment with diazomethane in dimethoxyethane transformed **18** into the
enol ether **33a**, the corresponding free aminoglycoside **33b** being obtained
upon alkaline hydrolysis. When the reaction of **18** with diazomethane was
carried out in a 2:1 chloroform–methanol mixture, together with **33a** the

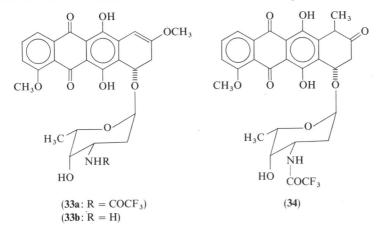

(33a: R = COCF₃)
(33b: R = H)

(34)

10-methylated compound **34** was also isolated. The structure of **34** was also proved by PMR spectrum of **35b**, the product arising upon aromatization of ring A with acid to **35a** followed by acetylation. In this spectrum, only the singlet of an olefinic methyl group at 2.62 δ and the signals of five aromatic protons (two doublets at 7.02 and 8.10 δ with J = 8 Hz corresponded to the two aromatic ring A protons) were discernible, besides the signals of the three acetyl groups and of the methoxyl group. Sodium cyanoborohydride reduction of **34** afforded **36a**, also deblocked to give **36b**. Acid hydrolysis of **36a** gave the aglycone **37a**, to which, because of the lack of reaction with dimethoxypropane to give a 7,9-isopropylidene derivative, the 7,9-trans-relative configuration was assigned. The H-9 signal in the PMR spectrum of **37b** appeared as two double doublets a 4.95 δ with one large

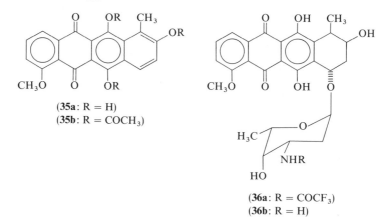

(**35a**: R = H)
(**35b**: R = COCH$_3$)

(**36a**: R = COCF$_3$)
(**36b**: R = H)

(J = 12.5 Hz) and two small (J = 5 Hz) coupling constants, suggesting the H-9$_{ax}$,H-10$_{eq}$ relationship, the large coupling constant being due to the interaction of H-9$_{ax}$ with H-8$_{ax}$.

Compound **33b** was inactive in the mouse P 388 test at the dose of 50 mg/kg. Compound **36b** displayed the same antitumor effect (prolongation of survival time of treated mice) as daunorubicin, albeit at 10 times higher dosage (NCI data).

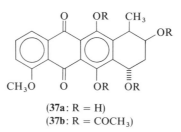

(**37a**: R = H)
(**37b**: R = COCH$_3$)

Treatment of **21b** with excess diazomethane afforded pyrazoline **38** in high yield. Photolysis or thermolysis of the latter gave 9-deoxy-9,10-methano *N*-trifluoroacetyldaunorubicin (**39a**) and 9,10-anhydro-10-methyldaunoru-bicin-*N*-trifluoroacetate (**40a**) (*55*). Both compounds were converted to the corresponding aminoglycosides **39b** and **40b**, which turned out to be inactive in the mouse P 388 system at the highest dose tested (50 and 100 mg/kg respectively) under the Q4D-5,9,13 treatment schedule (NCI data).

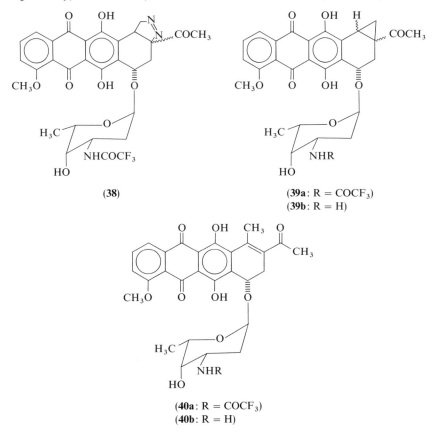

(**38**)

(**39a**: R = COCF$_3$)
(**39b**: R = H)

(**40a**: R = COCF$_3$)
(**40b**: R = H)

9-Deoxy-9-Methyl Derivatives

For the specific purpose of investigating the effect of a substituent different from OH and H at C-9, the total synthesis of 4-demethoxy-9-deoxy-9-meth-yldaunomycinone and its transformation to a daunosamine glycoside was carried out (*56*). Although these derivatives belong to the 4-demethoxy series which is dealt with in Chapter 7, the modification at C-9 seems of sufficient importance to allow their inclusion among the ring A analogues.

Starting material for the synthesis was 6-acetyl-1,4-dimethoxy-6-hydroxy-tetralin (**41**) (*57*), which was converted into **42** with concentrated sulfuric acid Reduction of **42** with lithium in liquid ammonia and in the presence of *t*-butanol followed by alkylation with methyl iodide of the C-9 anion gave the 6-methyl derivative **43**. The tetracyclic compound **45** was then obtained upon reaction of **43** with phthalic acid monomethyl ester in trifluoroacetic anhydride to give **44**, whose alkaline hydrolysis and cyclization in liquid HF

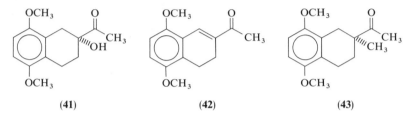

(**41**)   (**42**)   (**43**)

afforded **45**. Ketalization of **45** as in **46** and reaction of the latter with *N*-bromosuccinimide with concomitant photoirradiation gave a 7-bromo derivative that, without isolation, was methanolized and deketalized to the mixture of epimeric C-7 methoxy derivatives **47**. The latter product was treated with

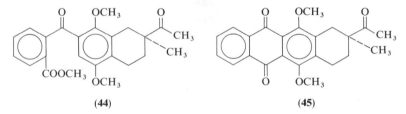

(**44**)   (**45**)

aluminium chloride in methylene chloride to remove the phenolic *O*-methyl groups, then treated with trifluoroacetic acid and finally with aqueous sodium bicarbonate to give, after a chromatographic separation step, comparable

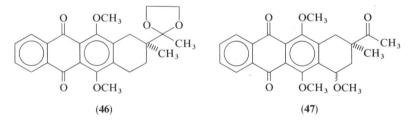

(**46**)   (**47**)

amounts of **48** and **49**. The structural assignments were based on the ready formation of cyclic ketal **50** when **49** was dissolved in methanol in the presence of a trace of *p*-toluenesulfonic acid.

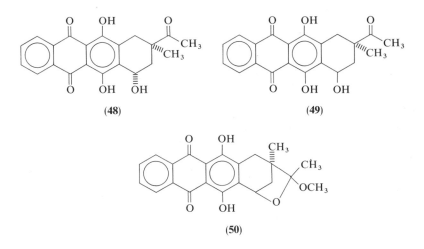

(48)   (49)

(50)

Condensation of **48** with *N,O*-ditrifluoroacetyldaunosaminyl chloride in dichloromethane and in the presence of silver trifluoromethanesulfonate gave glycosides **51a** and **52a**, easily separated by chromatography, from which daunorubicin analogues **51b** and **52b** were obtained after hydrolysis of

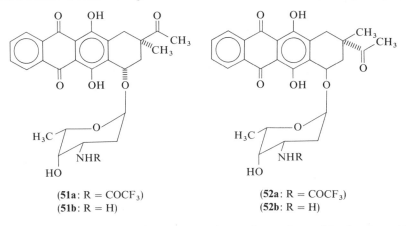

(**51a**: R = COCF₃)   (**52a**: R = COCF₃)
(**51b**: R = H)   (**52b**: R = H)

the N-protecting group. The α-anomeric configuration of both glycosides was deduced from the PMR spectra of **51a** and **52a** indicating the equatorial orientation of H-1′ which resonated at 5.46 δ (W_H 7.2 Hz) in the former and at 5.35 δ (W_H 10.8 Hz) in the latter. The spectra also showed that H-7 was equatorial in the two compounds, appearing as a broad singlet at 5.00 δ, W_H 12 Hz in **51a** and at 5.30 δ, W_H 8.2 Hz in **52a**, and therefore that both glycosides possessed the same half-chair conformation of ring A as daunorubicin. Acid hydrolysis of **51b** and **52b** afforded enantiomeric aglycones with $[\alpha]_D^{20} \pm 250$, but attempts to derive the absolute configurations were not made, since **51b** and **52b** displayed no activity in the mouse P 388 system at the highest dosage tested (50 mg/kg, treatment schedule Q4D-5,9,13).

Opening of Ring A between C-9 and C-10

Enol ether (**33a**) was used as the substrate for the ozonolysis at low temperature ($-78°C$) of the C-9–C-10 double bond to give a new type of daunorubicin derivative in which ring A was cleaved without loss of the aminosugar moiety. The compound obtained after decomposition of the ozonide was reduced with sodium cyanoborohydride to give, after hydrolysis of the N-protecting group, the acid **53a**, also characterized as the methyl ester **53b** (*55*). At the highest dose tested, the acid **53a** displayed no activity in the mouse P 388 test, whereas the ester **53b** was marginally active (NCI data), indicating the deleterious effect of ring A opening on the antitumor properties of the anthracycline glycosides.

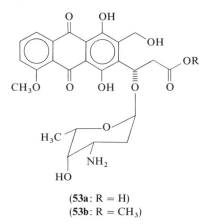

(**53a**: R = H)
(**53b**: R = CH$_3$)

SUBSTITUTION AT C-8

Derivatives modified at C-8 are of interest for two reasons. First, this position, which invariably corresponds to a methylene group in all classical biosynthetic anthracyclines as well as in doxorubicin and its congeners, appears bearing a methoxyl group in the related biologically active, mold metabolite, steffimycin (see Chapter 8). Second, as has been shown in Chapter 4, the main metabolic reaction inactivating the antitumor anthracyclines *in vivo* is an enzymatically catalyzed reductive deglycosidation leading to the corresponding 7-deoxyaglycones, apparently devoid of antitumor properties. The presence of a bulky group at the nearby C-8 position would possibly

affect the affinity of the substrate for the enzyme responsible of the transformation and therefore enhance the selectivity of action of the drugs.

The synthesis of new analogues bearing a hydroxyl, alkoxy, or acyloxy
group at C-8 takes advantage of the availability of intermediate **54**, which
is formed when daunomycinone is treated with dimethoxypropane and *p*-
toluenesulfonic acid in chloroform at reflux temperature (*58*). The compound
was obtained in pure form as a mixture of diastereoisomers in 28% yield
after a chromatographic separation step. Epoxidation of **54** with *m*-chloro-
perbenzoic acid in chloroform afforded **55a** in 80% yield, the latter being

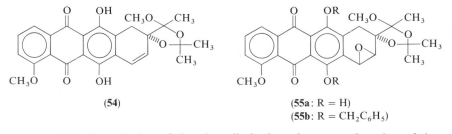

(54)

(55a: R = H)
(55b: R = CH₂C₆H₅)

protected by benzylation of the phenolic hydroxyl groups. Opening of the
oxirane ring with methanol in the presence of *p*-toluenesulfonic acid gave
7-methoxy-8-hydroxy compound **56a** in reasonable yields. Further elaboration to obtain the new aglycone, 8-methoxydaunomycinone, included methyl
lation of **56a** with sodium hydride and methyl iodide in tetrahydrofuran to
give **56b**, which was then deblocked to give **57a** by a 5-min treatment with
trifluoroacetic acid at 0°C. Treatment of **57a** with trifluoroacetic acid at room
temperature, followed by alkalinization with ammonium hydroxide, gave a
mixture of 8-(*R*)-methoxydaunomycinone (**57b**) and of the corresponding
7-epi derivative whose separation was carried out by fractional crystallization. Glycosidation of **57b** with *N,O*-ditrifluoroacetyldaunosaminyl chloride

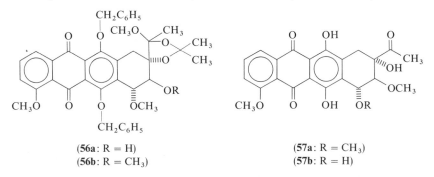

(56a: R = H)
(56b: R = CH₃)

(57a: R = CH₃)
(57b: R = H)

in the presence of silver triflate and collidine followed by chromatography
on a silicic acid column afforded **58a**, which was converted into **58b** with
dilute sodium hydroxide.

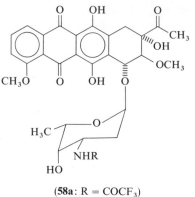

(58a: R = COCF$_3$)
(58b: R = H)

4-DEMETHOXY-7,10-ETHANODAUNOMYCINONE

The bridged daunomycinone analogue (59) and its epimer 60 have been synthetized by Krohn *et al.* (59), starting from naphthazarin (61), whose condensation with diene 62 in dichloromethane and at room temperature, followed by air oxidation in the presence of sodium hydroxide and finally acidification, afforded 63 in 62% yield. Further condensation of 63 with

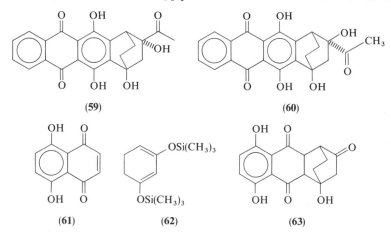

(59)   (60)

(61)   (62)   (63)

1-acetoxy-1,3-butadiene in toluene at 80°C followed by alkaline air oxidation and acidification, gave 64 in 69% yield. Reaction of the latter with ethinylmagnesium bromide and chromatographic separation of the products allowed recovery of two isomers (compound 65 and its C-9 epimer) in 1:2 ratio and almost 60% yield. Mercuric sulfate-catalyzed hydration of the side chain in the latter compounds resulted in aglycone analogues **59** and **60**, respectively. Application of the ethinylation–hydration sequence to **63** gave the tricyclic analog **66** and its epimer **67**.

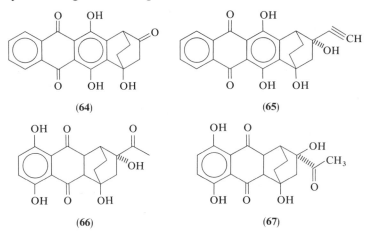

REFERENCES

1. J. Florent, J. Lunel, and J. Renaut, Ger. Patent 2,456,139 (May 28, 1975); *C.A.* **83**, 112355 (1975).
2. J. Florent and J. Lunel, Ger. Patent 2,610,557 (Sept. 23, 1976).
3. A. A. Aszalos, N. R. Bachur, B. K. Hamilton, A. F. Langlykke, P. P. Roller, M. Y. Sheikn, M. S. Sutpin, M. C. Thomas, D. A. Wareheim, and L. H. Wright, *Jpn. J. Antibiot.* **30**, 50 (1977).
4. J. Jolles and G. Ponsinet, Ger Patent 2,202,690 (July 27, 1972); *C.A.* **77**, 164320 (1972).
5. A. Di Marco, A. M. Casazza, T. Dasdia, F. Giuliani, L. Lenaz, A. Necco, and C. Soranzo, *Cancer Chemother. Rep., Part 1* **57**, 269 (1973).
6. G. Cassinelli, A. Grein, P. Masi, A. Suarato, L. Bernardi, F. Arcamone, A. Di Marco, A. M. Casazza, G. Pratesi, and C. Soranzo, *J. Antibiot.* **31**, 178 (1978).
7. T. H. Smith, A. N. Fujiwara, and D. W. Henry, *Am. Chem. Soc., 172nd Meet.* Abstr. Medi 88 (1976).
8. D. L. Kern, R. H. Bunge, J. C. French, and H. W. Dion, *J. Antibiot.* **30**, 432 (1977).
9. T. H. Smith, A. N. Fujiwara, and D. W. Henry, *J. Med. Chem.* **21**, 280 (1978).
10. K. Yamamoto, A. M. Acton, and D. W. Henry, *J. Med. Chem.* **15**, 872 (1972).
11. G. Jolles, Ger. Patent 1,803,892 (May 29, 1969); *C.A.* **71**, 70907 (1969).
12. R. Maral, G. Ponsinet, and G. Jolles, *C.R. Acad. Sci., Ser. D* **275D**, 301 (1972).
13. T. Skovsgaard, *Cancer Chemother. Rep., Part 1* **59**, 301 (1975).
14. R. K. Johnson, A. A. Ovejera, and A. Goldin, *Cancer Treat. Rep.* **60**, 99 (1976).
15. E. J. Gabbay, D. Grieg, R. E., Fingerle, R. Reimer, R. Levy, S. W. Pearce, and W. Wilson, *Biochemistry* **15**, 2062 (1977).
16. T. Skovsgaard, *Biochem. Pharmacol.* **26**, 215 (1977).
17. E. Bachmann, E. Weber, and G. Zbinden, *Agents Actions* **5**, 383 (1975).
18. E. Bachmann and G. Zbinden, *Toxicol. Lett.* **3**, 29 (1979).
19. G. Zbinden and E. Brändle, *Cancer Chemother. Rep., Part 1* **59**, 707 (1975).

20. C. Jaquillat, *Cancer (Philadelphia)* **37**, 653 (1976).
21. R. S. Benjamin, M. J. Keating, K. B. McCredie, G. P. Bodey, and E. J. Freireich, *Cancer Res.* **37**, 4623 (1977).
22. S. K. Carter, *Cancer Chemother. Pharmacol.* **1**, 263 (1978).
23. R. S. Benjamin, J. W. Mason, and M. E. Billingham, *Cancer Treat. Rep.* **62**, 935 (1978).
24. R. S. Benjamin, M. J. Keating, K. B. McCredie, M. A. Luna, T. L. Loo, and E. J. Freireich, *Proc. Am. Assoc. Cancer Res.* **17**, 72 (1976).
25. R. S. Benjamin, M. J. Keating, K. D. Swenerton, S. Legha, and K. B. McCredie, *Cancer Treat, Rep.* **63**, 925 (1979).
26. D. W. Henry and G. L. Tong, U.S. Patent 4,112,217 (Sept. 5, 1978).
27. J. B. Ducep, D. Farge, G. Ponsinet, and D. Reisdorf, U.S. Patent 4,075,328 (Feb. 21, 1978).
28. F. Arcamone, G. Franceschi, A. Minghetti, S. Penco, S. Redaelli, A. Di Marco, A. M. Casazza, T. Dasdia, G. Di Fronzo, F. Giuliani, L. Lenaz, A. Necco, and C. Soranzo, *J. Med. Chem.* **17**, 335 (1974).
29. B. Patelli, L. Bernardi, F. Arcamone, and A. Di Marco, Ger. Patent 2,627,146 (Dec. 30, 1976); *C.A.* **86**, 190419 (1977).
30. F. Arcamone, L. Bernardi, and B. Patelli, Ger. Patent 2,713,745 (Oct. 13, 1977); *C.A.* **88**, 23347 (1978).
31. L. Lenaz, A. Necco, T. Dasdia, and A. Di Marco, *Cancer Chemother. Rep., Part 1* **58**, 769 (1974).
32. E. Arlandini, A. Vigevani, and F. Arcamone, *Farmaco, Ed. Sci.* **32**, 315 (1977).
33. M. F. Goodman, G. M. Lee, and N. R. Bachur, *J. Biol. Chem.* **252**, 2670 (1977).
34. A. Goldin and R. K. Johnson, *in* "Adriamycin Review," Part 1 (M. Staquet *et al.*, eds.), p. 37. European Press Medikon, Ghent, 1975.
35. B. T. Hill and L. A. Price, *J. Natl. Cancer Inst.* **59**, 1311 (1977).
36. R. Goldmann, T. Facchinetti, D. Bach, A. Raz, and M. Shinitzky, *Biochim. Biophys. Acta* **512**, 254 (1978).
37. G. Zbinden, E. Bachmann, and E. Holderegger, *Antibiot. Chemother.* **23**, 255 (1978).
38. F. Arcamone, G. Franceschi, and S. Penco, Ger. Patent 1,917,874 (Nov. 6, 1969); *C.A.* **73**, 45799 (1970).
39. R. I. Geran, N. H. Greenberg, M. M. McDonald, A. M. Schumacher, and B. J. Abbott, *Cancer Chemother. Rep., Part 3* **3**, 1 (1972).
40. P. Masi, A. Suarato, P. Giardino, L. Bernardi, and F. Arcamone, *Farmaco, Ed. Sci.* **34**, 907 (1979).
41. Rhône-Poulenc, Fr. Patent 848,219 (May 10, 1977).
42. R. Maral, J. B. Ducep, D. Farge, G. Ponsinet, and D. Reisdorf, *C. R. Acad. Sci., Ser. D* **286**, 443 (1978).
43. C. Jaquillat, M. F. Auclerc, M. Well, J. Maral, L. Degos, G. Auclerc, G. Tobelem, G. Schaison, and J. Bernard, *Cancer Treat. Rep.* **63**, 889 (1979).
44. F. Arcamone, L. Bernardi, B. Patelli, and A. Di Marco, Ger. Patent 2,557,537 (July 8, 1976); *C.A.* **85**, 177886 (1976).
45. T. H. Smith, A. N. Fujiwara, and D. W. Henry, *J. Med. Chem.* **22**, 40 (1979).
46. G. Tong, W. W. Lee, D. R. Black, and D. W. Henry, *J. Med. Chem.* **19**, 395 (1976).
47. E. Arlandini, A. Vigevani, and F. Arcamone, *Farmaco, Ed. Sci.* **35**, 65 (1980).
48. S. Penco, F. Angelucci, and F. Arcamone, Ger. Patent 2,757,057 (July 6, 1978); *C.A.* **89**, 197892 (1978).
49. S. Penco, F. Angelucci, and F. Arcamone, Belg. Pat. 864,025 (Aug. 16, 1978).
50. S. Penco, F. Angelucci, A. Vigevani, E. Arlandini, and F. Arcamone, *J. Antibiot.* **30**, 764 (1977).
51. G. Cassinelli and F. Arcamone, *Ger. Offen.* 2,757,101 (July 6, 1978). *C.A.* **89**, 197890 (1979).
52. F. Zunino, A. Di Marco, and A. Zaccara, *Chem. Biol. Interact.* **24**, 217 (1979).

53. S. Penco, G. Franchi, and F. Arcamone, Belg. Pat. 876,100 (Nov. 8, 1979); *C.A.* **92**, 147141 (1980).
54. S. Penco, F. Gozzi, A. Vigevani, M. Ballabio, and F. Arcamone, *Heterocycles* **13**, 281 (1979).
55. S. Penco, F. Angelucci, F. Gozzi, G. Franchi, B. Gioia, A. Vigevani, and F. Arcamone, *Int. Symp. Chem. Nat. Prod., 11th, Golden Sands, Bulg.* **4**, Part 1, 448 (1978).
56. P. Giardino, A. Vigevani, L. Bernardi, and F. Arcamone, *Gazz Chim. Ital.* **110**, 101 (1980).
57. C. M. Wong, D. Popien, R. Schwenk, and T. Raa, *Can. J. Chem.* **49**, 2712 (1971).
58. S. Penco, F. Angelucci, M. Ballabio, A. Vigevani, and F. Arcamone, *Tetrahedron Lett.* **21**, 2253 (1980).
59. K. Krohn, H. H. Ostermeyer, and K. Tolkiehn, *Chem. Ber.* **112**, 2640 (1979).

6

Analogues Modified in the Aminosugar Residue

An important structural feature of daunorubicin and doxorubicin is the presence of the unique aminosugar daunosamine, namely 3-amino-2,3,6-trideoxy-L-*lyxo*-hexopyranose (**1**), bound glycosidically at position 7 of the aglycone moiety. This aminosugar has never been identified as a constituent of other antibiotics or natural products and therefore its presence seems restricted to the particular group of anthracycline glycosides which includes the said antitumor antibiotics. In fact, the other anthracyclines of biosynthetic origin have been shown in Chapter 1 to have the corresponding N-dimethyl derivative, rhodosamine (**2**), as the aminosugar component, and other nonaminated sugars as well. However, a number of 3-amino-2,3,6-trideoxyhexoses are presently known as components of antibiotic molecules. In addition to the already mentioned daunosamine and rhodosamine, the following members of this class of compounds have been found: acosamine, 3-amino-2,3,6-trideoxy-L-*arabino*-hexopyranose (**3**), from actinoidin (*1*); ristosamine, 3-amino-2,3-6-trideoxy-L-*ribo*-hexopyranose (**4**), from ristomycin (*2*); actinosamine, 3-amino-4-*O*-methyl-2,3,6-trideoxy-L-*arabino*-hexopyranose (**5**), from actinoidin (*1*); vancosamine, 3-amino-3-*C*-methyl-2,3,6-trideoxy-L-*lyxo*-hexopyranoside (**6**), from vancomycin (*3*); L-megosamine, 3-dimethylamino-2,3,6-trideoxy-L-*ribo*-hexopyranose (**7**),

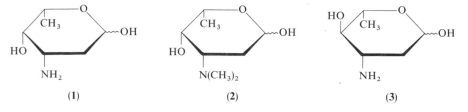

(**1**) (**2**) (**3**)

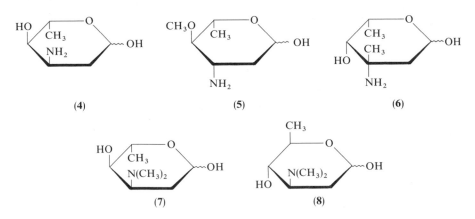

(4)   (5)   (6)

(7)   (8)

from the megalomycins (4); and angolosamine, 3-dimethylamino-2,3,6-trideoxy-D-*arabino*-hexopyranose (8), from angolamycin (5).

In the anthracycline antibiotics, the presence of the aminosugar residue is an important structural requirement for bioactivity, as a biological action due to the isolated aglycone moiety has never been recorded. As a matter of fact, the carbohydrate residue strongly modifies the solubility properties of the aglycones, generally highly insoluble in water, because the amino group allows the glycoside to dissolve in aqueous solutions at neutral pH values largely in the cationic, protonated form. The same carbohydrate residue contains four of the six chiral centers present in the molecule of the antitumor anthracyclines. As reported in Chapter 1, the absolute stereochemistry $1'(R)$, $3'(S)$, $4'(S)$ and $5'(S)$ corresponding to the L-*lyxo*-α-glycoside configuration, was assigned to these centers.

Starting from the information summarized in Chapters 3 and 4, it appears evident that analogues of doxorubicin (and of daunorubicin) showing modifications in the daunosamine moiety are of interest because alterations in sugar stereochemistry and substitution are expected to modify those parameters of anthracycline efficacy which reside on active transport or facilitated diffusion and on enzyme reactions, namely tissue distribution and metabolism of the drug, on the basis of the known dependence of such processes on structure and stereochemistry of carbohydrate derivatives. Because of the separate intracellular location of the main receptor responsible for the biological properties of the antitumor anthracyclines, intracellular distribution should also be considered a decisive factor in the pharmacological behavior of the drugs. The intracellular distribution is very likely dependent also on specific binding with cellular components such as nucleic acids, proteins, and other macromolecules, and the structure and configuration of the carbohydrate residue may be expected to play a role in the stabilization of the different intermolecular complexes.

Analogues of the antitumor anthracyclines modified in the aminosugar residue include those compounds in which the aglycone moiety is linked to a different carbohydrate as well as those obtained by derivatization of the biosynthetic glycosides. The former are configurational or functional analogues prepared following a general scheme involving the synthesis of the desired carbohydrate in the appropriately derivatized form in order to carry out the subsequent glycosidation of daunomycinone or of a protected adriamycinone derivative, and final deblocking of the glycosylation product, the doxorubicin analogues being alternatively (and often preferably) obtained from the corresponding daunorubicin analogues by introduction of the alcohol function at C-14. The second group of analogues are represented by the N-substituted derivatives and the 4′-glycosides. Mention will also be made in this chapter of those compounds in which the daunosamine residue is replaced by a nonsugar moiety.

THE L-ARABINO ANALOGUES AND THE DEVELOPMENT OF 4′-EPIDOXORUBICIN

The semisynthetic L-arabino analogues are those glycosides in which daunosamine (1) is replaced by acosamine (3). They will be described first, because they were the first configurational isomers of the antitumor anthracyclines reported in the literature, and also because of the importance of the L-arabino analogue of doxorubicin, 4′-epidoxorubicin, a compound already submitted to enlarged clinical trials.

Synthesis

The L-arabino analogue of daunorubicin was obtained by reaction of daunomycinone (9) with N,O-ditrifluoroacetyl-α-acosaminyl chloride (10) in the conditions of the Koenigs–Knorr reaction (i.e., in anhydrous methylene

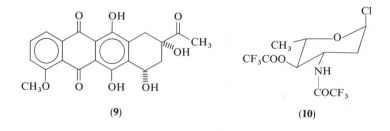

(9)   (10)

chloride and in the presence of mercuric oxide, mercuric bromide, and molecular sieve) to give, after a chromatographic separation and deblocking of the 4′-OH with methanol, the mixture of *N*-trifluoroacetates **11a** and **12a**. Removal of the N-protecting group with dilute aqueous sodium hydroxide at room temperature and chromatographic separation afforded the amino-glycosides **11b** and **12b**. The corresponding α and β acosaminides of adriamy-cinone were instead obtained by condensing **10** with adriamycinone

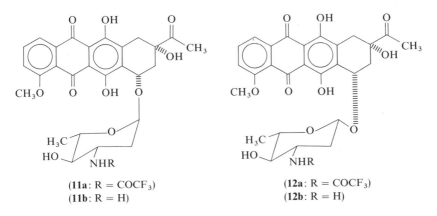

(**11a**: R = COCF₃)
(**11b**: R = H)

(**12a**: R = COCF₃)
(**12b**: R = H)

derivative **13** in the conditions indicated above to give, after methanolysis of the *O*-trifluoroacetyl group followed by chromatographic separation, the anomeric glycosides **14** and **15** in approximately ratio 9:1. Removal of the protecting groups first with alkali, as above, in order to hydrolyze the *N*-trifluoroacetyl group, and then with dilute acid at room temperature, in

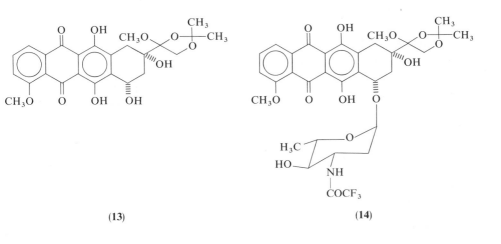

(13)   (14)

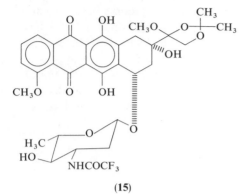 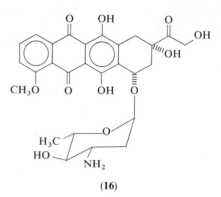

(15)   (16)

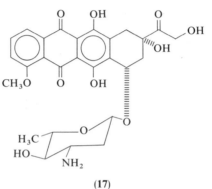

(17)

order to deblock the ketol side chain, afforded glycosides **16** and **17** respectively (6). The α and β anomeric glycosides were identified by PMR spectrometry. In the α anomers the signal of equatorial H-1′ was found as a broad singlet ($W_H \sim 6$ Hz) at about 5.5 δ, whereas the axial H-1′ of the β anomers was shifted to higher field values (e.g., to 4.92 δ in **12b** and appeared as a pair of doublets ($J_{ax, eq} \sim 2$ Hz; $J_{ax, ax} \sim 9$ Hz). On the other hand, the signal of H-7 resonated in the range 4.9–5.2 δ in the α glycosides and in the range 5.3–5.5 δ in the β glycosides.

Acosamine derivative (**10**) was prepared starting from daunosamine as shown in Scheme 1. Methyl N-trifluoroacetyl-α-daunosaminide (**19**), obtained upon trifluoroacetylation and methanolysis of methyl-α-daunosaminide (**18**), was oxidized to methyl-2,3,6-trideoxy-3-trifluoroacetamido-α-L-*threo*-hexopyranosid-4-ulose (**20**), whose reduction with sodium borohydride at 5°C gave, stereospecifically, acosamine derivative **21**. Hydrolysis of the latter gave N-trifluoroacetylacosamine (**22**), which was converted to (**10**) by treatment with dry hydrogen chloride of the corresponding 1,4-di-O-trifluoroacetate.

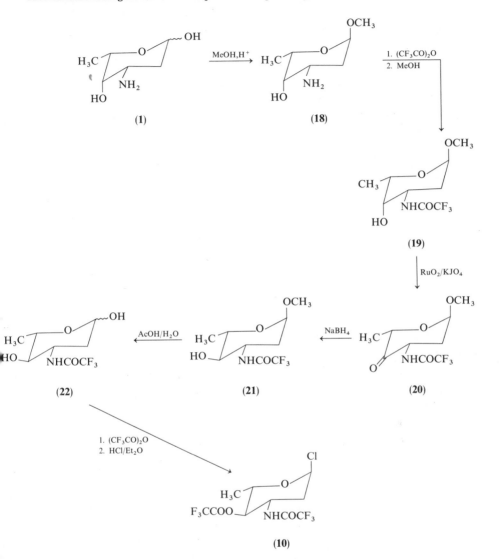

Scheme 1. Synthesis of N,O-ditrifluoroacetyl-α-acosaminyl chloride from daunosamine (6).

Other Syntheses of Acosamine

Different syntheses of acosamine (**3**) from commercially available sugars are now known. The first was carried out at SRI starting from the intermediate **23a** of daunosamine synthesis (see Chapter 2) from L-rhamnose. Catalytic hydrogenation of **23a** gave methyl α-acosaminide (**23b**), which was hydrolyzed to **3** with dilute acid (*7*).

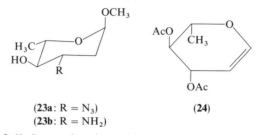

(**23a**: R = N₃)   (**24**)
(**23b**: R = NH₂)

Treatment of di-*O*-acetyl-L-rhamnal (**24**) with sodium azide and boron trifluoride etherate in acetonitrile resulted in the formation of **25** in equilibrium with the more stable **26**, and of a dimeric product, the yield of the mixture **25** and **26** being 65%. Iodomethoxylation of the equilibrium mixture with iodine and thallium acetate in methanol followed by catalytic hydrogenation and acetylation afforded methyl *N*,*O*-diacetyl-α-acosaminide (**27**) as the major product in 38.6% yield and the corresponding L-ribo compound in 24.6% yield (*8*).

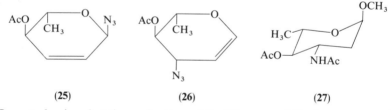

(**25**)   (**26**)   (**27**)

In a study aimed at the evaluation of the Klemer and Rodemeyer reaction, Horton and his co-workers (*9*) had already found that, although methyl α-L-rhamnopyranoside 2,3-benzylidene acetal (**28a**) and its 4-*O*-benzyl derivative (**28b**) failed to give useful products when treated with butyllithium, the 4-*O*-methyl derivative (**28c**) gave the desired methyl 2,6-dideoxy-4-*O*-methyl-α-L-*erythro*-hexopyranosid-3-ulose (**29**) in 40% yield. Hydroxylamine converted (**29a**) into the corresponding oxime. The potentiality of the Klemer and Rodemeyer reaction has been enhanced by the use of the tetrahydropyranyl residue as the hydroxyl protecting group. In fact, Klemer and Balkau (*10*) converted methyl 2,3-*O*-benzylidene-α-L-rhamnopyranoside (**28a**) to the 4-*O*-tetrahydropyranyl derivative (**28d**) in 71% yield. Reaction of (**28d**) with *s*-butyllithium afforded the ketone (**29b**) in 40% yield after a chromatographic step. Compound (**29b**) appears to be a versatile intermediate both to 3-amino-2,3,6-trideoxy-ʟ-hexoses, displaying the arabino or the ribo configuration, or to other derivatives, such as C-3 branched-chain 2,6-dideoxy sugars.

Together with a study concerning the synthesis of ᴅʟ-acosamine from sorbic acid, the following synthesis of ʟ-acosamine was reported by Dyong and Bondlin (*11*). Starting material was *trans*-4,5-epoxy-ᴅʟ-*threo*-hex-2-enoic acid (**30**), which was resolved with ʟ-(−)-phenylethylamine to give the ʟ form. Esterification of the latter with diazomethane and opening of the oxirane ring with *tert*-butyl alcohol and boron trifluoride etherate afforded stereospecifically and in 58% yield the ʟ-erythro compound (**31a**). Protection of the C-5 hydroxyl, as in tetrahydropyranyl derivative (**31b**),

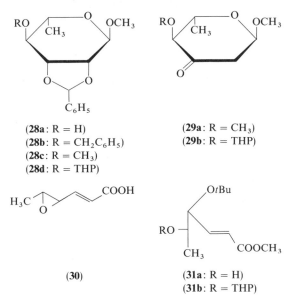

(**28a**: R = H)
(**28b**: R = CH₂C₆H₅)
(**28c**: R = CH₃)
(**28d**: R = THP)

(**29a**: R = CH₃)
(**29b**: R = THP)

(**30**)

(**31a**: R = H)
(**31b**: R = THP)

followed by addition of ammonia, acid hydrolysis, and acetylation, afforded the mixture of optically active lactones (**32**) and (**33**) in 70% yield. Reduction of the mixture with diisobutylaluminum hydride at −70°C gave *N*-acetyl-acosamine (**34**) in 39.2% yield, overall yield from ʟ-**30** being 10%.

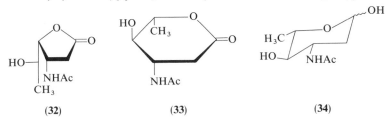

(**32**)   (**33**)   (**34**)

Molecular Properties

Both 4'-epidaunorubicin and 4'-epidoxorubicin displayed a higher R_f value than the corresponding parent compounds by thin-layer chromatography on silica gel plates buffered at pH 7 with phosphate (6). The two analogues were also found to behave as weaker bases in standard titration tests when compared to the parent antibiotics. Determined pK_a values of the protonated form were 8.46 and 8.34 for daunorubicin and doxorubicin respectively, but 8.2 and 8.08 for the corresponding L-arabino analogues (12). In the present author's laboratory the following pK_a values were found: daunorubicin, 8.33; doxorubicin, 8.22; 4'-epidoxorubicin, 7.7.

The DNA binding of the new analogues (Table I) was measured by Di Marco et al. (13), following the decrease of drug fluorescence resulting from the binding to the biopolymer. Linearization of the results according to Scatchard gave lower values for the apparent association constant of the 4'-epi analogues in comparison with the parent antibiotics. These differences were not in agreement with other studies based on the equilibrium dialysis method and Scatchard plot evaluation (14) or on the changes in extinction of the drugs on binding to DNA fitted to a two sites binding model by nonlinear regression analysis following a more adequate method for the separation of the independent and dependent variables (15). The different procedures used may explain the different results and make valid only comparisons within each particular study, differences between the analogues and parent compounds found by Di Marco et al. (13), however, indicating that a lower affinity for DNA can be evidenced in some experimental conditions (as for instance at the low drug concentrations used in the spectrofluorometric assay of binding). The lower affinity shown by the 4'-epi analogues would

Table I

Comparison of Binding Parameters of 4'-Epianthracycline Aminoglycosides with Native Calf Thymus DNA with Those of the Parent Antibiotics

Antibiotic	Apparent association constant (K_{app}, M^{-1})			Apparent number of bridging sites (n, moles/DNA-P)		
4'-Epidaunorubicin	2.0×10^{6} [a]	3.8×10^{5} [b]	—	0.185[a]	0.15[b]	—
Daunorubicin	3.3×10^{6} [a]	4.5×10^{5} [b]	1.3×10^{6} [c]	0.176[a]	0.16[b]	0.20[c]
4'-Epidoxorubicin	2.2×10^{6} [a]	3.6×10^{5} [b]	1.9×10^{6} [c]	0.235[a]	0.18[b]	0.27[c]
Doxorubicin	4.8×10^{6} [a]	3.7×10^{5} [b]	1.9×10^{6} [c]	0.18 [a]	0.18[b]	0.25[c]

[a] Spectrofluorimetric determinations (13).

[b] Equilibrium dialysis determinations (14).

[c] Spectrophotometric determinations (15). All compounds with a free amino group described thoughout this chapter were tested as the hydrochlorides.

also be in agreement with the weaker basic character of the same if account is taken of the stabilizing effect on the drug–DNA complex due to the protonated amino group interacting with the phosphate anionic groups on the DNA double helix (see Chapter 3). In addition, a slightly lower effect on the thermal transition temperature of calf thymus DNA was found for 4'epidoxorubicin in respect to doxorubicin: $\triangle T_m = 12.50$ versus 14.5°C (13) and 15 versus 16.25°C (15). The same was not found for 4'-epidaunorubicin in respect to daunorubicin: $\triangle T_m = 12.4$ versus 12.0°C (13). On the other hand, 4'-epidoxorubicin binding to DNA was accompanied by a distinctly more pronounced enhancement of intrinsic viscosity of the solution than was the case with doxorubicin itself (14).

The effects of the 4'-epi analogues on E. coli DNA polymerase I and RNA polymerase was studied by Di Marco et al. (13). The enzyme preparations were incubated in the presence of the required precursors, 6 mM magnesium chloride and calf thymus DNA, the activity being measured by the incorporation of radioactivity from a labeled precursor ([³H]dTTP and [³H]UTP respectively) into acid-insoluble material at the end of the incubation. Inhibition curves obtained with 4'-epidoxorubicin and with 4'-epidaunorubicin were practically coincident with the ones obtained with the parent drugs. Concentrations required for 50% inhibition of the DNA polymerase-catalyzed reaction were the following: 4'-epidoxorubicin, 11.5 μM (13 μM), doxorubicin 11.5 μM (12 μM), 4'-epidaunorubicin, 12 μM (17 μM), and daunorubicin, 16 μM (16 μM). The values in parentheses are those given by the authors in a subsequent paper (12). Similarly, the following concentrations of the drugs resulted in 50% inhibition of the RNA polymerase reaction: 4'-epidoxorubicin, 6 μM, doxorubicin, 6 μM, 4'-epidaunorubicin, 9 μM, daunorubicin, 8 μM.

Evaluation of Antitumor Activity in Experimental Models

The 4'-epi analogues inhibited the colony-forming ability of cultured HeLa cells at higher dose levels (by 50% or more) than the parent compounds and inhibited the proliferation of mouse embryo fibroblasts in vitro, as well as tritiated thymidine incorporation in the latter, the activity being in these cases of the same order of magnitude as that of the parent drugs (6,12,13).

In the experimental L 1210 leukemia in mice, the 4'-epi analogues exhibited antitumor activity at dose values close to those of the parent antibiotics (13) in both ascites and solid sarcoma 180 and in transplanted Gross leukemia in mice, the activity of 4'-epidoxorubicin in the latter tumor being noteworthy (6).

The results of the laboratory evaluation of antitumor activity and some pharmacological properties of 4'-epidoxorubicin have been reported (16,17).

Table II

Comparison of 4'-Epidoxorubicin with Doxorubicin in
Murine Experimental Leukemias[a]

Tumor	Dose (mg/kg)	Doxorubicin T/C^b	Doxorubicin LTS^c	4'-Epidoxorubicin T/C^b	4'-Epidoxorubicin LTS^c
P 388	2.5	182		190	
	5	212		230	16
	10	$\geq 475^d$	55	≥ 400	40
	15	e		396^d	35
L 1210	2	133	3.3	137	3.3
	5	145		146	
	10	140		155	3.3

[a] Treatment ip on day 1.
[b] Median survival time of treated mice over median survival time of control tumor-bearing mice, $\times$ 100.
[c] Long-time survivors, as percent of treated animals.
[d] Number of toxic deaths $\geq 10\%$ of treated animals.
[e] Toxic dose.

Table II shows the comparison of the semisynthetic analogue with the parent drug in two experimental leukemias of the mouse. In both these tumors, 4'-epidoxorubicin exerted the same antitumor activity as doxorubicin but a reduced toxicity. The therapeutic index, calculated as the ratio of LD_{10} over ED_{200} (the dose that caused a 200% increase of lifespan in treated animals) in P 388 leukemia-bearing mice was found to be 1.09 for the parent antibiotic but 1.81 for the analogue, indicating an enhanced selectivity of action for the latter. Similarly, 4'-epidoxorubicin was compared favorably with doxorubicin when tested in experimental solid tumors in mice. In mice bearing the transplanted mammary carcinoma, the two drugs exhibited comparable activity and optimal dose values at different treatment schedules, the 4'-epi analogue appearing however, better tolerated than the parent compound. The analogue exhibited noticeable activity in the metastatic tumor, Lewis lung carcinoma, as it significantly increased the lifespan and, at the highest dose tested, it cured half of the treated animals without evident signs of toxicity (Table III). In mice infected with the Maloney sarcoma virus, the higher tolerability of 4'-epidoxorubicin allowed the use of higher doses resulting in a more marked inhibition of tumor growth in respect to doxorubicin with no interference with the process of spontaneous regression of this tumor. Interestingly, 4'-epidoxorubicin afforded a higher protection from recurrence of surgically removed murine MS-2 sarcoma in metastatic form than did doxorubicin.

Comparison of 4'-epidoxorubicin with doxorubicin in the P 388 mouse leukemia system under different schedules of treatment is shown in Table IV.

Table III

Comparison of 4'-Epidoxorubicin with Doxorubicin in Experimental Solid Tumors of the Mouse: Transplanted Mammary Carcinoma and Lewis Lung Carcinoma[a]

Tumor	Schedule	Dose (mg/kg)	Doxorubicin T/C[b]	Doxorubicin Cures[c]	4'-Epidoxorubicin T/C[b]	4'-Epidoxorubicin Cures[c]
Mammary	Q7D, 1–15	10	350[d]	60	350	80
carcinoma	Q3D, 1–16	5	205[d]		223	
	Q2D, 1–11 and 17–27	2.5	140		146	
Lewis	Q3D, 13–28	5	170	40		
lung	Q3D, 13–28	7.5	150	30	140	15
carcinoma	Q3D, 13–28	10			200	50

[a] Treatment iv.

[b] As in Table I.

[c] Mice surviving without palpable tumors and in healthy conditions 3 months after inoculation.

[d] As in Table I.

Table IV

Comparison of Optimal Dose (mg/kg) and Activity of 4'-Epidoxorubicin with Doxorubicin in the P 388 Mouse Leukemia System[a,b]

Control number	Treatment schedule	4'-Epidoxorubicin O.D. (mg/kg)	4'-Epidoxorubicin T/C[c]	Doxorubicin O.D. (mg/kg)	Doxorubicin T/C[c]
3410	day 1	5.6	233	10	245
3942	day 1	10	225	10	225
3445	QD 1–9	0.39	204	1	192
3602	QD 1–9	1.6	225	1	207
4775	Q4D 5,9,13	5	166	8	150
0007[d]	QD 1–9	Inactive		Inactive	

[a] Experiments performed by A.D. Little under the auspices of NCI.

[b] For experimental procedure used, see Geran et al. (18).

[c] Survival time of treated animals expressed as percent of controls.

[d] Doxorubicin-resistant subline.

Table V

Comparison of Optimal Dose and Activity of 4'-Epidoxorubicin with Doxorubicin in Different Experimental Mouse Tumors[a]

Control number	Tumor system	Treatment and schedule	4'-Epidoxorubicin		Doxorubicin	
			O.D.	T/C	O.D.	T/C
R072[b]	L 1210	ip, QD 1–9	3.13	176[c]	2	138[c]
0385[b]	B16 melanocarcinoma	ip, day 1	7.5	283	4	283
0866[b]	" "	ip, day 1	1.88	308	4	308
0862[b]	" "	ip, day 5	15	157	8	159
B011[d]	Colon 26	iv, days 1,8,15	14	117	10.5	133
B014[d]	" "	iv, days 1,8	14	115	6.3	197
102000[d]	" 38	sc, days 3,10	21	306	8.1	217
042100[d]	" "	sc, days 3,10,17	14	190	8.1	157
101000[d]	" "	sc, days 3,10,17	15	233	7.1	244
100300[d]	C3H mammary adenocarcinoma	sc, days 13,20,27	11.3 (5)	296 (271)	6.0	298
0150[e]	CD8F1 mammary tumor	ip, Q7D 1–29	3	29[f]	2	31[f]

[a] Experiments performed under the auspices of NCI.
[b] Screener A.D. Little.
[c] Median survival time expressed as percent of controls.
[d] Screener SRI.
[e] Screener The Catholic Medical Center.
[f] Median tumor weight as percent of controls.

In all cases the analogue was equally or more effective than the parent. No activity was discernible up to a 10 mg/kg dosage on doxorubicin-resistant P 388 leukemia. When compared with doxorubicin in different experimental systems included in current screen within the drug research and development program, N.C.I., Division of Cancer Treatment, the analogue revealed remarkable activity over a wide spectrum of mouse tumors (Table V).

Toxicological Studies with 4′-Epidoxorubicin

Toxicological effects of 4′-epidoxorubicin in rabbits treated iv for 3 consecutive days a week for 6 weeks were found to be qualitatively similar to those exhibited by doxorubicin and included bone marrow depression, gastrointestinal lesions, and cardiac damage. However, a quantitative comparison showed that 4′-epidoxorubicin was about 25% less toxic than the parent antibiotic (16). The same authors demonstrated the carcinogenic properties of the analogue in infant rats as being of the same order of magnitude as those of doxorubicin. The animals, however, did not develop cateracts and dental malformations as instead was the case after doxorubicin treatment.

The distribution of 4′-epidoxorubicin in mice bearing transplanted mammary carcinoma was determined and compared with that of doxorubicin using a total fluorescence assay (16). The results (Fig. 1) indicated that the distribution of fluorescent materials at 6 hr after treatment was similar for the two drugs, but the analogue was retained less strongly than the parent compound in the heart, the kidneys, and the spleen, as shown by the 24 and 48 hr data. Such findings would suggest that the lower toxicity of 4′-epidoxorubicin with respect to doxorubicin might be related to a lower concentration in some relevant tissues.

According to results obtained by G. Zbinden, ETH, Zurich, the minimal cumulative cardiotoxic dose of 4′-epidoxorubicin in the rat model is 16 mg/kg, which compares favorably with the value obtained for doxorubicin (10–12 mg/kg) (19). The compound was reported to exhibit strong mutagenic activity in a bacterial and a mammalian cell system (20).

Clinical Evaluation of 4′-Epidoxorubicin

A total of 56 patients had entered the phase 1 clinical study in April, 1978 (21,22). Single doses up to 90 mg/m² were administered by rapid iv injection at 3-week intervals. The highest cumulative dose administered was 555 mg/m². At the higher doses, a lower incidence of vomiting, stomatis, alopecia, and marrow suppression were observed than with doxorubicin at comparable doses.

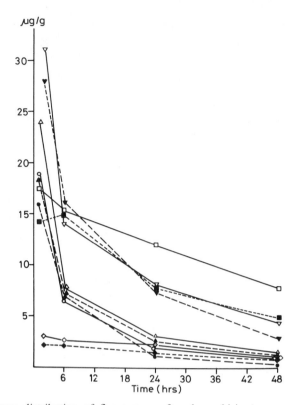

Fig. 1. Tissue distribution of fluorescence after doxorubicin (open symbols) and 4'-epidoxorubicin (full symbols) iv administration (10 mg/kg) to C3H/He mice bearing mammary carcinoma (○ ●, heart; △▲, liver; □ ■, spleen; ▽ ▼, kidney; ◇ ◆, tumor). Data deduced from (16).

Objective regressions in a variety of tumors were observed in 32% of patients, responses of renal cancer (2/6), melanoma (2/6), and rectal cancer (1/3) being of particular interest, as these tumors are known to be refractory to doxorubicin treatment.

OTHER ANALOGUES MODIFIED AT C-4'

The remarkable antitumor activity and improved pharmacological properties of the 4'-epi analogue prompted the synthesis of new compounds showing functional modifications at the same position. The aminosugar residues corresponding to these analogues were obtained starting from daunosamine and subsequently coupled with daunomycinone, the doxo-rubicin analogues being prepared from the corresponding daunorubicin analogues by introduction of the alcoholic functionality at C-14.

4'-Deoxy Analogues

The previously unknown 3-amino-2,3,4,6,-tetradeoxy-L-*threo*-hexose (4-deoxydaunosamine) was obtained as the *N*-trifluoroacetyl derivative **37** in three steps (Scheme 2) from methyl *N*-trifluoroacetyldaunosaminide (**19**), which was brosylated to **35**, the latter compound being converted to the iododerivative **36**. Catalytic hydrogenation of **36** followed by hydrolysis of the glycoside gave **37**. The glycosylating agent **38** was prepared from **37** by treatment with dry hydrogen chloride of the corresponding 1-*p*-nitro benzoate.

The glycosylation reaction was carried out in methylene chloride and in the presence of silver trifluoromethane sulfonate (*23*) to give, stereoselectively the *N*-trifluoroacetyl derivative of 4'-deoxydaunorubicin. Removal of the

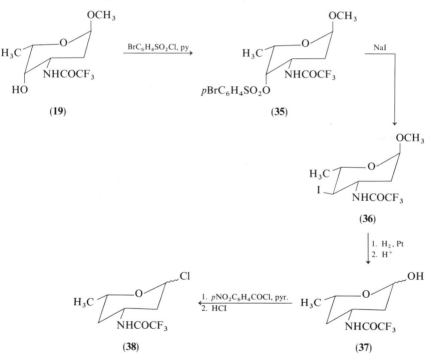

Scheme 2. Synthesis of 2,3,4,6-tetradeoxy-3-trifluoroacetamido-L-*threo*-hexopyranosyl chloride from daunosamine.

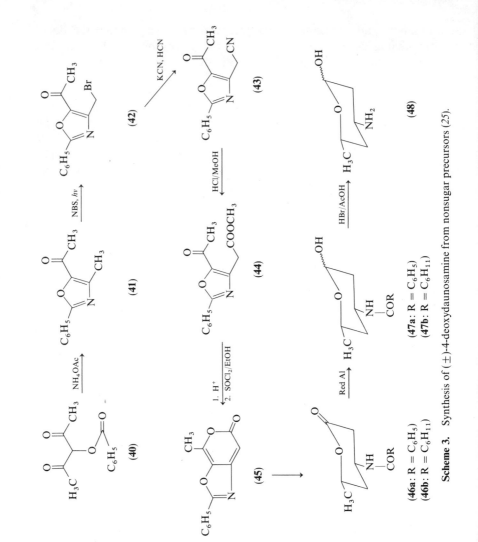

Scheme 3. Synthesis of (±)-4-deoxydaunosamine from nonsugar precursors (25).

protecting group with dilute sodium hydroxide afforded 4′-deoxydauno-rubicin (**39a**), from which the corresponding doxorubicin analogue **39b** was prepared in approximately 50% yield via the 14-bromoderivative **39** and nucleophilic substitution of the halogen with hydroxyl ion (*24*).

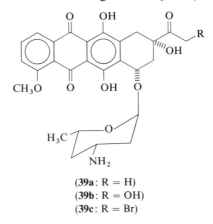

(**39a**: R = H)
(**39b**: R = OH)
(**39c**: R = Br)

A synthesis of racemic 4-deoxydaunosamine has been reported (Scheme 3). Oxazolino-α-pyrone (**45**), obtained in four steps from **40**, was hydrogenated in the presence of Adam's catalyst to the mixture of **46a** and **46b** or to **46b**, the relative stereochemistry of the products being ascertained by PMR analysis. Both **46a** and **46b** were converted to 3-amino-2,3,4,6-tetradeoxy-DL-*threo*-hexopyranose by reduction of the lactone function to the hemiacetal as in **47a** and **47b**, followed by hydrolysis with hydrogen bromide (*25*).

Determination of the binding parameters with calf thymus DNA of the 4′-deoxy analogues by the equilibrium dialysis methods gave values of the apparent association constants (3.1×10^5 and 4.4×10^5 respectively) and of the number of binding sites (0.14 and 0.17 moles/DNA-P respectively) for 4′-deoxydaunorubicin and 4′-deoxydoxorubicin of the same order of magnitude as those found for the parent compounds. 4′-Deoxydoxorubicin affected intrinsic viscosity of native DNA very similarly to doxorubicin, an additional indication of the absence of consequences in the removal of the 4′-hydroxyl as far as the DNA complexation reaction is concerned (*14*). These results were in agreement with those of Di Marco *et al.* (*12*), who found values of the apparent association constant practically identical to those of the parent antibiotics on the basis of the fluorescence quenching measurements. These authors also determined the pK_a values of the 4′-deoxy analogues that resulted, as expected because of the absence of the electronegative C-4′ substituent, in stronger bases ($pK_a \simeq 8.7$) in respect to the parent compounds.

The 4'-deoxy analogues inhibited by 50% the reactions catalyzed by *E. coli* RNA polymerase and DNA polymerase *in vitro* at lower concentration values when compared with the parent antibiotics and with the 4'-epi analogues (*12*). The authors related this finding to the higher basic character of the 4'-deoxyaminoglycosides that would enhance the DNA binding ability of the compounds. The hypothesis is not in agreement with the affinities as evaluated on the basis of the equilibrium constants. Alternatively, the rates of association and dissociation of the DNA complex could be influenced by the structural modification. The importance of the said rates for the interpretation of the biochemical behavior of actinomycin derivatives is well established (*26*).

When tested on cultured HeLa cells, the 4'-deoxy analogues reduced by 50% the colony-forming capacity of the cells at very low concentration, namely, 4 nM for 4'-deoxydaunorubicin and 17 nM for 4'-deoxydoxorubicin, whereas the parent compounds exhibited ED_{50} of 64 nM and 310 nM, respectively. This marked effect is probably related to different distribution properties, as the 4'-deoxy analogues were taken up in a greater extent by cultured L 1210 cells in comparison with the parent compounds and with the 4'-epi analogues, this behavior being in agreement with the higher partition coefficient of the 4'-deoxy derivatives in the biphasic system *n*-butanol/ 0.01 M, pH 7.4 Tris buffer, plus 0.1 M sodium chloride (*12*).

Table VI

Comparison of the 4'-Deoxy Analogues with the Parent Compounds in L 1210 Leukemia and Solid Sarcoma 180 in Mice[a].

Tumor	Compound	Dose (mg/kg)	T/C[b]	Tumor growth[c]
L 1210[d]	4'-Deoxydaunorubicin	4	162	
	Daunorubicin	2	162	
	4'-Deoxydoxorubicin	4	177	
	Doxorubicin	5	155	
S 180[e]	4'-Deoxydoxorubicin	0.8	90	47
		1	143	46
	Doxorubicin	1.6	95	52
		2	184	51

[a] From Arcamone *et al.* (*24*).

[b] Average survival time expressed as percent of untreated controls.

[c] Tumor size on day 11 after tumor implant expressed as percent of untreated controls.

[d] Treatment ip on day 1, only optimal doses are reported.

[e] Treatment iv, on days 1–5.

Table VII

Comparison of Optimal Dose (mg/kg) and Activity of 4'-Deoxydoxoru-
bicin with Doxorubicin in the P 388 Mouse Leukemia System[a]

Control number	Treatment schedule	4'-Deoxydoxorubicin		Doxorubicin	
		O.D.	T/C	O.D.	T/C
4283	QD 1 to 9	0.78	280	0.78	245
4585	QD 1 to 9	1.56	226	0.78	198
4801	Q4D 5,9,13	3.13	175	8.00	178
4987	Q4D 5,9,13	3.13	158	8.00	165

[s] Experiments performed by A. D. Little under the auspices of NCl.
See footnotes to Table IV.

The 4'-deoxy analogues, and especially 4'-deoxydoxorubicin, displayed
remarkable activity in experimental tumors in mice such as L 1210 leukemia
and solid sarcoma 180 (Table VI) and on P 388 leukemia (Table VII). These
results are of greater interest if account is taken of the lower cardiotoxicity
exhibited by 4'-deoxydoxorubicin in the Zbinden's rat model (19), a finding
that, when confirmed in other animal species and under prolonged treatment
schedules, would make this compound one of the most promising new
doxorubicin analogues.

4'-Methyl Derivatives

Treatment of **19** with diazomethane and boron trifluoride etherate gave
49, which was converted to the halide **50c** by hydrolysis of the methyl glycoside **50a**, p-nitrobenzoylation to **50b**, and treatment of the latter with dry
hydrogen chloride. Glycosylation of daunomycinone with **50c** in the presence of silver triflate and detrifluoroacetylation of the condensation product
afforded 4'-O-methyldaunorubicin (**51a**), from which 4'-O-methyldoxoru-
bicin (**51b**) was also obtained. Similarly, the L-arabino analogues **52a** and

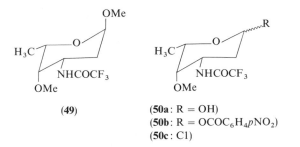

(**49**)

(**50a**: R = OH)
(**50b**: R = OCOC$_6$H$_4$pNO$_2$)
(**50c**: Cl)

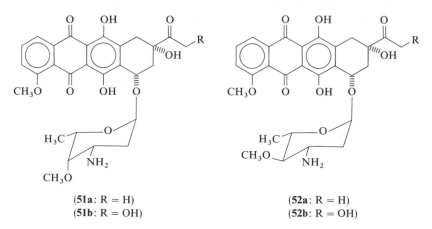

(51a: R = H)   (52a: R = H)
(51b: R = OH)   (52b: R = OH)

52b were prepared starting from methyl *N*-trifluoroacetyl-α-acosaminide (**21**), whose *O*-methylation afforded methyl *N*-trifluoroacetyl-α-actinosaminide (**53**). Further conversion of the latter to **54c** via **54a** and **54b**, followed by reaction of **54c** with daunomycinone in the presence of silver triflate, gave **52a**, whose transformation to **52b** was carried out by standard methods (*27*).

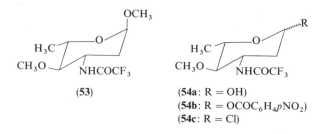

(53)   (54a: R = OH)
                  (54b: R = OCOC₆H₄*p*NO₂)
                  (54c: R = Cl)

The 4′-*O*-methyl derivatives of daunorubicin and doxorubicin displayed an affinity for calf thymus DNA of the same order of magnitude as the parents, and an outstanding antitumor activity in experimental tumors. However, the DNA association constant of 4′-*O*-methyldoxorubicin, as measured by the equilibrium dialysis method, was 3.0×10^5, a value not very different from that of doxorubicin (4.0×10^5) obtained in the same study (*28*). Table VIII in particular shows the remarkable efficacy of **51b** on mouse transplantable L 1210 ascitic leukemia, a system somewhat less sensitive, compared to other experimental tumors, to doxorubicin and to other active anthracyclines as well. This analogue is currently under evaluation under the auspices of NCI. Results obtained so far indicate a higher potency but equal activity when compared with doxorubicin in the P 388 and L 1210 mouse test, but no activity on a P 388 line resistant to doxorubicin. In mice, **51b** was significantly less cardiotoxic than doxorubicin when both were administered under a

Table VIII

Average Survival Times (T/C) and Toxicity of 4'-O-Methyldoxorubicin and of 4'-Epi-4'-O-Methyldoxorubicin as Compared with Doxorubicin in L 1210 Leukemia Bearing Mice[a]

Compound	Dose (mg/kg)	T/C (%)		Toxic deaths
		Experiment 1	Experiment 2	
Doxorubicin	4.4	169		
	6.6	175	175	
	10.0	187	187	3/20
4'-O-Methyldoxorubicin	4.4	287	312	
	6.6	231	275	1/20
	10.0	75	62	17/18
4'-Epi-4'-O-methyldoxorubicin	6.6	169		
	10.0	187		
	15.0	181		2/10
	22.5	87		

[a] Treatment ip on day 1 (27).

chronic schedule at the same dosages of 1 and 2 mg/kg. Cardiotoxicity was evaluated on the basis of the severity and extension of heart lesions (29).

4'-C-Methylated Analogues

C-Methylated aminosugars are of not rare occurrence as components of antibiotic molecules. The methyl branch is situated in position 3, 4, or 5 of the hexose chain, the biosynthetic origin of the methyl group being in the S-methyl group of L-methionine. C-Methylation apparently occurs with S-adenosyl-L-methionine as the methyl donor and a nucleotide-bound aldo-sulose as the acceptor (30). Many of the known C-methylated antibiotic sugars are derivatives of 2,6-dideoxy-L-hexoses. Grisebach and Schmid (31) reported 11 compounds, out of which five belonged to the above-mentioned series, the latter being L-mycarose (55a), L-cladinose (55b), L-olivomycose (56a), L-chromose B (56b), and L-arcanose (57a). Axenose (57b) was isolated as a component of the antibiotic axenomycin (32). Although the importance of the branched sugars moieties as far as their contribution to biological activity is not fully understood (31), the synthesis of C-methylated analogues of daunosamine and their use for the preparation of new glycosides was carried out in the author's laboratory owing to the important results obtained with the other modifications of the sugar moiety.

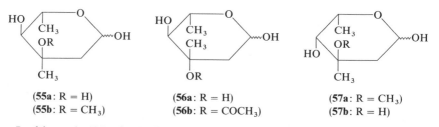

(55a: R = H)   (56a: R = H)   (57a: R = CH₃)
(55b: R = CH₃)   (56b: R = COCH₃)   (57b: R = H)

In this study (*33*), the 4′-C-methyl-4′-*O*-methyl analogues of daunorubicin and doxorubicin in both the L-lyxo and the L-arabino configuration were prepared. Starting material for the synthesis of the corresponding sugar moieties was methyl 2,3,6-trideoxy-3-trifluoroacetamido-α-L-*threo*-hexopyranoside-4-ulose (**20**), whose treatment with the Grignard reagent at low temperature gave exclusively the L-lyxo alcohol **58**, whereas when the reaction was carried out in refluxing tetrahydrofuran the L-arabino isomer **62** was obtained as the major product in 75% yield and **58** as the minor product in 15% yield (Scheme 4). Compound **58** was then methylated to **59** and hydrolyzed with hot aqueous acetic acid to give **60**, from which the glycosylating agent **61** was obtained via the 1-*p*-nitrobenzoate. Similarly, the L-arabino derivative **62** was converted to **65** via **63** and **64**. Carbon-13 NMR spectrum of **58** showed the signal of the C-4 equatorial methyl group at 21.3 ppm downfield from tetramethylsilane used as internal reference, whereas the axial methyl group in **62** appeared at 13.6 ppm.

Reaction of **61** and of **65** with daunomycinone in the presence of silver triflate gave 4′-C-methyl-4′-*O*-methyl-*N*-trifluoroacetyldaunorubicin and 4′-C-methyl-4′-*O*-methyl-*N*-trifluoroacetyl-4′-epidaunorubicin, respectively, the corresponding aminoglycosides **66a** and **67a** being obtained after removal of the *N*-trifluoroacetyl group with dilute alkali. Doxorubicin analogues **66b** and **67b** were prepared by bromination at C-14 followed by hydrolysis of

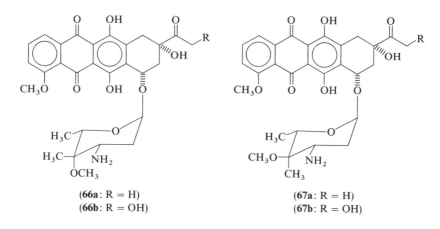

(66a: R = H)   (67a: R = H)
(66b: R = OH)   (67b: R = OH)

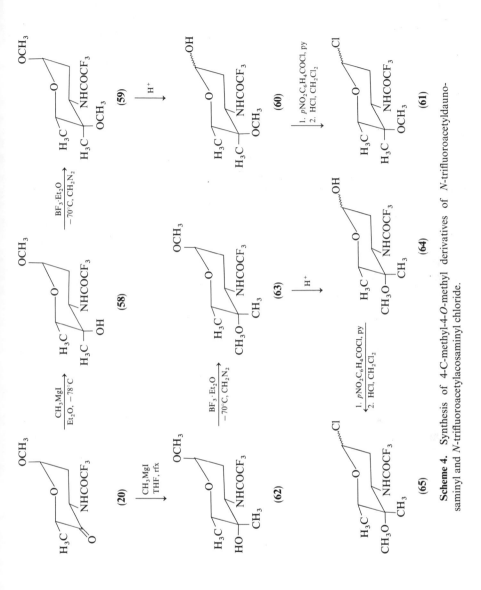

Scheme 4. Synthesis of 4-C-methyl-4-O-methyl derivatives of N-trifluoroacetyldauno-saminyl and N-trifluoroacetylacosaminyl chloride.

the bromo derivative with aqueous sodium formate. No β glycosides were isolated as products of the coupling reaction.

OTHER CONFIGURATIONAL ANALOGUES

Configurational analogues of daunorubicin and doxorubicin, in addition to the L-arabino compounds, have been synthesized and their biological activity, with some exception, reported. The said analogues can be divided into: (a) those belonging, as the parent antibiotics, to the L series, but possessing the same configuration at C-1' (α-glycosides), namely the L-ribo and the L-xylo analogues (b) those belonging to the L series but showing inverted configuration at C-1' (β-glycosides); and, (c) those belonging to the D series, both in the α-anomeric and β-anomeric forms.

The L-ribo and L-xylo Analogues

Ristosamine (4) is the other configurational analogue of daunosamine already known as a constituent of an antibiotic. It was isolated as a product of the hydrolysis of ristomycin, an antibiotic obtained from *Proactinomyces fructiferi* var. *ristomycini*, and is composed of a peptide moiety linked to a tetrasaccharide side chain and an aminosugar (2). Different syntheses of ristosamine or its derivatives are now available. The procedures used by Lee *et al.* (7) and by Sztaricskai *et al.* (34) both used methyl 2,6-dideoxy-3-*O*-tosyl-L-*arabino*-hexopyranoside (68), a compound prepared in three steps from L-rhamnal, the starting intermediate. The *O*-tosyl group was displaced with sodium azide to give 69, whose catalytic reduction afforded methyl-α-ristosaminide (70a). Ristosamine was obtained as the free sugar or as the *N*-benzoyl derivative upon acid hydrolysis of 70a or 70b, respectively.

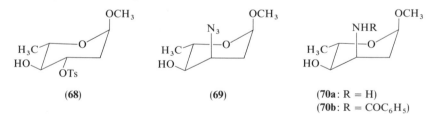

(68)   (69)   (70a: R = H)
(70b: R = COC$_6$H$_5$)

An alternative procedure was developed in the author's laboratory. Startting material was methyl 4,6-*O*-benzyliden-2-deoxy-α-L-*arabino*-hexopyranoside (71a), an intermediate accessible by well-established methods from L-arabinose (35–38). In a first study (39), compound 71a was oxidized with ruthenium tetroxide to methyl 4,6-*O*-benzylidene-2-deoxy-α-L-*erythro*-hexopyranosid-3-ulose (72a), and the latter converted to oxime 72b, whose reduction with lithium aluminium hydride afforded a mixture of **73a** and of the corresponding L-arabino isomer in the ratio 85:15, yield of **73a** from **71a** being 65% (*38*). This conversion had already been investigated in the D series (*40,41*). However, methyl 3-amino-4,5-*O*-benzylidene-2-deoxy-α-L-*ribo*-hexopyranoside (**73a**) was also prepared by another route involving tosylation of **71a**, nucleophilic displacement of the tosyloxy group with azide, and catalytic hydrogenation of **73b** to **73a** in 85% overall yield (*38*). The D form of **73b** had been obtained starting from the 3-*O*-mesyl and the 3-*O*-brosyl analogues of **71b**, albeit in low yields (*41,42*). Hydrolysis of the acetal function in **73a** with methanolic hydrogen chloride afforded methyl 3-amino-2,3-dideoxy-α-L-*ribo*-hexopyranoside, which was N-trifluoroacetylated to give **74a**, a key intermediate for the synthesis of anthracycline analogues possessing the L-ribo and L-xylo configurations.

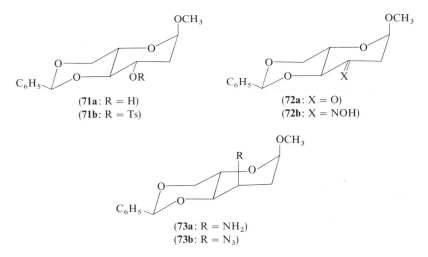

(71a: R = H)
(71b: R = Ts)

(72a: X = O)
(72b: X = NOH)

(73a: R = NH₂)
(73b: R = N₃)

The transformation of **74a** into the corresponding 6-deoxy compound was carried out by treatment with triphenylphosphine and *N*-bromosuccinimide in dimethylformamide (*43*) to give the 6-bromo derivative **74b**, which was reduced catalytically to **74c**.

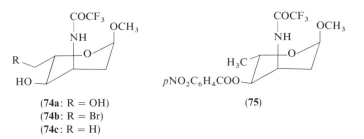

(74a: R = OH)
(74b: R = Br)
(74c: R = H)

(75)

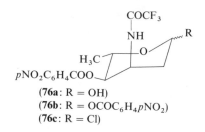

(76a: R = OH)
(76b: R = OCOC$_6$H$_4$pNO$_2$)
(76c: R = Cl)

The glycosylating reagent **76c** was obtained by p-nitrobenzoylation of **74c** to **75**, followed by hydrolysis to **76a**, conversion of the latter to the di-p-nitrobenzoate **76b**, and treatment with dry hydrogen chloride (44). The synthesis of the L-ribo configurational isomer **77a** of daunorubicin was carried out by coupling **76c** with daunomycinone in the presence of silver triflate, followed by removal of the protecting groups by an alkaline treatment. Hydroxylation of **77a** via the 14-bromo derivative afforded 3',4'-diepidoxorubicin (**77b**) (44).

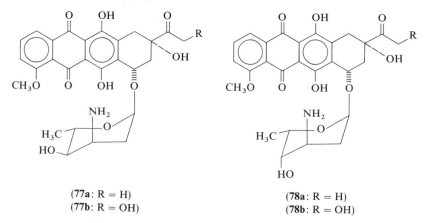

(77a: R = H)   (78a: R = H)
(77b: R = OH)   (78b: R = OH)

Synthesis of the L-xylo analogues of daunorubicin (**78a**) and of doxorubicin (**78b**) was carried out using intermediate **74c** for the access to the previously unknown derivatives of 3-amino-2,3,6-trideoxy-L-*xylo*-hexopyranose (**79**) (45). Treatment of **74c** with mesyl (methanesulfonyl) chloride in pyridine afforded **80** which was submitted to a nucleophilic displacement by heating with sodium benzoate in dimethylformamide. Methanolysis of the resulting **81a** in the presence of a catalytic amount of sodium methoxide afforded methyl 2,3,6-trideoxy-3-trifluoroacetamido-α-L-*xylo*-hexopyranoside (**81b**) in approximately 58% yield from **74c**. Further steps to sugar halide **82b** were the conversion of **81b** to the 4-O-p-nitrobenzoate **81c** and of the latter to **82b** via the 1,4-di-O-p-nitrobenzoate **82a**. Coupling of **82b** with daunomycinone in the presence of silver triflate and molecular sieve in methylene chloride afforded 4'-*O*-*p*-nitrobenzoyl-*N*-trifluoroacetyl-3'-epidaunorubicin, which was converted to 3'-epidaunorubicin (**78a**) by deblocking with sodium hydroxide in aqueous acetone. Transformation of **78a** to 3'-epidoxorubicin (**78b**) was finally carried out by the usual procedure. Preferred conformation of the mentioned L-xylo derivatives was deduced from 90 MHz PMR studies and found to be the $^1C_4$ conformation on the basis of the values of the coupling constants of H-1' and of H-4' indicating the equatorial orientation of the corresponding protons (unpublished results from author's laboratory).

Other syntheses of derivatives of the L-xylo analogue of daunosamine are now available. The one developed in Horton's laboratory (*46*) started from methyl 3-azido-4,6-*O*-benzylidene-2,3,-dideoxy-α-D-*arabino*-hexopyranoside

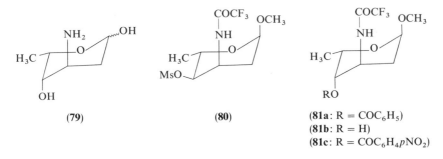

(**79**)   (**80**)   (**81a**: R = COC₆H₅)
                                                                               (**81b**: R = H)
                                                                               (**81c**: R = COC₆H₄*p*NO₂)

(**83**), and was based on a reaction sequence whose pivotal step was the epimerization of the asymmetric center at C-5. Compound **83** was converted into **84** in 75% yield according to Hanessian procedure (*47*) and the latter compound treated with dry silver fluoride in pyridine to give **85** in 96% yield. Hydrogenation of **85** in the presence of palladium on carbon followed by acetylation afforded a mixture whose major component in 40% yield was however the desired methyl 3-acetamido-4-*O*-benzoyl-2,3,6-trideoxy-β-L-*xylo*-hexopyranoside (**86**).

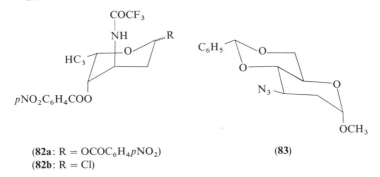

(**82a**: R = OCOC₆H₄*p*NO₂)   (**83**)
(**82b**: R = Cl)

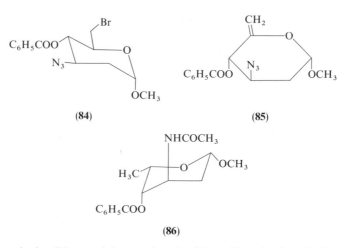

(84)   (85)

(86)

Alternatively, **85** was debenzoylated with sodium hydroxide in aqueous methanol to give **87a**, which was reduced with lithium aluminum hydride to **87b**. Conversion of the latter into the desired L-xylo analogue of daunosamine was best accomplished by hydrogenation in the presence of palladium on charcoal and of an equimolar amount of *p*-toluenesulfonic acid, followed by acetylation of the resulting mixture in order to allow separation of **88a**, overall yield of **88a** from **85** being 63%. Transesterification of **88a** with methanol in the presence of a catalytic amount of sodium methoxide afforded **88b**. In the same study, an attempt was made to treat compound **89**, an intermediate in the synthesis of D-acosamine (*48*) with silver fluoride, but the anhydro compound **90**, arising through a nucleophilic attack of the 3-acetamido nitrogen atom on C-6, was obtained in the place of the expected 5,6-unsaturated product.

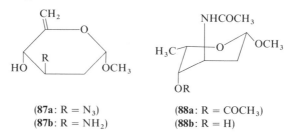

(87a: R = N$_3$)   (88a: R = COCH$_3$)
(87b: R = NH$_2$)   (88b: R = H)

The same approach for the synthesis of derivatives of the L-xylo isomer was used by Biovin *et al.* (*49*), who (*inter alia*) treated intermediate **87a** with Raney nickel in a hydrogen atmosphere to give methyl 3-amino-2,3,6-trideoxy-β-L-*xylo*-hexopyranoside (**91**) in 98% yield.

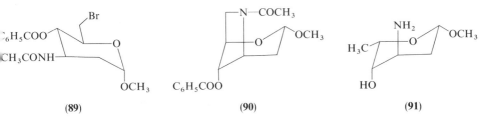

(89) (90) (91)

The two configurational analogues 3',4'-diepidaunorubicin (**77a**) and 3'-epidaunorubicin (**78a**) show a lower affinity for DNA when compared with daunorubicin. Apparent association constants as determined by the equilibrium dialysis method were $2.6 \times 10^5 \ M^{-1}$ and $1.3 \times 10^5 \ M^{-1}$, respectively (daunorubicin, $K_{app} = 4.5 \times 10^5 \ M^{-1}$) (unpublished results from author's laboratory). According to Zunino et al. (*50*), who used the fluorescence quenching method, the apparent association constants for **77a** and **78a** with calf thymus DNA were 0.95×10^6 and 0.86×10^6 respectively (daunorubicin, $K_{app} = 3.3 \times 10^6$), the different behavior of the two analogues being not explained in terms of the relative amount of protonated and nonprotonated forms at neutral pH as was suggested in the case of the 4'-epi analogues. In fact, pK_a values were determined by titration and found to be 8.40 for the L-ribo and 8.18 for the L-xylo analogues (daunorubicin, $pK_a = 8.46$). Also, the complex of the two analogues with DNA appeared intrinsically different from that of the parent drug because the ratio of the quantum yield of fluorescence of totally bound antibiotic to that of free antibiotic was 0.098 and 0.097 for **77a** and **78a**, respectively, but 0.0235 for daunorubicin and 0.027 for 4'-epidaunorubicin. The inversion of the 3'-center appears to be responsible for a somewhat different DNA intercalation complex endowed with lower stability in respect to that formed by the L-lyxo and L-arabino glycosides.

The antitumor activity of the L-ribo analogues **77a** and **77b** on L 1210 experimental leukemia in mice was similar to that exhibited by the L-lyxo and L-arabino stereoisomers, but the optimal dose was 12 times higher (Table IX). Preliminary testing of 3',4'-diepidaunorubicin performed at A.D. Little under the auspices of NCI indicated a noticeable activity in the P 388 murine leukemia test. The average survival time, expressed as percent of controls, at the maximal dose used under the QD 1–9 ip treatment schedule (25 mg/kg) was T/C = 231 (daunorubicin, optimal dose = 0.5 mg/kg, T/C = 165), and at the maximal dose used under the day 1 single ip treatment schedule (100 mg/kg) was T/C = 201 (doxorubicin, optimal dose = 10 mg/kg, T/C = 221). No activity was instead recorded for the L-*xylo*-daunorubicin analogue in the L 1210 test at the highest dose used (Table IX).

Table IX

Antitumor Activity of Configurational Analogues Belonging to
the L Series on the L 1210 Experimental Leukemia in Mice[a]

Compound	Configuration	Optimal dose (mg/kg)	T/C[b]
Daurubicin	L-lyxo	4	150
4'-Epidaunorubicin	L-arabino	4	143
3',4'-Diepidaunorubicin	L-ribo	50	137
3'-Epidaunorubicin	L-xylo	50[c]	100
Doxorubicin	L-lyxo	5	166
4'-Epidoxorubicin	L-arabino	5	150
3',4'-Diepidoxorubicin	L-ribo	60	161

[a] Treatment ip on day 1 (17).
[b] Average survival time expressed as percent of controls.
[c] Maximal dose tested (A. Di Marco and A. M. Casazza, personal communication.

Configurational Analogues Belonging to the D Series

The synthesis of the α and β anomers of 7-(3-amino-2,3,6-trideoxy-D-arabino-hexopyranosyl)daunomycinone (**92** and **93**) has been recently reported by Fuchs et al. (51). These compounds represent the first daunorubicin analogues containing a D-aminosugar (in this case, D-acosamine) configurationally related with daunosamine. The two glycosides were obtained by condensing N-trifluoroacetyl-O-trifluoroacetyl-D-acosaminyl chloride (**94a**) or its O-p-nitrobenzoyl analogue **94b** with daunomycinone in tetrahydrofuran and in the presence of mercuric cyanide, mercuric bromide,

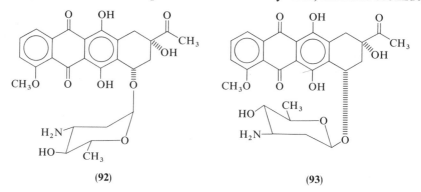

(92)   (93)

and molecular sieve, followed by chromatographic separation and deblocking of the two anomers. The protected aminosugar halides were prepared starting from **95** following standard procedure. Greater yields in the coupling reaction were obtained when **94b** was used as the glycosylating agent. In this case, the ratio of the α to the β anomer was approximately 7:1 (overall yield of the single glycosylation step 83%). The α glycoside **92** was

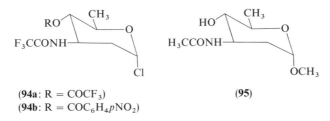

(94a: R = COCF$_3$)   (95)
(94b: R = COC$_6$H$_4p$NO$_2$)

weakly active (average survival time at the maximal dose tested of 100 mg/kg T/C = 125%) on P 388 murine leukemia under the Q4D 5,9,13 ip treatment schedule, whereas the β glycoside **93** was inactive at 50 mg/kg.

The synthesis of D-acosamine and of its derivative **95** had been previously reported by Horton *et al.* (*48*). Starting material for the synthesis was methyl 3-acetamido-4,6-*O*-benzylidene-2,3-dideoxy-α-D-*arabino*-hexopyranoside (**96**), preferably prepared according to the procedure developed by Overend and co-workers (*41*). Treatment of **96** with *N*-bromosuccinimide (*52*) afforded **97a**, which was reductively dehalogenated with Raney nickel in the presence of triethylamine to **97b**. Removal of the benzoyl group by catalytic transesterification led to the already known **95** (*53*), and subsequent deacetylation with aqueous barium hydroxide followed by mild acid hydrolysis gave D-acosamine (**98**) in 80% yield from **96**.

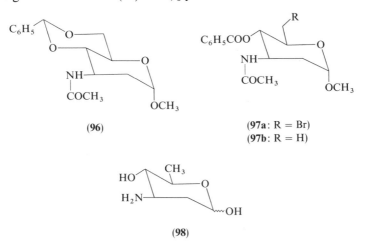

(96)

(97a: R = Br)
(97b: R = H)

(98)

Syntheses of other configurational variants of daunorubicin have not yet been published, although mention of 7-(3-amino-2,3,6-trideoxy-β-D-*ribo*-hexopyranosyl)daunomycinone was made in an abstract (*54*). On the other hand, syntheses of 3-amino-2,3,6-trideoxy-D-hexoses have been reported by different investigators.

The preparation of D-arabino and D-lyxo derivatives from methyl 4,6-*O*-benzylidene-2-deoxy-α-D-*ribo*-hexopyranoside (**99a**), an intermediate easily accessible from D-glucose (*53*), should be mentioned. Compound **99a** was converted to the *O*-mesyl derivative **99b**, which gave **100a** when treated with sodium azide. Catalytic hydrogenation of **100a** followed by acetylation afforded **100b**. Hydrolysis of the latter gave **101a**, whose conversion into the 6-deoxy compound was carried out by selective tosylation to **101b**, displacement of the tosyl group with iodide, and reduction to methyl 3-acetamido-2,3,6-trideoxy-α-D-*arabino*-hexopyranoside (**95**). Mesylation of **95** to **102** and hydrolysis with a weak base afforded the methyl *N*-acetyl-α-D-daunosaminide **103**. The latter compound was deacetylated with base, treated with benzoic anhydride, and hydrolyzed with aqueous acetic acid to give *N*-benzoyl-D-daunosamine (**104**).

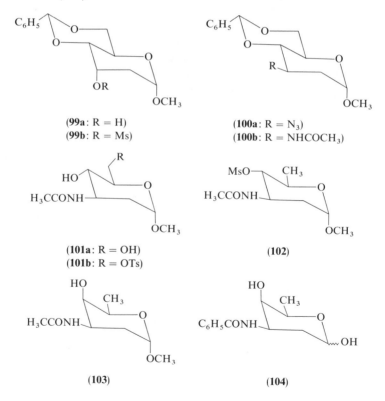

(**99a**: R = H)   (**100a**: R = N₃)
(**99b**: R = Ms)   (**100b**: R = NHCOCH₃)

(**101a**: R = OH)   (**102**)
(**101b**: R = OTs)

(**103**)   (**104**)

Baer's synthesis of D-daunosamine consisted of an approach to D-arabino and D-lyxo derivatives starting from the 4,6-benzylidene derivatives of methyl 3-nitro-β-D-glucopyranoside and methyl 3-nitro-β-D-galactopyranoside, both intermediates deriving from the periodate oxidation of methyl β-D-glucopyranoside followed by reaction with nitromethane (*55*). According to this approach, compound **105a** was converted to the corresponding 2-deoxy derivative by acetylation followed by heating in benzene in the presence of sodium bicarbonate to give a nitroolefin, whose catalytic reduction afforded **105b**. Acid hydrolysis, hydrogenation with Adam's catalyst, and N-acetylation gave **106a**, whose 4-*O*-acetyl-6-*O*-tosyl derivative **107** was converted to methyl N-acetyl-β-D-acosaminide (**106b**) by replacement of the tosyl group with iodine followed by hydrogenation in the presence of Raney nickel. Inversion of the C-4 hydroxyl via *O*-mesylation and heating with sodium acetate in aqueous ethylene glycol monomethylether gave methyl N-acetamido-2,3,6-trideoxy-β-D-*lyxo*-hexopyranoside (methyl N-acetyl-β-D-daunosaminide, **108**). The D-lyxo derivative (**108**) was also obtained from the D-galacto isomer of **105a**, namely **109**, following a reaction sequence similar but not necessitating the inversion of the C-4 center.

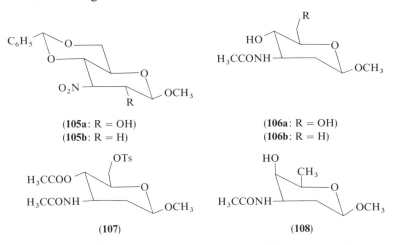

(**105a**: R = OH)
(**105b**: R = H)

(**106a**: R = OH)
(**106b**: R = H)

(**107**)

(**108**)

The first reported synthesis of 3-amino-2,3,6-hydroxy-D-*ribo*-hexopyranose (D-ristosamine) is that of Horton and Weckerle (*56*), who used compound (**110**), obtained in 53.5% yield and five steps from methyl α-D-mannopyranoside (*57*), as the starting intermediate. Debromination by catalytic hydrogenation of (**110**), followed by a treatment with methanol in the presence of a catalytic amount of sodium methoxide, gave (**111**), which was converted to D-ristosamine (**112**) by deacetylation with barium hydroxide and acid hydrolysis of the methyl glycoside. In two other syntheses, carried out by Hungarian chemists (*58*) and by Baer and Georges (*59*),

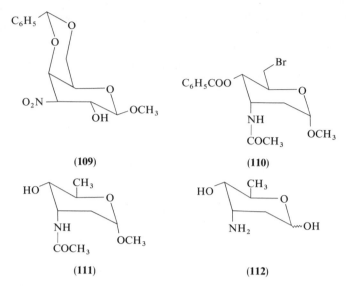

(109)   (110)

(111)   (112)

tri-*O*-acetyl-D-glucal (**113**) was the starting point for the preparation of intermediates **114a** and **114b**, respectively. Treatment of these intermediates with sodium azide afforded **115**, which was converted to **116** upon reaction with *N*-bromosuccinimide (*47*). Compound **116** was converted by Pelyvas *et al.* (*58*) to *N*-benzoyl-D-ristosamine (**118**) in a four-step sequence involving catalytic hydrogenation followed by N-benzoylation to **117**, then methanolysis of the 4-*O*-benzoate and hydrolysis with aqueous acetic acid of the methyl glycoside. D-Ristosamine (**112**) was obtained by Baer and Georges by a procedure involving first methanolysis of the 4-*O*-benzoate ester **116**, followed by catalytic hydrogenation, and finally hydrolysis with dilute hydrogen chloride.

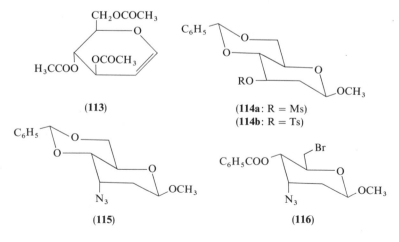

(113)   (114a: R = Ms)
                         (114b: R = Ts)

(115)   (116)

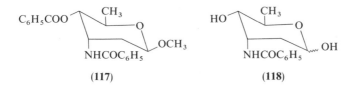

(117)   (118)

The β Glycosides

The β anomer of doxorubicin, 1'-epidoxorubicin (see Chapter 2, **237**) showed a distinctly lower affinity for heat-denatured calf thymus DNA ($K_{app} = 0.2 \times 10^5$) when compared with doxorubicin ($K_{app} = 1.5 \times 10^5$), and affected intrinsic viscosity of native DNA to a much lower extent than did the parent drug (*14*). In a comparative study, Di Marco *et al.* (*13*) had found that the compound inhibited by approximately 20% the *in vitro* synthesis of DNA, catalyzed by *E. coli* DNA polymerase, at 60 μM concentration, and that of RNA, catalyzed by *E. coli* RNA polymerase, at 40 μM concentration, whereas doxorubicin showed EC_{50} values of 11.5 and 6 μM; respectively. The β anomer **237** did not show any inhibitory effect on [^{3}H]thymidine incorporation in cultured mouse embryo fibroblasts up to 3.5 μM concentration and was definitely less active than the parent drug on cell proliferation. A similar behavior was shown by the β anomers **12b** and **17** of 4'-epidaunorubicin and 4'-epidoxorubicin when compared with the corresponding α glycosides. All above-mentioned β-glycoside analogues were found to bind to native calf thymus DNA much less than the α anomers, as shown by the fluorescence quenching method and by the effect on the melting temperature of the helix-to-coil transition of the same DNA preparation. Further investigations on the interaction of 1'-epidoxorubicin with DNA (*60*) indicated that the binding properties of the compound were different from those of the parent compound. Binding studies included the determination of thermal denaturation curves and of the binding isotherms, calorimetric measurements (the enthalpy change of binding of the β anomer to DNA was found to be -0.9 kcal/mole, whereas that of doxorubicin was -5.1 kcal/mole), and viscosimetric determinations. The mode of binding of the β anomer remains uncertain, as both an external binding or a different intercalation complex could be possible. These findings are in agreement with the originally reported lower cytotoxic effect of 1',4'-diepidaunorubicin (**12b**) in respect to 4'-epidaunorubicin (*6*). The former compound inhibited the colony-forming ability of cultured HeLa cells at concentrations 10 times or more greater than those of the latter, and a similar difference was recorded in the mouse embryo fibroblast proliferation test *in vitro*. *In vivo*, **12b** was devoid of activity in the transplanted Gross leukemia test in mice up to

3 mg/kg dosage, whereas 4′-epidaunorubicin displayed considerable anti-tumor effect at the same and even lower dose. The β glycosides do not seem to be endowed with biological activity also in the D-series, as indicated by the reported results concerning the D-arabino analogue 93 (*51*).

OTHER FUNCTIONAL ANALOGUES

The synthesis of daunorubicin and doxorubicin analogues containing structurally modified sugar moieties has been actively pursued in this author's laboratory as well as by other investigators. Although at present time these studies have not resulted in promising antitumor compounds, valuable information concerning the molecular requirements for biological activity can be deduced from the pharmacological evaluation of the new glycosides.

Hydroxylated Analogues

All 3-amino-2,3-dideoxy-L-hexopyranosyl derivatives of daunomycinone, namely the 6-hydroxylated analogues of daunorubicin possesing the L-lyxo, L-arabino, L-ribo, and L-xylo configuration, as well as three of the corresponding doxorubicin analogues, have been synthetised and tested. In order to determine the relevance of the C-2′ deoxy group, 2-(R)-2-hydroxy-daunorubicin (L-talo configuration) was also prepared.

Synthesis of the 6′-hydroxy analogues required the supply of the proper derivatives of the 3-amino-2,3-dideoxy-L-hexoses, access to which could be reasonably provided on the basis of the information also available in the literature for the D series. In fact, none of the aminosugars corresponding to the L-configurations indicated above had been synthetised before (*38,61,62*).

The synthesis of the derivatives belonging to the L-arabino and the L-lyxo series was performed starting from methyl 4,6-O-benzylidene-2-deoxy-α-L-*ribo*-hexopyranoside (**119**), whose preparation was carried out either from the corresponding L-arabino derivative **71a** by oxidation with ruthenium tetraoxide followed by lithium aluminum hydride reduction in 82% yield or from L-glucose in 30% yield, according to the procedures already established in the D series. Conversion of **119** to **120** as described in the D series (*53*) and in 59% yield, followed by debenzylidenation with methanolic hydrogen chloride, gave methyl 3-amino-2,3-dideoxy-α-L-*arabino*-hexopyranoside (**121**). Acid hydrolysis afforded **122a**, whose N-trifluoroacetyl derivative **122b** was p-nitrobenzoylated and heated with aqueous sodium bicarbonate to give 4,6-di-O-p-nitrobenzoyl-1,2,3-trideoxy-3-trifluoroacetamido-L-*arab-ino*-hex-1-enopyranose (**123**) in 70% overall yield from **120** (*63*). Reaction of **123** with daunomycinone in benzene and in the presence of p-toluenesulfonic

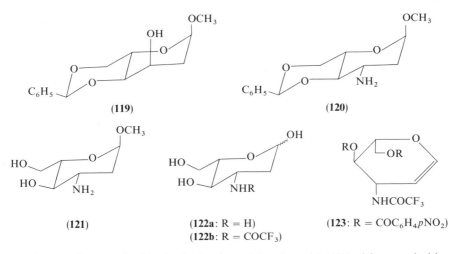

(119)   (120)

(121)   (122a: R = H)   (123: R = COC₆H₄pNO₂)
               (122b: R = COCF₃)

acid as catalyst resulted in the formation of the glycoside **124** with remarkable stereoselectivity. Removal of the protecting groups allowed 4′-epi-6′-hydroxydaunorubicin (**125a**), which was also transformed into 4′-epi-6′-hydroxydoxorubicin (**125b**) (56% yield from daunomycinone). When the glycosidation was carried out allowing daunomycinone to react with halo-sugar **126** in methylene chloride and in the presence of mercuric oxide, mercuric bromide, and molecular sieve, a mixture of α and β anomeric glycosides was obtained. After deprotection, the respective yields of the anomers from daunomycinone were 15 and 6%.

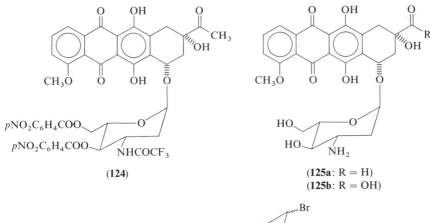

(124)   (125a: R = H)
               (125b: R = OH)

(126)

For the synthesis of the L-lyxo analogue, intermediate **120** was *N*-trifluoroacetylated and treated with methanolic hydrogen chloride to give **127a**, which was converted to the 6-*O*-trityl derivative **127b**. Oxidation of **127b** with ruthenium tetraoxide gave **128**, whose reduction with lithium tri-*sec*-butyl borohydride afforded stereoselectively **129a**. Detritylation with aqueous acetic acid gave methyl 2,3-dideoxy-3-*N*-trifluoroacetamido-α-L-*lyxo*-hexopyranoside **129b**, which was converted to 3-amino-2,3-dideoxy-L-*lyxo*-hexose (6-hydroxydaunosamine) (**130**) with dilute acid (*38*). The glycosylating agent **132** was prepared from **130**, which was trifluoroacetylated, and the thus formed *N,O*-trifluoroacetate heated with isopropanol to give **131a**. Isopropyl α-glycoside **131a** was *O*-*p*-nitrobenzoylated to **131b** and treated with dry hydrogen chloride in anhydrous acetic acid to give **132**.

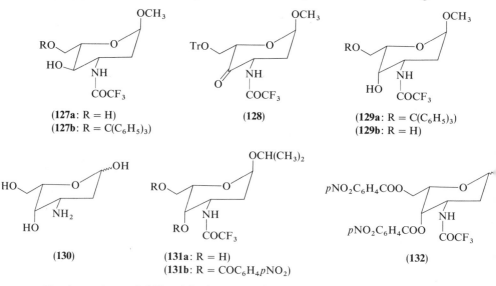

(**127a**: R = H)
(**127b**: R = C(C$_6$H$_5$)$_3$)

(**128**)

(**129a**: R = C(C$_6$H$_5$)$_3$)
(**129b**: R = H)

(**130**)

(**131a**: R = H)
(**131b**: R = COC$_6$H$_4$*p*NO$_2$)

(**132**)

Condensation of **132** with daunomycinone by the silver triflate method followed by deblocking of the resulting glycoside afforded 6'-hydroxydaunorubicin (**133**) (*64*).

Synthesis of the L-ribo and L-xylo analogues was carried out starting from methyl 2,3-dideoxy-3-trifluoroacetamido-α-L-*ribo*-hexopyranoside (**74a**), which was converted to the di-*p*-nitrobenzoate **134**, and the latter hydrolyzed to **135a** and finally converted, via the 1,4,6-tri-*O*-*p*-nitrobenzoate, to the haloderivative **135b**. Condensation of **135b** with daunomycinone by the silver triflate method gave, after deacylation, 3', 4'-diepi-6'-hydroxydaunorubicin (**136a**), also converted to 3', 4'-diepi-6'-hydroxydoxorubicin (**136b**) (*63*). On the other hand, the mesylation of **74a** to **137** and treatment of the latter with sodium benzoate in anhydrous dimethylformamide at 120°C

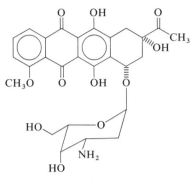

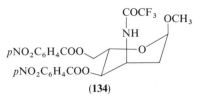

(134)

(133)

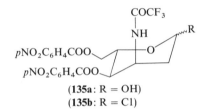

(135a: R = OH)
(135b: R = Cl)

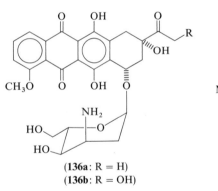

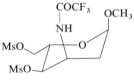

(136a: R = H)
(136b: R = OH)

(137)

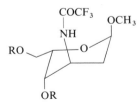

(138a: R = COC$_6$H$_5$)
(138b: R = H)
(138c: R = COC$_6$H$_4$pNO$_2$)

afforded the L-xylo derivative **138a**, yield of the nucleophilic displacement reaction being 80%. Methanolysis of **138a** in the presence of sodium methoxide as catalyst afforded methyl 2,3-dideoxy-3-trifluoroacetamido-α-L-*xylo*-hexopyranoside **138b**, which was transformed to **138c** with *p*-nitrobenzoyl chloride and pyridine. Compound **138c** was converted to **139a** by solution in chloroform containing acetic acid and treatment with dry hydrogen chloride, followed by *p*-nitrobenzoylation of the residue obtained upon evaporation of the solvent. The chloroderivative **139b** was prepared from **139a** with dry hydrogen chloride in methylene chloride and condensed with daunomycinone by the silver triflate procedure to give **140** in 73% yield

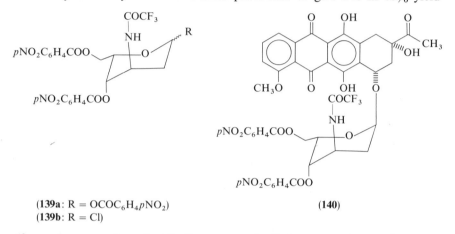

(**139a**: R = OCOC_6H_4*p*NO_2)
(**139b**: R = Cl)

$$(139a: R = OCOC_6H_4pNO_2)$$

(**140**)

(from daunomycinone). Alkaline removal of the protecting acyl groups afforded 3′-epi-6′-hydroxydaunorubicin (**141a**), from which 3′-epi-6′-hydroxydoxorubicin (**141b**) was obtained via the 14-bromo derivative and treatment of the latter with an aqueous solution of sodium formate (*65*).

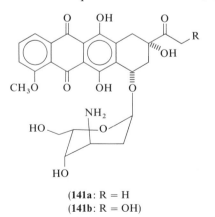

(**141a**: R = H
(**141b**: R = OH)

The daunorubicin analogue containing an axial hydroxyl group at C-2′ was prepared by condensation of the bromoderivative **143b** with daunomycinone in methylene chloride and in the presence of mercuric oxide and mercuric bromide, followed by alkaline deprotection of the reaction product to give 2′(R)-2′-hydroxydaunorubicin (**144**) (*66*). The glycosylating agent **143b** was obtained starting from known 3-amino-3,6-dideoxy-L-*talo*-hexopyranose (**142a**) (*67*), which was converted to the *N*-trifluoroacetyl derivative **142b**, and the latter to the di-*p*-nitrobenzoate **143a**. Treatment of **143a** with hydrogen bromide in methylene chloride afforded **143b**.

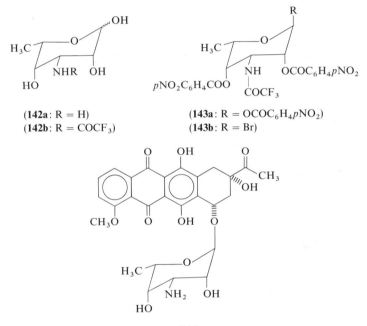

(**142a**: R = H)
(**142b**: R = COCF₃)

(**143a**: R = OCOC₆H₄*p*NO₂)
(**143b**: R = Br)

(**144**)

The presence of the additional hydroxyl group at C-6′ in the L-lyxo analogue **133** and in the L-arabino analogues **125a** and **125b** did not abolish the DNA-complexing ability of the corresponding 6′-deoxy compounds. Using the equilibrium dialysis method, 6′-hydroxydaunorubicin (**133**) showed an affinity constant $K_{app} = 2.0 \times 10^5$ (daunorubicin, $K_{app} = 4.5 \times 10^5$), the number of binding sites ($n = 0.15$ moles/nucleotide) being practically the same (daunorubicin, $n = 0.16$ moles/nucleotide) (*14*). Using the fluorescence quenching method, 6′-hydroxydaunorubicin also was found to bind strongly to double-stranded DNA, albeit less effectively than the parent drug (Table IX). In agreement with the said measurements, the analogue inhibited the DNA-dependent nucleic acid enzymatic synthesis *in vitro* at concentrations only 20 to 30% higher than those of the parent. On the other hand, the concentration of 6'-hydroxydaunorubicin required for 50% inhibition of the colony-forming ability of cultured HeLa cells was 28 times higher than that of daunorubicin, indicating that cell uptake of the hydroxylated analogue should play an important role in the pharmacological properties of the compound. In the same study (*12*), it was in fact demonstrated that 6'-hydroxydaunorubicin was taken up to a lower extent by cultured L 1210 leukemia cells than was daunorubicin, in agreement with the relative values of the partition coefficients of the two compounds in the *n*-butanol, pH 7.4, 0.01 *M* Tris buffer biphasic system. The analogue was also much less effective than the parent drug in an *in vivo* system, namely the sarcoma 180 ascites in the mouse, as the maximal dose tested of 16 mg/kg showed marginal, if any, activity, whereas daunorubicin was remarkably active at the optimal dose of 4 mg/kg (*17*).

Similar observations were made with the 6'-hydroxy derivatives belonging to the L-arabino series. The new analogues exhibit DNA-binding properties similar to those of the 4'-epi-6-deoxy glycosides as shown by the values of the apparent association constant and the concentrations required for the inhibition of DNA template function (Table X). On the other hand, the activity on HeLa cells cloning ability as compared with the corresponding 6'-deoxy compounds was more than 10 times lower for the daunorubicin

Table X

Calf Thymus DNA Binding Properties and Effects on the Colony-Forming Ability of HeLa Cells of Hydroxylated Analogues of Daunorubicin and Doxorubicin[a]

		Concentration required for 50% inhibition (μM)		
Compound	K_{app} ($M^{-1} \times {}^{-6}$)	DNA polymerase[b]	RNA polymerase[b]	HeLa cells[c]
Daunorubicin	2.27	16	8	0.064
6'-Hydroxydaunorubicin	1.23	19	11	1.800
4'-Epidaunorubicin	1.95	17	9	0.099
6'-Hydroxy-4'-epidaunorubicin	1.33	19	10	1.800
2'-Hydroxydaunorubicin	1.30	22	12	
Doxorubicin	3.30	12	6	0.310
4'-Epidoxorubicin	2.18	13	6	0.600
6'-Hydroxy-4'-epidoxorubicin	1.90	16	9	1.725

[a] From Di Marco *et al.* (*12*).

[b] *E. coli* enzymes.

[c] After 8 hr of exposure to the test compound.

Table XI

Comparison of 6′-Hydroxylated L-Arabino Glycosides with the Parent Drugs and their 4′-Epi Analogues in Experimental Mouse Tumors[a]

| | S 180 ascites | | | |
Compound	Optimal dose (mg/kg)	T/C[b]	LST[c]	L 1210 leukemia, dose required for 50% ILS (mg/kg)[d]
Daunorubicin	2	192	16/68	4
4′-Epidaunorubicin				5
6′-Hydroxy-4′-epidaunorubicin	10	167	0/10	
Doxorubicin	2	210	30/125	3
4′-Epidoxorubicin				5
6′-Hydroxy-4′-epidoxorubicin	10	162	2/10	40

[a] Treatment ip on day 1 after tumor transplantation. Data from Arcamone *et al.* (*63*) and Di Marco *et al.* (*12*).

[b] Average survival time expressed as percent of untreated controls.

[c] Long-term survivors (60 days from tumor transplantation).

[d] Increase of lifespan relative to untreated controls.

analogue and 3 times for the doxorubicin analogue. Similar behavior was also recorded in other cell culture tests with mouse embryo fibroblasts (*63*). *In vivo*, the 6′-hydroxy derivatives displayed distinctly lower activity than both the parent drugs and their 4′-epi analogues (Table XI). The different behavior in the cell culture and in the animal systems, not fully ascribable to the differences in the DNA-binding properties, have been tentatively related by Di Marco *et al.* to variations in pK_a values and in water–lipid partition. Although it appears likely that cellular uptake and metabolic modification would account for the low biological activity of these analogues, it should be noted that the mechanism of the said processes, as regards the 6′-hydroxy derivatives, has not been investigated and is therefore still unknown.

Fewer data are available on the biological properties of the L-ribo glycosides **136a** and **136b** and of L-xylo analogues **141a** and **141b**. The L-ribo analogues were still able to bind to DNA (*28*).

Both 6′-hydroxy-3′, 4′-diepidaunorubicin and 6-hydroxy-3′, 4′-epidoxorubicin were active in experimental tumors of mice (*44*), data available so far not allowing evaluation of the biological activity of the compounds.

The L-xylo derivatives, 6′-hydroxy-3′-epidaunorubicin and 6′-hydroxy-3′-epidoxorubicin were respectively 711 and 166 times less effective than daunorubicin and doxorubicin on the cloning capacity of cultured HeLa cells. Both compounds appeared devoid of activity in the L 1210 leukemia test in the mouse (single ip treatment on day 1) up to dosages of 75 and 100 mg/kg respectively (*65*).

2 -Hydroxydaunorubicin (**144**), although less basic than 6'-hydroxydaun-orubicin (the pK_a values were found to be 6.82 and 8.28 respectively) showed similar affinity for DNA (Table X). The analogue, similarly to the 6'-hydroxy derivative, exhibited a low activity in the mouse L 1210 leukemia system (*12*), indicating the apparent strict requirement of the deoxy group at C-2' for the expression of bioactivity.

The 3'-Deamino-3'-hydroxyglycosides

The synthesis of 7-*O*-(2,6-dideoxy-α-L-*lyxo*-hexopyranosyl)daunomycin-one has been reported by Fuchs *et al.* (*68*). The glycosylating agent **146b** was obtained from 2-deoxy-L-fucose (**145**), which was acetylated to **146a**, the latter being converted to **146b** with dry hydrogen chloride in anhydrous ether. Condensation of **146b** with daunomycinone in the presence of mer-curic oxide, mercuric bromide, and molecular sieve gave, after a chromato-graphic separation, **147a** in 84% yield (based on daunomycinone). Only the α anomer was isolated. Deacetylation of **147a** by treatment with methanol and sodium methoxide as catalyst afforded daunorubicin analogue **147b**.

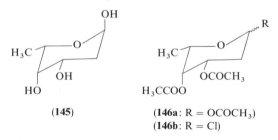

(**145**)
(**146a**: R = OCOCH₃)
(**146b**: R = Cl)

Compound **147b** displayed marked antitumor activity in the P 388 test in mice, the optimal dose being, however, approximately 6 times higher than that of daunorubicin (*69*). This result, together with the activity exhibited at high dosage by the *N*-acyl derivatives (see below), would indicate that the presence of the basic group at C-3' is not so strict a requirement as was thought before, at least in this particular test system (ip treatment of ip inoculated ascitic P 388 leukemia).

The preparative synthesis of 2-deoxy-L-fucose and of its 5-epimer, digi-toxose, was reported by the same group (*70*).

The following glycosides have also been prepared (*54*): 7-*O*-(2,6-dideoxy-α,β-D-*ribo*-hexopyranosyl)daunomycinone; 7-*O*-(2,6-dideoxy-α,β-D-*arabino*-hexopyranosyl)daunomycinone; 7-*O*-(2-deoxy-α,β-D-*arabino*-hexopyrano-syl)daunomycinone. The D-ribo compounds were biologically inactive (*69*).

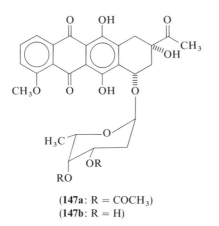

(147a: R = COCH₃)
(147b: R = H)

The 4-Amino Analogues of Daunosamine

As the first part of a study aimed to investigate the biological properties of analogues possessing a sugar moiety having the amino group at C-4 rather than C-3, methyl 4-amino-2,3,4,6-tetradeoxy-α-L-*threo*-hexopyranoside (**150b**) was prepared from **148**, the 4-*O*-mesyl derivative of **23a**, by Wu *et al.* (*71*). The interesting synthetic sequence developed by the authors was based on the reaction of **148** with sodium benzylsulfinate and excess thiobenzyl alcohol in methanol to give **150a**. According to Wu *et al.*, reduction of the azide would result in the intermediate **149**, with subsequent opening of the aziridine ring and formation of the thiobenzyl derivative **150a**. Desulfiniza-tion of **150a** with Raney nickel afforded **150b**.

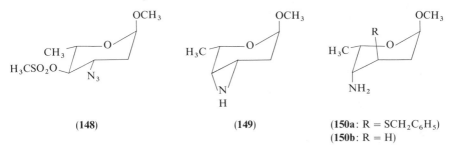

(148)   (149)   (150a: R = SCH₂C₆H₅)
                                                  (150b: R = H)

A synthesis of 4-aminosugars related with daunosamine, namely of methyl 4-amino-3-*O*-methyl-2,4,6-trideoxy-β-L-*arabino*-hexopyranoside (**151**), also known as methyl β-holantosaminide or methyl 4-amino-4-deoxy-β-oland-roside, of the corresponding a anomer **152**, and of methyl 4-amino-3-*O*-methyl-2,4,6-trideoxy-α-L-*lyxo*-hexopyranoside **153**, has been reported by Monneret *et al.* (*72*). Synthesis of **151** was performed starting from **99a**, which was methylated and converted into **154** by an established procedure (*52*).

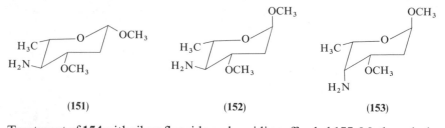

(151)   (152)   (153)

Treatment of **154** with silver fluoride and pyridine afforded **155**. Methanolysis of the latter in the presence of a catalytic amount of sodium methoxide, followed by hydrogenation with palladium on barium sulfate, gave, stereospecifically, the L-*lyxo*-glycoside **156**, whose transformation into **152** was accomplished by standard methods (tosylation, nucleophilic displacement with sodium azide, catalytic hydrogenation).

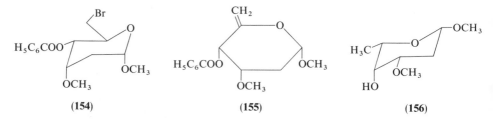

(154)   (155)   (156)

The synthesis of **152** and of **153** was carried out starting from **68**, an intermediate of daunosamine and ristosamine synthesis from L-rhamnose (*34,73*). Treatment of **68** with sodium methoxide in methanol gave methyl α-L-oleandroside (**157**) via the intermediary formation of a 3,4-epoxide. Oxidation of **157** with pyridinium chlorochromate to **158** was followed by formation of the oxime **159** and reduction of the latter with lithium aluminum hydride to afford, after acetylation, a mixture of **160** and **161**. Compound **161** was also obtained from **157** by tosylation, displacement reaction with sodium azide, catalytic hydrogenation, and acetylation. It is worth noting that **162**, derived similarly to **155** from the β anomer of **154**, was not hydrogenated stereospecifically, as a mixture of the corresponding D-ribo and L-lyxo sugars was obtained in the conditions under which **155** was converted into the L-lyxo derivative (**156**).

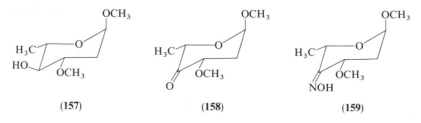

(157)   (158)   (159)

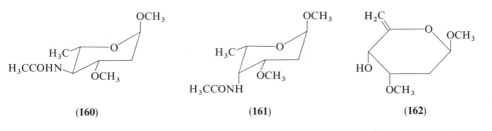

(160)   (161)   (162)

Diaminodeoxy Sugar Derivatives

The synthesis of 7-(3,6-diamino-2,3,6-trideoxy-α-D-*ribo*-hexopyranosyl) daunomycinone (**163**) has been reported by Fuchs *et al.* (*69*). The preparation of **163** was best carried out by condensing the aglycone with glycal **164** in benzene and in the presence of a catalytic amount of *p*-toluenesulfonic acid, without formation of the β anomer. The glycal **164** was obtained starting from bromide **165a**, an intermediate of the daunosamine synthesis from D-mannose (see Chapter 2), via the azide **165b** whose deacetylation and reduction with lithium aluminum hydride afforded **166**. The diaminosugar **166**, a positional isomer of nebrosamine (a component of the aminocyclitol antibiotic tobramycin), was then transformed to **164** in a four-step sequence including N-trifluoroacetylation, O-*p*-nitrobenzoylation, acetolysis to **167**,

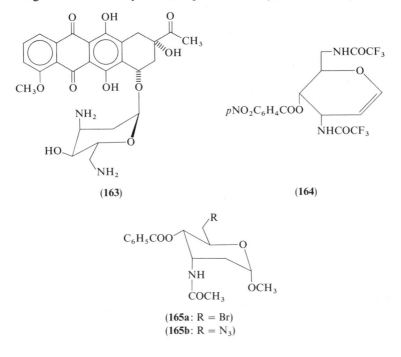

(163)   (164)

(165a: R = Br)
(165b: R = N₃)

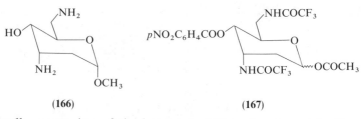

(166)   (167)

and finally conversion of the latter into **164** by heating with silica gel in xylene. Compound **163** was devoid of antitumor activity in the P 388 mouse test at the dose levels tested (up to 12.5 mg/kg).

Daunomycinone β-Glucoside and β-Glucosaminide

Daunomycinone glycosides with D-glucose and with D-glucosamine were prepared by condensing 2,3,4,6-tetraacetyl-α-D-glucosyl bromide or 2-deoxy-3,4,6-tri-O-acetyl-2-trifluoroacetamido-α-D-glucosyl bromide with daunomycinone in 1,2-dichloroethane and in the presence of silver carbonate. Upon hydrolysis with dilute alkali, the acyl groups were removed and a single glycoside was obtained as reaction product in both instances. The β configuration was assigned to the glycosidic linkage in **168a** and **168b** on the basis of the known effect of a participating group at C-2 on the steric course of the Koenigs–Knorr condensation (74). Compound **168b** displayed a much lower affinity for DNA when compared with daunorubicin (75), and no activity in cultured HeLa cells or in sarcoma 180 ascites tumor bearing mice was detected (76). Compound **168a** showed no cytotoxic activity in the standard test systems (Di Marco, personal communication).

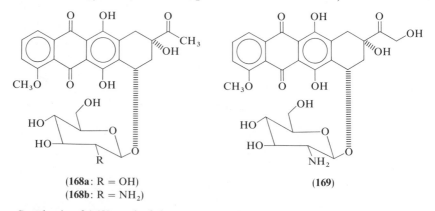

(168a: R = OH)
(168b: R = NH₂)   (169)

Synthesis of **168b** and of the corresponding doxorubicin analogue **169** was more recently reported (77). The two analogues, although essentially inactive in the *in vitro* tests, appeared equally or even more active than doxorubicin in the experimental murine L 1210 leukemia at high dosages (respectively 25 and 34 times that of doxorubicin). The corresponding N-trifluoroacetyl derivatives were also tested and were found devoid of biological activity.

Pentopyranosyl Derivatives

Because of the biological activity associated with the corresponding semisynthetic derivative of ε-rhodomycinone, El Khadem and Swartz (78) prepared 7-O-(2-deoxy-D-erythro-pentopyranosyl)daunomycinone (170) by allowing the aglycone to react with di-O-acetyl-2-deoxy-D-erythro-pentopy-ranosyl chloride in anhydrous tetrahydrofuran and in the presence of mercuric bromide, mercuric cyanide, and moleculer sieve. The resulting acetylated glycoside was obtained in 80% yield and transformed to 170 with methanol containing sodium methoxide. The structure of 170 was confirmed by NMR spectroscopy.

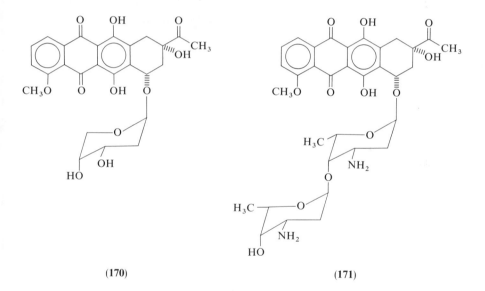

(170)   (171)

DISACCHARIDES

During a study on the pigments produced by different strains of *S. peuce-tius*, a compound showing the presence of two daunosaminyl residues per mole of glycoside was isolated and characterized (79). Purity of this material was not confirmed in later analytical investigations, but the main component of the isolated fraction appeared to be a glycoside to which structure **171**,

4'-O-daunosaminyldaunorubicin, was attributed. The biosynthetic material did not markedly differ from daunorubicin with respect to the effect of calf thymus DNA on visible absorption of the compound, the effect of the same on viscosity of DNA solutions, and the displacement of methyl green from its complex with calf thymus DNA (*80*). The material was however, 5 to 6 times less effective than daunorubicin in inhibiting HeLa cells or mouse embryo fibroblasts *in vitro*. Antitumor activity in mice, at optimal doses, was just less than that displayed by daunorubicin on sarcoma 180 solid and sarcoma 180 ascites tumor. When tested in the MSV (Moloney) induced rhabdomyosarcoma, the biosynthetic material did not significantly affect the development of the tumor, but it prevented spontaneous tumor regression to a greater extent than did daunorubicin, suggesting a strong immunodepressant activity of daunosaminyldaunorubicin (*75*).

As part of a semisynthetic approach to disaccharide derivatives, the compounds 4'-O-α-daunosaminyldaunorubicin (**171**), 4'-O-α-acosaminyl-daunorubicin (**172a**) and 4'-O-(2,6-dideoxy-α-L-*arabino*-hexopyranosyl) daunorubicin (**172b**) were prepared in the author's laboratory (*81*).

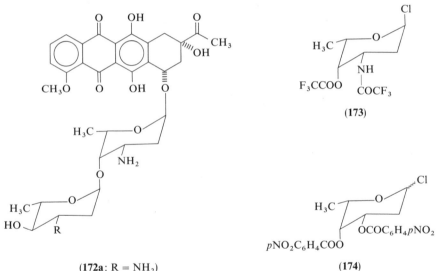

(**172a**: R = NH$_2$)
(**172b**: R = OH)

(**173**)

(**174**)

The procedure used involved the reaction of *N*-trifluoroacetyl dauno-rubicin with the appropriate protected 1-halosugar as, for instance, di-*N,O*-trifluoroacetyl-α-daunosaminyl chloride (**173**), di-*N,O*-trifluoro-acetyl-α-acosaminyl chloride (**10**), 2,6-dideoxy-3,4-O-*p*-nitrobenzoyl-L-*ara*-*bino*-hexopyranosyl chloride (**174**), for respectively the synthesis of **171**, **172** and **172b** in methylene chloride and in the presence of molecular sieve, silver triflate, and 2,6-lutidine. The resulting protected glycosides were deblocked with dilute alkali to give, after a chromatographic separation step, the desired free aminoglycosides. The latter compounds, tested in the P 388 murine leukemia, showed appreciable antitumor activity which, in the case of **171** and under the reported experimental conditions, was even higher than that of the parent drug (Table XII).

Table XII

Antitumor Activity of Semisynthetic Disaccharide Derivatives on P 388 Leukemia in Mice[a]

Compound	Schedule of treatment	Optimal dose (mg/kg)	T/C[b]
Daunorubicin[c]	QD 1–9	1.0	166
4'-α-Daunosaminyldaunorubicin[c]	QD 1–9	3.13	196
Daunorubicin[d]	Q4D 5,9,13	8.0	126
4'-α-Acosaminyldaunorubicin[d]	Q4D 5,9,13	25.0	121
Daunorubicin[e]	Q4D 5,9,13	16.0	134
4'-(2,6-dideoxy-α-L-*arabino*-hexopyranosyl)daunorubicin[e]	Q4D 5,9,13	50.0[f]	135

[a] Experiments performed at A.D. Little under the auspices of NCI.
[b] Average survival time expressed as percent of controls.
[c] Experiment no. 4109.
[d] Experiment no. 5275.
[e] Experiment no. 5622.
[f] Maximal dose tested.

AMIDES

Amide derivatives of daunorubicin and/or doxorubicin have been prepared and studied in different laboratories. The *N*-trifluoroacetyl derivatives have been known as protected intermediates for at least 10 years (*82*) and *N*-acetyldaunorubicin was used for PMR studies (*83,84*). Other amide compounds, both with simple organic acids or with functionalized derivatives of the same, including amino acids or small peptides, have been synthetized. The scope of such studies was that of obtaining compounds that have more favorable pharmacological properties and able to be transformed *in vivo* to the parent drugs by enzymatic deacylation, although the possibility of discovering bioactive compounds with a different mechanism of action were considered by some investigators. In fact, the aminoglycoside function present in the clinically useful antitumor anthracyclines, as well as in all their biologically active congeners, is such an important structural feature as a determinant of chemical and physicochemical behavior of these compounds, that it appears very unlikely that the blocking of the same as in the amide derivatives may result in analogs with improved biological activity. As has been shown in Chapter 3, the basic amino group is an important molecular requirement for a stable DNA intercalation complex and probably for other pharmacologically relevant molecular interactions as well.

N-Acyl Derivatives

N-Acetyl daunorubicin (175a) exhibited a low affinity for calf thymus DNA when compared with the parent antibiotic. The solutions of the compound showed a measurable but small variation of the absorbance at 480 nm upon addition of the DNA preparation. Viscosity of the DNA solution was not modified appreciably by N-acetyldaunorubicin, and the latter was the least effective of a number of daunorubicin derivatives in inducing the displacement of methyl green from its DNA complex (80). In the same study, the ID_{50} of the compound on cell proliferation of cultured HeLa cells was found to be higher than 8.3×10^{-6} M, whereas the same value for daunorubicin was 0.89×10^{-6} M, the effect of the compound on the mitotic index or on DNA synthesis in the same system being comparably lower than that of the parent. The stability constant of the complex of N-acetyldaunorubicin with calf thymus DNA was 100 times lower than that of daunorubicin (75). Optimal antitumor activity of N-acetyldaunorubicin in mice bearing L 1210 leukemia was recorded as increasing by 26% the average survival time under the Q4D-1,5,9 days schedule, at 40 mg/kg daily dose, whereas in the same experimental conditions daunorubicin afforded a 39–44% increase at 1 mg/kg dosage, different regimens of treatment giving similar indications of low, albeit measurable, activity (85). N-Acetyldaunorubicin was found less cardiotoxic than daunorubicin in the isolated dog heart (86), and no ECG or heart mitocondrial changes appeared in rats treated daily for 20 days with a total cumulative dose of 120 mg/kg, corresponding to 6 times a toxic dose of daunorubicin (87).

A sample of N-acetyldoxorubicin (175b) was prepared in the author's laboratory and tested on P 388 leukemia in mice in comparison with doxorubicin (Table XIII). Considerable activity was shown by the compound, but the dose giving the longest survival time was more than 100 times higher under one treatment schedule and at least 50 times under the other in respect to that of doxorubicin. It is worth noting that the apparent association constant of this compound was also 50 times lower than that of doxorubicin, the mode of binding also being probably different, as shown by the numer of apparent binding sites ($n = 0.02$ moles per DNA nucleotide) (28).

Table XIII

**Comparison of *N*-Acetyldoxorubicin with Doxorubicin on
P 388 Leukemia in Mice Treated ip on Days 1 to 9, or on
Days 5,9,13 after Tumor Inoculation**[a]

Compound	Regimen	Optimal daily dose[b] (mg/kg)	T/C[c]
N-Acetyldoxorubicin[b]	QD 1–9	100	201
Doxorubicin[d]	QD 1–9	0.78	233
N-Acetyldoxorubicin[e]	Q4D 5,9,13	400[f] (400)[f]	146 (159)
Doxorubicin[e]	Q4D 5,9,13	8 (8)	150 (148)

[a] Screener A.D. Little, experiments performed under the auspices of NCI.

[b] Dose giving the highest T/C value.

[c] Average survival time expressed as percent of controls.

[d] Experiment no. 4695.

[e] Experiments nos. 5423 and 5597.

[f] Maximal dose tested.

The accumulation of *N*-acetyldaunorubicin in cultured rat embryo fibroblast was about 3 times greater than that of *N*-acetyldoxorubicin, and the distribution of the former appeared diffuse and not corresponding to the distribution of particular subcellular fractions, these being identified by the determination of marker enzymes (*88*). *N*-Acetyldaunomycin was found to antagonize the cardiotoxic effects of doxorubicin in rats (*89*).

In addition to acetamide **175a**, different *N*-acylderivatives were prepared and tested by Yamamoto *et al.* (*85*). These were the *N*-propionyl, *N*-butyryl, *N*-methylcarbamoyl, *N*-butylcarbamoyl, methyl-, butyl-, and phenylthiocarbamoyl derivatives, *N*-carboxydaunorubicin methyl ester, and *N*-carboxydaunorubicin γ-lactam. With the exception of the last compound, which showed activity in a single high-dose regimen at 200 and 400 mg/kg, the other derivatives were ineffective when tested in murine L 1210 leukemia under the Q4D-1,5,9 treatment schedule up to doses in the range from 16 mg/kg to 128 mg/kg.

The physicochemical and biological properties of some *N*-acyl derivatives of daunorubicin have been studied (*90,91*). In the first paper, a detailed presentation of high-resolution mass spectra of various compounds was reported. In the second one, it was shown that daunorubicin *N*-octanoate, *N*-dodecanoate, *N*-hexadecanoate, and *N*-isonicotinate, at a compound-to-DNA nucleotide ratio equal to 0.37, did not interact with calf thymus DNA, as could be deduced from circular dichroism, thermal denaturation, and exhaustive dialysis determinations. In addition, mouse embryo DNA polymerase α and DNA polymerase β activities were inhibited *in vitro* by daunorubicin but not by the above-mentioned derivatives. Similar results were recorded using avian myeloblastosis virus reverse transcriptase and poly(rA)·oligo(dT) as the primer–template (drug concentrations used in the enzyme studies were 50 and 100 μg/ml). On the other hand, the *N*-acetylated derivatives exhibited noticeable inhibition of the proliferation of cultured LLC monkey cells, ID$_{50}$ values being in the range of 2 to 5 times that of the parent drug. As no hydrolysis of the derivatives to give daunorubicin was detected after a 3-day incubation in the presence of growing mammalian cells, the authors concluded that the biological activity of *N*-acyldaunorubicins were due to a mechanism not involving an interaction with DNA, as has been proposed for the parent compound.

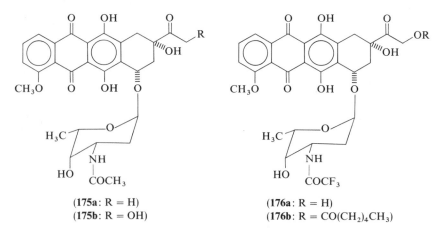

(175a: R = H)
(175b: R = OH)

(176a: R = H)
(176b: R = CO(CH$_2$)$_4$CH$_3$)

The preparation of the *N*-citraconyl derivatives of daunorubicin and doxorubicin, *N*-dimethylmaleyldaunorubicin and *N*-(3,4,5,6-tetrahydro)-phthalyldaunorubicin has been described in a patent. The synthetic procedure consisted in the reaction of the corresponding acid anhydrides with the antibiotic free base in aqueous buffered solution and in the presence of a lower alcohol. The compounds were active at dosages in the range 0.1–5 mg/kg in mouse experimental tumors (*92*).

N-Trifluoroacetyldoxorubicin (**176a**) was found to be endowed with an antitumor effect similar to that of the parent drug when tested on P 388 experimental leukemia in mice (Table XIV), optimal doses being lower than those displayed by the corresponding *N*-acetyl derivative (Table XIII). In agreement with these results, the *N*-trifluoroacetyl derivatives of a number of doxorubicin 14-esters, prepared by nucleophilic displacement of the halogen atom in the 14-iododerivative of *N*-trifluoroacetyldaunorubicin, were

Table XIV

Comparison of *N*-Trifluoroacetyldoxorubicin with Doxorubicin on P 388
Leukemia in Mice Treated ip on Days 5,9,13 after Tumor Inoculation[a]

Compound	Experiment (number)	Optimal dose (mg/kg)	T/C[b]
N-Trifluoroacetyldoxorubicin	5423	50[c]	148
Doxorubicin·HCl	5423	8	150
N-Trifluoroacetyldoxorubicin	5598	200[c]	206
Doxorubicin·HCl	5598	8	176
N-Trifluoroacetyldoxorubicin	5765	100	189
Doxorubicin·HCl	5765	8	187

[a] Screener A.D. Little, experiments performed under the auspices of NCI.
[b] Average survival time expressed as percent of untreated controls.
[c] Maximal dose tested.

found biologically active (*93*). Among these, *N*-trifluoroacetyldoxorubicin 14-valerate (**176b**) was reported to show remarkable activity, superior to doxorubicin, on murine P 388 and L 1210 leukemia, optimal doses being 10–15 times those of the parent drug (*94*). The compound was also evaluated in Di Marco's laboratory and, in agreement with the above-mentioned report, it was found to be endowed with significant antitumor activity in experimental animal systems, at doses about 10 times higher than those of doxorubicin (*95*). However, *N*-trifluoroacetyldoxorubicin 14-valerate was only slightly superior to doxorubicin in the mouse L 1210 test, the optimal dose of 40 mg/kg (treatment ip on days 1 to 4) affording average survival time equal to 225% of controls, whereas doxorubicin treatment at 4 mg/kg gave T/C = 194%. In P 388 leukemia bearing mice, a single ip dose of 100 mg/kg of derivative **176b** exerted the same antitumor effect as a 10 mg/kg dose of doxorubicin, and similar antitumor activity was recorded in the murine Gross leukemia involving iv treatment with the drugs. When the intravenous route was used for drug administration in L 1210 ascites tumor bearing mice, a single dose of 8 mg/kg of doxorubicin on day 1 equaled the antitumor effect of the maximal nontoxic dose of **176b** (80 mg/kg). In the same study, the presence of a dispersing agent such as Tween 80 in the drug formulation was found to remarkably affect the biological response to doxorubicin, and the use of dispersing agents is necessary for the formulation of an otherwise water-insoluble compound as **176b**. This argument was put forward in order to explain the different results obtained in different laboratories, although a different evaluation of the toxicity of the compounds was also considered. On the other hand, further data published by Parker *et al.* (*96*) allowed the authors to claim an activity of *N*-trifluoroacetyldoxorubicin 14-valerate on a

Table XV

Comparison of *N*-Trifluoroacetyldoxorubicin 14-Valerate (AD-32) with Doxorubicin
on P 388 Leukemia in Mice Treated ip According to Different Regimens by Different Screeners[a]

		AD-32		Doxorubicin	
Experiment	Schedule	O.D. (mg/kg)	T/C[b]	O.D. (mg/kg)	T/C[b]
6249[c]	Q4D 5,9,13	90	221	15	195
6359[c]	Q4D 5,9,13	60	177	10	203
6243[c]	Q4D 1–9	30	303	3	264
1598[d]	QD 1–4	30	351	2.6	536
2686[d]	QD 1–4	30	333	3.2	243
1598[d]	QD 4–7	30	263	3.2	243
2686[d]	QD 4–7	30	196	3.2	181
0052[e]	QD 1–4	36	353	1.3	212
0073[e]	Q3D 1,4,7	70	506	4	330
0036[d,f]	QD 1–4	30	246	2.1	184
0036[d,f]	QD 4–7	30	173	3.2	148
0014[e,g]	QD 1–4	36	130	6.7	133
0019[e,g]	Q4D 1,5,9	70	155	6.7	139

[a] Experiments performed under the auspices of NCI.
[b] Average survival time expressed as percent of untreated controls.
[c] Screener: A.D. Little.
[d] Screener: Southern Research Institute.
[e] Screener: Assoc. Chief Lab. Res.
[f] Tumor line resistant to vincristine.
[g] Tumor line resistant to doxorubicin.

doxorubicin-resistant P 388 subline and on solid Ridgway osteogenic sarcoma. Interestingly, although the new derivative was found to interact poorly
with DNA (*97*) and to show a different intracellular distribution (*98*), it
exhibited an inhibition of incorporation of [³H]thymidine in gastrointestinal mucosa, bone marrow, and ascitic tumor cells in L 1210 bearing mice,
both qualitatively and quantitatively similar to that shown by doxorubicin
at a 10-fold lower dosage. The results of unpublished experiments in which
compound **176b** was compared with doxorubicin on P 388 leukemia by
different screeners (Table XV) and on a number of other experimental tumors
of the mouse (Table XVI) may be of interest to the reader and allow the
conclusion that, exception being made for the large difference in the dose
levels needed for the expression of the antitumor activity, the latter is substantially both qualitatively and quantitatively equivalent to that exhibited
by the parent compound, making very unlikely the hypothesis of a basically
different mechanism of action between the two drugs.

Table XVI

Comparison of *N*-Trifluoroacetyl 14-Valerate (AD-32) with Doxorubicin on Different
Experimental Tumors in Mice

Tumor	Experiment	Schedule	AD-32		Doxorubicin	
			O.D. (mg/kg)	T/C[b]	O.D. (mg/kg)	T/C[b]
B16 Melamocarcinoma	033600	QD 3 to 20	30	129	1	102
C3H Mammary tumor	129000	Days 3,10	150	128	4.3	130
C3H Mammary tumor	106400	Days 3,10,17	79	156	5.6	131
Colon 38	113200	Days 3,10	390	247	11	231
Colon 38	111500	Days 3,10,17	150	141	10	168
Ridgway osteogenic sarcoma	013300	Q4D 12–24	40	157	2	187
C3H Mammary adenocarcinoma 13/C	108400	Q7D 20–34	79	200	7.5	191
C3H Mammary adenocarcinoma 16/C	117700	Q7D 9,16,23[c]	150	198	4.4	225

[a] Screener: Southern Research Inst.; experiments performed under the auspices of NCI.
[b] See Table XIV.
[c] Treatment by sc route.

This conclusion is also supported by the recent work of Kanter and Schwartz (99), who found that both **176a** and **176b** or their biotransformation products display DNA-damaging effects in cultured human lymphoblastic cells similar to those exhibited by doxorubicin and daunorubicin. The formation of activated forms of the two compounds is suggested, owing to the low DNA affinity of the two derivatives. In this connection, the importance of information about the metabolic fate of the said derivatives is evident. Investigations on this subject have been carried out by comparing the urinary anthracycline metabolites from mice treated with doxorubicin and with *N*-trifluoroacetyldoxorubicin 14-valerate (100), and by investigating the hepatobiliary metabolism and excretion of the two compounds in the rat (101). Analyses were performed using two HPLC systems, one normal phase and the other reversed phase affording fluorometric detection of as low as 1–10 ng (102). In the first investigation, only 3.3% of a 4 mg/kg doxorubicin ip dose and only 2.3% of a 40 mg/kg ip dose of **176b** were recovered as total fluorescence in the 96 hr cumulative urine samples. Although doxorubicin accounted for approximately half of the said fluorescence in the doxorubicin-treated animals, it was present in traces in the urine of the animals treated with the derivative. The conclusion of the authors was that doxorubicin was not a metabolite of AD-32. It should however be noted that in the urine of the animals treated with **176b**, approximately 50% of the 0–24-hr fluorescence was attributed to unknowns (metabolites A and B, polar fractions) also characterized as doxorubicin metabolites, an observation that could affect the said conclusion when account is taken of the different tissue distribution and presumably different rates of metabolic conversions of the various fluorescent species originated from the administered drug. On the other hand, N-trifluoroacetyldoxorubicin (**176a**) and the corresponding C-13 secondary alcohol 13-dihydro-N-trifluoroacetyldoxorubicin (N-tri-fluoroacetyldoxorubicinol) appeared clearly to be the major urinary metab-olites of **176b**, the latter being absent in all samples analyzed. The bile excretion studies confirmed that extensive said transformation of **176b** to **176a** with no evidence that doxorubicin were a significant metabolite. The results so far obtained strongly point to **176a** as the main component respon-sible for bioactivity *in vivo*, while the possibility that the antitumor effect were due to formation of tightly intracellularly bound doxorubicin was not ruled out by the authors. The question is still an open one and is now cen-tered on the *in vivo* behavior of **176a**, which is, as has been shown above, a remarkably active compound although the acylation of the amino group strongly reduced the DNA-complexing properties typical of the antitumor anthracyclines (*103*).

Cardiotoxicity of **176b** has been evaluated in the rat. Minimal cumulative cardiotoxic dose was found to be 48 mg/kg, whereas the same value for doxorubicin was 10–12 mg/kg (*104*).

N-Aminoacyl Derivatives

N-(L-Leucyl)daunorubicin **177a** was prepared by Buchandon and Jolles (*105*) by treatment of daunorubicin as the free base with L-leucin-N-carboxy-anhydride, while N-(D-leucyl)daunorubicin **177b** was obtained upon re-action of daunorubicin with N-trityl-D-leucyl-N-hydroxysuccinimide ester in the presence of DCCD followed by removal of the protecting group with aqueous acetic acid. The two new derivatives were equally active on mouse L 1210 experimental leukemia, but the L-analogue was more potent and displayed a slightly higher therapeutic index. The biological activity of the new derivatives was studied in more detail by Deprez-de Campaneere *et al.* (*106*). Both L- and D-leucyldaunorubicin inhibited [³H]thymidine incorpo-ration by cultured L 1210 cells more slowly than daunorubicin, the cyto-static effect shown by the derivatives on the same cells being clearly less marked than that exhibited by the parent. On the other hand the L-leucyl derivative was definitively active when tested in mice bearing the L 1210 leukemia, while the D-leucyl analogue was ineffective in this system. The authors pointed out that the L-analogue, but not the D-analogue was hydro-lyzed *in vivo* to regenerate daunorubicin.

The synthesis of derivatives **177c,d** and **e** was performed by Wilson *et al.* (*107*) using the mixed anhydride method of peptide synthesis. The compounds inhibited the DNA-dependent *E. coli* RNA polymerase reaction less efficiently than did daunorubicin; and it was also found, by stop-flow techniques to monitor the hyperchromic change accompanying the dissociation of the corresponding DNA complex with sodium dodecyl sulfate, that the dissociation rate of the DNA complex with **177c,d**, and **e** was higher than

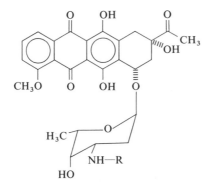

(**177a**: R = L-leucyl)
(**177b**: R = D-leucyl)
(**177c**: R = COCH$_2$N(CH$_3$)$_2$)
(**177d**: R = COCH$_2$NHCOCH$_2$N(CH$_3$)$_2$)
(**177e**: R = COCH$_2$N(C$_3$H$_7$)$_2$)

that with the parent drug. In agreement with these observations, the peptide derivatives were less active than daunorubicin in the P 388 leukemia test in mice. These results, also extended to other analogues of the same type, were further reported and discussed in other publications (*108,109*).

N-Aminoacyl derivatives of daunorubicin have been prepared upon reaction of daunorubicin, as free base, with the *N*-carboxyanhydrides of various aminoacids. Further reaction of the products with the same or with a different *N*-carboxyanhydride allowed homo- or heteropeptide derivatives. The ε-amino group of lysine was protected as the *N*-trifluoroacetate. N-succinylation of the parent compound and of the derivatives with succinic anhydride afforded compounds with reversed ionic charge (*110*). The biological activity of the resulting compounds was tested through the measurement of percent inhibition of [^{3}H]thymidine incorporation into cultured EL4 lymphoma cells induced by 10^{-5} and 5×10^{-5} *M* concentrations of the drugs. Unfortunately, EL$_{50}$ values were not determined and the relative effects of the new derivatives in respect to the drug are not clear. More then 90% inhibition at 10^{-5} *M* was exhibited by *N*-L-alanyl, *N*-L-leucyl, ε-*N*-trifluoroacetyl-L-lysyl, L-lysyl, and L-lysyl-L-phenylalanyldaunorubicin (daunorubicin inhibited by 99.7% at 10^{-5} *M*). Activity was markedly reduced in

the Ala$_2$, Ala$_3$, DL-Ala$_5$, Lys$_2$, and Lys-Tyr peptide derivatives and in the
N-succinyl compounds including N-succinyldaunorubicin, but more than
90% inhibition was shown by the peptidyl derivatives in the presence of the
proteolytic enzyme pronase. The activity in the [^{3}H]thymidine incorporation assay was paralleled by the extent of binding to calf thymus DNA as
measured from the quenching of fluorescence of the drugs in the presence of
varying amounts of the nucleic acid. The new derivatives were presented as
potentially useful antitumor agents with lower toxicity and higher efficiency
when compared with the parent compound in animal tests (unpublished
results cited by the same authors).

N,N-DIMETHYLDAUNORUBICIN

Methylation of daunorubicin and doxorubicin with formaldehyde and
cyanoborohydride allowed the preparation of the corresponding N,N-
dimethyl tertiary amines in which the aminosugar, daunosamine, was substituted with its natural analogue rhodosamine (111). The daunorubicin
derivative appeared to be the most active against P 388 murine leukemia,
albeit not superior to doxorubicin. The compound was found, however, to
be markedly more cardiotoxic than doxorubicin in the rat (112).

NONSUGAR DERIVATIVES

Stereoisomeric compounds of general structure 178, differing in the abso-
lute configuration of the C-7 substituents, were prepared and tested (113).
The DNA-binding parameters of the same compounds were determined by
Molinier-Jumel et al. (114) using electrochemical techniques. It was not

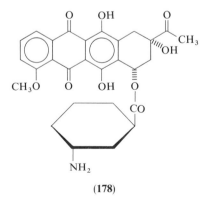

(178)

possible to establish a correlation between the binding data and the antitumor activity, as the two trans isomers, displaying a very low biological activity, showed affinity constants similar to the highly active cis compounds and the parent drug, daunorubicin.

REFERENCES

1. N. N. Lomakina, I. A. Spiridonova, Y. N. Sheinker, and T. F. Vlassova, *Khim. Prir. Soedin.* **9**, 101 (1973); *C.A.* **78**, 148117 (1973).
2. R. Bognar, F. Sztaricskai, M. F. Munk, and J. Tamas, *J. Org. Chem.* **39**, 2971 (1974).
3. D. H. Williams and J. R. Kolman, *Tetrahedron Lett. No. 52*, 4829 (1976).
4. T. That Thang, G. Lukacs, S. Onura, P. Bartner, D. L. Boxler, R. Brambilla, A. K. Mallams, J. B. Morton, P. Reichert, F. D. Sancillo, H. Suprenant, and G. Tomalesky, *J. Am. Chem. Soc.* **100**, 663 (1978).
5. M. Brufani and W. Keller-Schierlein, *Helv. Chim. Acta* **49**, 1962 (1966).
6. F. Arcamone, S. Penco, A. Vigevani, S. Redaelli, G. Franchi, A. Di Marco, A. M. Casazza, T. Dasdia, F. Formelli, A. Necco, and C. Soranzo, *J. Med. Chem.* **18**, 703 (1975).
7. W. W. Lee, H. Y. Wu, J. E. Christensen, L. Goodman, and D. W. Henry, *J. Med. Chem.* **18**, 768 (1975).
8. K. Heyns, M.-J. Lim, and J. I. Park, *Tetrahedron Lett. No. 18*, 1477 (1976).
9. D. M. Clode, D. Horton, and W. Weckerle, *Carbohydr. Res.* **49**, 305 (1976).
10. A. Klemer and D. Balkau, *J. Chem. Res. (S)* p. 303 (1978).
11. I. Dyong and H. Bendlin, *Chem. Ber.* **111**, 1677 (1978).
12. A. Di Marco, A. M. Casazza, T. Dasdia, A. Necco, G. Pratesi, P. Rivolta, A. Velcich, A. Zaccara, and F. Zunino, *Chem. Biol. Interact.* **19**, 291 (1977).
13. A. Di Marco, A. M. Casazza, R. Gambetta, R. Supino, and F. Zunino, *Cancer Res.* **36**, 1962 (1976).
14. E. Arlandini, A. Vigevani, and F. Arcamone, *Farmaco, Ed. Sci.* **32**, 315 (1977).
15. T. W. Plumbridge and J. R. Brown, *Biochem. Pharmacol.* **27**, 1881 (1978).
16. A. M. Casazza, A. Di Marco, C. Bertazzoli, F. Formelli, F. Giuliani, and G. Pratesi, *Curr Chemother., Proc. Int. Congr. Chemother., 10th* p. 1257 (1978).
17. F. Arcamone, A. Di Marco, and A. M. Casazza, *Adv. Cancer Chemother.* p. 297 (1978).
18. R. I. Geran, N. H. Greenberg, M. M. McDonald, A. M. Schumacher, and B. J. Abbott, *Cancer Chemother. Rep., Part 3* **13**, 1 (1972).
19. F. Arcamone, *Adv. Med. Oncol. Res. Educ.* **5**, 21 (1979).
20. H. Marquardt and H. Marquardt, *Cancer (Philadelphia)* **40**, 1930 (1977).
21. V. Bonfante, G. Bonadonna, F. Villani, G. Di Fronzo, A. Martini, and A. M. Casazza, *Cancer Treat. Rep.* **63**, 915 (1979).
22. V. Bonfante, F. Villani, G. Bonadonna, and U. Veronesi, *Proc. Annu. Meet. Clin. Oncol., 15th, New Orleans, La.* **20**, 172 (1979).
23. S. Hanessian and J. Banoub, *Carbohydr. Res.* **44**, C14 (1975).
24. F. Arcamone, S. Penco, S. Redaelli, and S. Hanessian, *J. Med. Chem.* **19**, 1424 (1976).
25. H.-K. Hung, H.-Y. Lam, W. Niemczura, M.-C. Wang, and C.-M. Wong, *Can, J. Chem.* **56**, 638 (1978).
26. M. Muller and D. M. Crothers, *J. Mol. Biol.* **35**, 251 (1968).
27. G. Cassinelli, D. Ruggieri, and F. Arcamone, *J. Med. Chem.* **22**, 121 (1979).

28. E. Arlandini, A. Vigevani, and F. Arcamone, *Farmaco, Ed. Sci.* **35**, 65 (1980).
29. A. M. Casazza, A. Di Marco, G. Bonadonna, V. Bonfante, C. Bertazzoli, O. Bellini, G. Pratesi, L. Sala, and L. Ballerini, *in* "Anthracyclines" (S. T. Crooke and S. D. Reich eds.), Academic Press, 1980, p. 403.
30. H. Grisebach, *Adv. Carbohyd. Chem. Biochem.* **35**, 81 (1978).
31. H. Grisebach, and R. Schmid, *Angew. Chem., Int. Ed. Engl.* **11**, 159 (1972).
32. F. Arcamone, W. Barbieri, G. Franceschi, S. Penco, and A. Vigevani, *J. Am. Chem. Soc.* **95**, 2008 (1973).
33. A. Bargiotti, G. Cassinelli, F. Arcamone, and A. Di Marco, German Offenlegungschrift 2,942,818 (May 8, 1980).
34. F. Sztaricskai, I. Pelyvas, and R. Bognar, *Tetrahedron Lett.* No. 13, 1111 (1975).
35. J. C. Sowden and H. O. L. Fisher, *J. Am. Chem. Soc.* **69**, 1048 (1947).
36. G. B. Howart and J. K. N. Jones, *Can. J. Chem.* **45**, 2253 (1967).
37. I. W. Hughes, W. G. Overend, and M. Stacey, *J. Chem. Soc.* p. 2846 (1949).
38. A. Bargiotti, G. Cassinelli, G. Franchi, B. Gioia, E. Lazzari, S. Redaelli, A. Vigevani, F. Arcamone, and S. Hanessian, *Carbohydr. Res.* **58**, 353 (1977).
39. F. Arcamone, A. Bargiotti, G. Cassinelli, S. Penco, and S. Hanessian, *Carbohydr. Res.* **46**, C3 (1976).
40. E. H. Williams, W. A. Szarek, and J. K. N. Jones, *Can. J. Chem.* **47**, 4467 (1969).
41. P. J. Beynon, P. M. Collins, and W. G. Overend, *J. Chem. Soc. C* p. 272 (1969).
42. J. Kovar, V. Dienstbierova, and J. Jary, *Collect. Czech. Chem. Commun.* **32**, 2498 (1967).
43. S. Hanessian, M. M. Pompipom, and P. Lavallee, *Carbohydr. Res.* **24**, 45 (1972).
44. F. Arcamone, A. Bargiotti, A. Di Marco, and S. Penco, Ger. Patent 2,618,882 (Nov. 11. 1976); *C.A.* **86**, 140416 (1977).
45. A. Bargiotti, G. Cassinelli, and F. Arcamone, Ger. Patent 2,752,115 (June 1, 1978); *C.A.* **89**, 180312 (1979).
46. T. M. Cheung, D. Horton, T. J. Sorenson, and W. Weckerle, *Carbohydr. Res.* **63**, 77 (1978).
47. S. Hanessian and N. R. Plessas, *J. Org. Chem.* **34**, 1045 (1969).
48. D. Horton, R. J. Sorenson, and W. Weckerle, *Carbohydr. Res.* **58**, 125 (1977).
49. J. Boivin, M. Païts, and C. Monneret, *Carbohydr. Res.* **64**, 271 (1978).
50. F. Zunino, A. Di Marco, and A. Velcich, *Cancer Lett.* **3**, 271 (1977).
51. E. F. Fuchs, D. Horton, W. Weckerle, and B. Winter, *J. Antibiot.* **32**, 223 (1979).
52. S. Hanessian, *Carbohydr. Res.* **2**, 86 (1966).
53. A. C. Richardson, *Carbohydr. Res.* **4**, 422 (1967).
54. T. M. Cheung, E. F. Fuchs, D. Horton, R. G. Nickol, W. R. Turner, W. Weckerle, B. Winter, and E. Winter, *Am. Chem. Soc. Natl. Meet., 176th*, CARB 8 (1978). Miami Beach (Flo), Sept. 10–15.
55. H. H. Baer, K. Čapek, and M. C. Cook, *Can. J. Chem.* **47**, 89 (1969).
56. D. Horton and W. Weckerle, *Carbohydr. Res.* **46**, 227 (1976).
57. D. Horton and W. Weckerle, *Carbohydr. Res.* **44**, 227 (1975).
58. L. Pelyvas, F. Sztaricskai, L. Szilagyi, and R. Bognar, *Carbohydr. Res.* **68**, 321 (1979).
59. H. H. Baer and F. F. Z. Georges, *Carbohydr. Res.* **55**, 253 (1977).
60. F. Zunino, R. Gambetta, A. Di Marco, A. Velcich, F. Quadrifoglio, and V. Crescenzi, *Biochim. Biophys. Acta* **476**, 38 (1977).
61. A. C. Richardson, in MTP International Review of Science, Organic Chemistry Series 1, vol. 7, *Carbohydrates* (G.O. Aspinall Ed.), Butterworths, London 1973, p. 105.
62. F. Arcamone, *Lloydia* **40**, 45 (1977).
63. F. Arcamone, A. Bargiotti, G. Cassinelli, S. Redaelli, S. Hanessian, A. Di Marco, A. M. Casazza, T. Dasdia, A. Necco, P. Reggiani, and R. Supino, *J. Med. Chem.* **19**, 733 (1976).
64. F. Arcamone, A. Di Marco, and E. Lazzari, Br. Patent 1,502,121 (Feb. 22, 1978).

65. A. Bargiotti, G. Cassinelli, and F. Arcamone, Ger. Patent 2,743,675 (Apr. 6, 1978).
66. S. Penco, G. Franchi, F. Arcamone, and A. Di Marco, Ger. Patent 2,731,286 (Jan. 19, 1978); *C.A.* **88**, 152939 (1978).
67. A. C. Richardson and K. A. McLauchlan, *J. Chem. Soc.* p. 2499 (1962).
68. E. F. Fuchs, D. Horton, and W. Weckerle, *Carbohydr. Res.* **57**, C36 (1977).
69. E. F. Fuchs, D. Horton, W. Weckerle, and E. Winter-Mihaly, *J. Med. Chem.* **22**, 406 (1976).
70. T.-M. Cheung, D. Horton, and W. Weckerle, *Carbohydr. Res.* **58**, 139 (1977).
71. H. Y. WU, W. W. Lee, T. H. Smith, and D. W. Henry, *Am. Chem. Soc. Natl. Meet.*, *172nd*, CARB 98 (1976). San Francisco, Aug. 29-Sept. 3.
72. C. Monneret, C. Conreur, and Q. Khoung-Huu, *Carbohydr. Res.* **65**, 35 (1978).
73. J. P. Marsh, Jr., C. W. Mosher, E. M. Acton, and L. Goodman, *Chem. Commun.* p. 973 (1967).
74. S. Penco, *Chim. Ind. (Milan)* **50**, 908 (1968).
75. F. Zunino, R. Gambetta, A. Di Marco, and A. Zaccara, *Biochim. Biophys. Acta* **227**, 489 (1972).
76. A. Di Marco, A. M. Casazza, T. Dasdia, F. Giuliani, L. Lenaz, A. Necco, and C. Soranzo, *Cancer Chemother. Rep.*, *Part 1* **57**, 269 (1973).
77. M. Israel and R. J. Murray, *Am. Chem. Soc.*, *Natl. Meet.*, *172nd*, MEDI 89 (1976). San Francisco, Aug. 29–Sept. 3.
78. H. S. El. Khadem and D. L. Swartz, *Carbohydr. Res.* **65**, Cl (1978).
79. F. Arcamone, G. Cassinelli, S. Penco, and L. Tognoli, Ger. Patent 1,923,885 (Jan. 29, 1970); *C.A.* **72**, 131086 (1970).
80. A. Di Marco, F. Zunino, R. Silvestrini, C. Gambarucci, and R. A. Gambetta, *Biochem. Pharmacol.* **20**, 1323 (1971).
81. S. Penco, G. Franchi, and F. Arcamone, Ger. Patent 2,751,395 (May 18, 1978); *C.A.* **89**, 110283 (1979).
82. F. Arcamone, W. Barbieri, G. Franceschi, and S. Penco, *Chim. Ind. (Milan)* **51**, 834 (1969).
83. F. Arcamone, G. Cassinelli, G. Franceschi, P. Orezzi, and R. Mondelli, *Tetrahedron Lett.* No. 30, 3353 (1968).
84. F. Arcamone, G. Cassinelli, G. Franceschi, R. Mondelli, P. Orezzi, and S. Penco, *Gazz. Chim. Ital.* **100**, 949 (1970).
85. K. Yamamoto, E. M. Acton, and D. W. Henry, *J. Med. Chem.* **15**, 872 (1972).
86. R. Mhatre, E. Herman, A. Huidobro, and V. Waravdekar, *J. Pharmacol. Exp. Ther.* **178**, 216 (1971).
87. G. Zbinden and E. Brändle, *Cancer Chemother. Rep.*, *Part 1* **59**, 707 (1975).
88. C. Peterson and A. Trouet, *Cancer Res.* **38**, 4645 (1978).
89. G. Zbinden, *Experientia* **31**, 1058 (1975).
90. P. P. Roller, M. Sutphin, and A. A. Aszalos, *Biomed. Mass Spectrosc.* **3**, 166 (1976).
91. A. Aszalos, M. L. Macy, V. Sagas Sethi, V. Luc, and C. Kalita, *Biochem. Pharmacol.* **28**, 335 (1979).
92. R. Baurain, Ger. Patent 2,756,604 (June 22, 1978).
93. M. Israel, S. K. Tinter, H. Lazarus, B. Brown, and E. J. Modest, *Int. Cancer Congr.*, *11th.* *Florence* **4**, 752 (1974).
94. M. Israel, E. J. Modest, and E. Frei, III, *Cancer Res.* **35**, 1365 (1975).
95. G. Pratesi, A. M. Casazza, and A. Di Marco, *Cancer Treat. Rep.* **62**, 105 (1978).
96. L. M. Parker, M. Hirst, and M. Israel, *Cancer Treat. Rep.* **62**, 119 (1978).
97. S. K. Sengupta, R. Seshadri, E. J. Modest, and M. Israel, *Proc. Am. Assoc. Cancer Res.* **17**, 109 (1976).
98. A. Kristian, M. Israel, E. J. Modest, and E. Frei, III, *Cancer Res.* **36**, 2114 (1976).
99. P. M. Kanter and H. S. Schwartz, *Cancer Res.* **39**, 448 (1979).

100. M. Israel, W. J. Pegg, and M. Wilkinson, *J. Pharmacol. Exp. Ther.* **204**, 696 (1978).

101. M. Israel, P. M. Wilkinson, W. J. Pegg, and E. Frei, III, *Cancer Res.* **38**, 365 (1978).

102. M. Israel, W. J. Pegg, P. M. Wilkinson, and M. B. Garnick, *J. Liq. Chromatogr.* **1**, 795 (1978).

103. T. Facchinetti, A. Raz, and R. Goldman, *Cancer Res.* **38**, 3944 (1978).

104. G. Zbinden, E. Bachmann, and C. Holderegger, *Antibiot. Chemother.* **23**, 255 (1978).

105. J. Bouchandon and J. Jolles, Ger. Patent 1,813,518 (July 10, 1969), *C.A.* **71**, 91866 (1969).

106. D. Deprez-Decampaneere, M. Masquelier, R. Baurain, and A. Trouet, *Curr. Chemother. Proc. Int. Congr. Chemother., 10th* p. 1242 (1978).

107. D. W. Wilson, D. Grier, R. Reimer, J. D. Bauman, J. F. Preston, and E. J. Gabbay, *J. Med. Chem.* **19**, 381 (1976).

108. E. J. Gabbay, D. Grier, R. E. Fingerle, R. Reimer, R. Levy, S. W. Pearce, and W. D. Wilson, *Biochemistry* **15**, 2062 (1976).

109. E. J. Gabbay, *Int. Quantum Chem.: Quantum Biol. Symp.* No. 3,217 (1976).

110. Y. Levin and B. A. Sela, *FEBS Lett.* **98**, 119 (1979).

111. D. W. Henry, G. Tong, A. N. Fujiwara, and W. W. Lee, *Am. Chem. Soc., Natl. Meet., 172nd*, MEDI 90 (1976). San Francisco, Aug 29–Sept. 3.

112. G. Zbinden, M. Pfister, and C. Holderegger, *Toxicol. Lett.* **1**, 267 (1978).

113. R. Maral, J. B. Ducep, F. Farge, G. Ponsinet, and D. Reisdorf, *C. R. Acad. Sci., Ser. D* **286**, 443 (1978).

114. C. Molinier-Jumel, B. Malfoy, J. A. Reynaud, and G. Aubel-Sadron, *Biochem. Biophys. Res. Commun.* **84**, 441 (1978).

7

Analogues Modified in the Anthraquinone Chromophore

The anthraquinone chromophore system is an important structural feature of all anthracyclines and of the useful antitumor antibiotics, daunorubicin and doxorubicin in particular. A wide range of oxygenated substitution patterns appear to be compatible with biological activity among the biosynthetic glycosides, although the existence of a direct contribution of the said substitution patterns on antitumor activity is not established at present time. In this chapter, modifications on the chromophoric system in daunorubicin and doxorubicin, as obtained by total synthesis or by semisynthesis, will be reviewed. New analogues originated by fermentation are dealt with, together with the developments of the biosynthetic-related compounds, in Chapter 8.

SYNTHESIS OF 4-DEMETHOXYDAUNORUBICINS

The synthesis of 4-demethoxydaunorubicin and of 4-demethoxy-7,9-diepidaunorubicin has been carried out by performing the total synthesis of the corresponding 4-demethoxy aglycones and by coupling the same with the natural aminosugar, daunosamine (1). The synthetic scheme for aglycone synthesis was largely based on the work of Wong et al. (2), which will be summarized next. In fact, the work of the Canadian authors represents the first published study concerning the synthesis of a fully functionalized anthracyclinone derivative, that is, 4-demethoxy-7-O-methyldaunomycinone (1), and their synthetic approach, with proper modifications, has been exploited in the author's laboratory for the development of a number of important analogues. Wong's synthesis of **1** started from racemic 6-acetyl-1,4-dimethoxy-6-hydroxytetralin (**2**), whose acylation with phthalic acid monomethylester in trifluoroacetic anhydride solution and at reflux temperature gave **3a** (not isolated). Alkaline hydrolysis to **3b**, followed by treatment with liquid hydrogen fluoride, afforded tetracyclic compound **4**, namely (±)-4-demethoxy-7-deoxy-daunomycinone. These steps, tracking the classical synthetic route to napthacene derivatives based on the condensation of a substituted tetralin with a phthalic acid derivative (*3,4*) and a previously

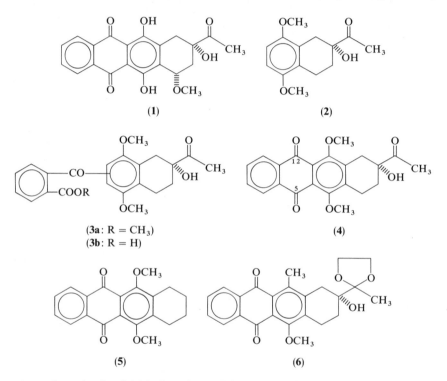

(**1**)

(**2**)

(**3a**: R = CH$_3$)
(**3b**: R = H)

(**4**)

(**5**)

(**6**)

reported synthesis of 6,11-dimethoxy-7,8,9,10-tetrahydro-5,12-naphthacene-quinone **5** (*5*), afforded a 23% yield of **4** from **2**. Functionalization of ring **A** was completed by conversion of **4** to **6** and treatment of the latter with N-bromosuccinimide and a trace of benzoyl peroxide to give a mixture of **7** and **8**, which was refluxed in anhydrous methanol to give, after a chromatographic separation, **9a**, **9b**, and **10**. The regioselectivity of the bromination reaction was explained by considering the C-7 benzylic position less hindered than that at C-10 by the ketalized side chain. Treatment of **9a**, the major product of the methanolysis, with aluminum chloride in benzene gave **1** in reasonable yield (74%).

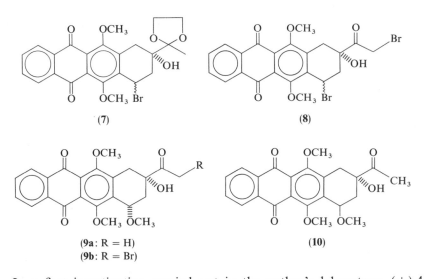

(7)

(8)

(9a: R = H)
(9b: R = Br)

(10)

In a first investigation carried out in the author's laboratory, (±)-4-demethoxy-7-O-methyldaunomycinone (**4a**), prepared according to Wong's procedure, was treated with trifluoroacetic acid at room temperature, and the resulting crude 7-O-trifluoroacetate hydrolyzed with sodium bicarbonate to give (±)-4-demethoxydaunomycinone. Condensation of the latter with N,O-ditrifluoroacetyl-α-daunosaminyl chloride in chloroform and in the presence of mercuric oxide, mercuric bromide, and molecular sieve followed by a methanolysis and a chromatographic separation afforded two products in 61 and 34% yield respectively, the former constituted by a mixture of α-anomeric glycosides **11a** and **12a**, the second by a mixture of β-anomeric glycosides **13a** and **14a**. Alkaline hydrolysis of the N-trifluoroacetyl groups gave the corresponding mixture of α-anomeric (**11b** and **12b**) and β-anomeric

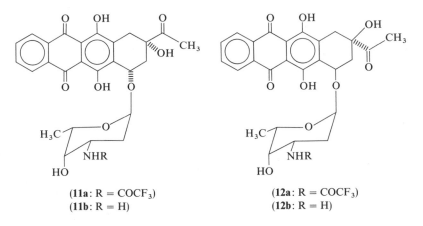

(11a: R = COCF₃)
(11b: R = H)

(12a: R = COCF₃)
(12b: R = H)

(**13b** and **14b**) aminoglycosides. The α-anomeric mixture appeared to be endowed with remarkable activity in cultured cell systems and in experimental animal tumors (*6*).

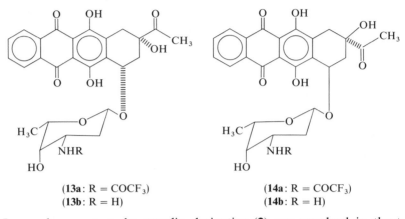

(**13a**: R = COCF₃)   (**14a**: R = COCF₃)
(**13b**: R = H)   (**14b**: R = H)

In a subsequent study, tetralin derivative (**2**) was resolved in the two enantiomeric forms by reaction of the racemic material with (−)-1-phenyl-ethylamine in acetonitrile to give the two diastereomeric Schiff bases corresponding to structure **15** with 6(*R*) and 6(*S*) configuration, the former being insoluble and the latter soluble in the reaction solvent. Hydrolysis of the two diastereomers afforded (*R*)-(−)-acetyl-1,4-dimethoxy-6-hydroxy-tetralin (**12**) and the corresponding (*S*)-(+) enantiomer **16** respectively (*7*). It should be noted here that, as already remarked by Kelly (*8*), compound **2** was incorrectly indicated as (*S*) in different publications (*1,9*). Both enantiomers were then converted to the corresponding 4-demethoxydaunomy-cinones, taking care to avoid racemization during the necessary reaction sequences. The objective was achieved by allowing the optically active tetralins **2** or **16** to react at room temperature with phthalic acid mono-methylester monochloride in dichloromethane and in the presence of aluminum chloride, hydrolyzing the product with base and then cyclizing the resulting acid to respectively levorotatory (**4**) and dextrorotatory (**17**). The

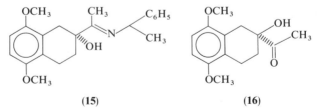

(**15**)   (**16**)

synthesis proceeded by converting **4** and **17** to the corresponding C-13 cyclic acetals with ethylene glycol and *p*-toluenesulfonic acid, followed by

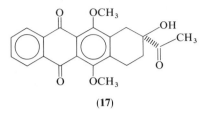

(17)

treatment with *N*-bromosuccinimide with concomitant light irradiation to give, after methanolysis and acid treatment, the mixtures respectively of the 7(*S*) and 7(*R*) diastereoisomers **18** and **19**. Demethylation of the phenolic

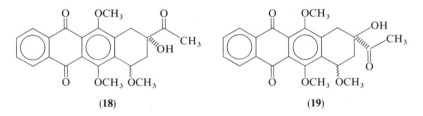

(18) **(19)**

hydroxyl groups of **18** was carried out with aluminum chloride in benzene, and the resulting products were directly treated with trifluoroacetic acid and then with sodium bicarbonate in aqueous acetone to afford, after a chromatographic separation, **20** (4-demethoxydaunomycinone) and **21** (4-demethoxy-7-epidaunomycinone) in respectively 25 and 21% yield from **2**. Recycle of **21** in trifluoroacetic acid and hydrolysis allowed conversion of the 7-epi compound to **20** in 48% yield. Similarly, 7,9-diepi-4-demethoxy-daunomycinone (**22**) was obtained from intermediate **17**. Condensation of **20** or of **22** with glycal **23** in benzene and in the presence of a catalytic amount

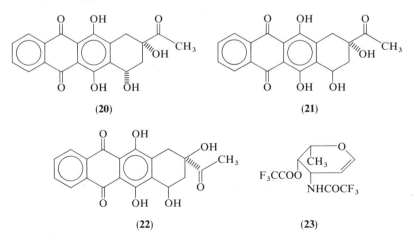

(20) **(21)**

(22) **(23)**

of *p*-toluenesulfonic acid followed by methanolysis and chromatographic separation gave a 60% yield of the α-7(*S*),9(*S*) and β-7(*S*),9(*S*) glycosides (**11a** and **13a**), or of the α-7(*R*),9(*R*) and β-7(*R*),9(*R*) glycosides (**12a** and **14a**), the α glycosides being the main products of the reaction. Alkaline deblocking of each diastereomer afforded aminoglycosides **11b**, **13b** or **12b** and **14b**, which were isolated as the hydrochlorides. Glycosidation of **20** was also carried out by a Koenigs–Knorr reaction with *N*,*O*-ditrifluoroacetyl-α-daunosaminyl chloride as described above for the racemic aglycone to give **11a** in 36% yield. Glycosidation of racemic 4-demethoxydaunomycinone with *N*,*O*-ditrifluoroacetyl-α-daunosaminyl chloride in dichloromethane and in the presence of silver triflate was also reported (*10*). A high conversion rate was obtained, the reaction affording, after a chromatographic separation and crystallization, an overall yield of 88% of two glycosides, *N*-trifluoroacetyl-4-demethoxydaunorubicin (**11a**, 46%) and a strongly levorotatory compound (42%) to which the 7(*R*),9(*R*) and β-glycoside configuration as in **14a** was assigned (*9*). Reexamination of the reaction products has, however, indicated that the latter isomer is an α-glycoside (unpublished work).

A further improvement to the synthesis of 4-demethoxydaunomycinone was subsequently obtained (*11*) by performing the synthesis of 4-demethoxy-7-deoxydaunomycinone (**24**) directly upon heating to melting the levorotatory enantiomer **2** with phthalic anhydride in the presence of aluminum chloride and sodium chloride, to give **24** in good yield without apparent racemization. Ketalization of **24** to **25** followed by treatment with bromine and 2,2′-azo-bis-isobutyronitrile, hydrolytic work-up and silica gel chromatography, afforded **20**, the yield of the latter being approximately 20% from **2** and 29% from **24** (*9*).

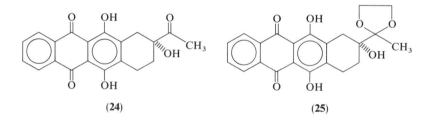

(24)   (25)

PROPERTIES OF 4-DEMETHOXYDAUNORUBICINS

The biological activity of daunorubicin is markedly increased, on a weight basis, upon substitution of the 4-methoxyl group with a hydrogen atom. This makes both the comparison of the different configurational variants and the evaluation of the actual potential therapeutic value of 4-demethoxy-daunorubicin important steps in the development of new analogues.

In Vivo and *in Vitro* Comparison of 7(*S*),9(*S*) and 7(*R*),9(*R*) Stereomers

The 4-demethoxydaunorubicins were compared with daunorubicin in two experimental mouse leukemias and in cultured cells (Table I). In both animal tests, 4-demethoxydaunorubicin displayed the same antitumor effect as dau-norubicin but at 8 times lower dose. The higher potency was, however, accompanied by higher toxicity as evaluated by the number of treated animals dying because of drug toxicity (not shown in the table). The β anomer with the 7(*S*),9(*S*) configuration also showed noticeable activity, the effective doses being of the same order of magnitude as those of daunorubicin. The latter observation was a remarkable one, if account is taken of the very low, if any, biological activity exhibited by other β glycosides (see Chapter 6). On the other hand the 7(*R*),9(*R*) analogues were found to be inactive in the anti-tumor tests, clearly indicating the strict requirement of natural aglycone stereochemistry for the expression of biological activity. The results of the *in vitro* test were in agreement with those of the above mentioned *in vivo* systems.

The DNA binding ability of diastereoisomers **11b**, **12b**, **13b**, and **14b** par-alleled the biological activity (*13*). Although all compounds stabilized to a certain extent the helix of native calf thymus DNA, the effect of the 7(*S*),9(*S*) isomers on the melting temperature of the same DNA was distinctly greater than that of the 7(*R*),9(*R*) glycosides, and the α anomers afforded a greater stabilization than the β anomers (Fig. 1). DNA binding studies using the fluorescence quenching method indicated a similar affinity constant for 4-demethoxydaunorubicin ($2.4 \times 10^6 \ M^{-1}$) and for daunorubicin ($3.3 \times 10^6 \ M^{-1}$). However, anomalous binding isotherms were observed for the compounds with unnatural configuration that exhibited much lower DNA binding properties. Different effects were shown by the compounds on DNA-dependent *E. coli* DNA and RNA polymerase reactions in an *in vitro* assay system. 4-Demethoxydaunorubicin was markedly effective as an inhi-bitor, being as active as daunorubicin in the DNA polymerase system, but somewhat less active on the RNA polymerase catalyzed reaction. A dis-tinctly lower inhibition was shown, as expected, by compounds **12b**, **13b**, and **14b**, with the exception of the noticeable effect of the β glycoside **12b** on the RNA polymerizing system. This observation was related with the bio-logical activity displayed by this isomer and with its higher effectiveness in

Table I

Activity of Diastereoisomeric 4-Demethoxydaunorubicins on Average Survival Time (T/C) of Mice Bearing L 1210[a] or Gross[b] Leukemia or on Colony-Forming Ability of Cultured HeLa Cells[c]

Compound[d]	L 1210		Gross		Cytotoxicity[g] (EC$_{50}$, nM/ml)
	Dose[e] (mg/kg)	T/C[f]	Dose[e] (mg/kg)	T/C[f]	
Daunorubicin	4	150	6	185	21.2
4-Demethoxydaunorubicin (**11b**)	0.5	150	0.75	185	0.3
4-Demethoxy-1′-epidaunorubicin (**13b**)	8	150	6	143	13.2
7(R),9(R)-4-Demethoxydaunorubicin (**12b**)	8[h]	100	6[h]	100	>200
7(R),9(R)-4-Demethoxy-1′-epidaunorubicin (**14b**)	10[h]	100	13.5[h]	100	>200

[a] Treatment ip on day 1.
[b] Treatment iv on days 1,2,3.
[c] From Arcamone et al. (1) and Supino et al. (12).
[d] In this and following tables, all free aminoglycosides are tested as the hydrochlorides.
[e] Optimal nontoxic dose.
[f] Expressed as percent of controls.
[g] After 24 hr of exposure.
[h] Highest dose tested.

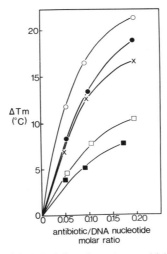

Fig. 1. Effect of daunorubicin (X), 4-demethoxydaunorubicin α (○) and β (●) anomers, and 4-demethoxy-7,9-diepidaunorubicin α (□) and β (■) anomers on the midpoint of thermal denaturation curve of calf thymus DNA. From Zunino *et al.* (*13*).

stabilizing the secondary structure of native DNA, the latter property being apparently the one which best correlated with antitumor activity *in vivo* of the demethoxy analogues.

Plumbridge and Brown (*14*) have recorded a 9-nm bathochromic shift in the λ_{max} of the absorption peak at longest wavelength and a 47% (daunorubicin 13 nm and 40%) decrease of the extinction at 480 nm when calf thymus DNA was added to a pH 7.0 solution of 4-demethoxydaunorubicin with the DNA-P to drug ratio of 10:1. As with the parent intercalating agent, no bathochromic shift was found upon changing the pH at 9.6 in the presence of DNA. Using a two-site binding model and a nonlinear regression analysis of spectrophotometric and fluorescence determinations, the compound was found to show binding parameters for the interaction with DNA comparable to those of daunorubicin. The effect on thermal transition of double-stranded DNA was also similar. In a more recently published study (*15*), the same authors demonstrated that, like the parent compound, 4-demethoxydaunorubicin did not afford appreciable stabilization of poly(I·C), a nucleic acid known to exist in the A conformation. In the same paper, the DNA binding properties of compounds **26** and **27** were reported. Although the 7(*R*) compound **27** did not intercalate into calf thymus DNA, the 7(*S*) analogue **26** displayed an affinity constant (as measured by spectrophotometric titration) of 6.1×10^5 (daunorubicin 13.3×10^5) and appreciably stabilized the DNA helix to thermal denaturation, confirming the importance of the absolute configuration at C-7 for the expression of DNA binding properties.

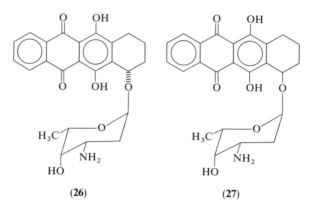

(26)　　　　　　　　　　　　　　　(27)

4-Demethoxydaunorubicin

Preliminary evaluation of **11b** had shown that, in addition to the remarkable activity on experimental murine L 1210 and Gross leukemias, the compound was equally or more effective than daunorubicin in sarcoma 180 ascites and sarcoma 180 solid tumors in mice, the optimal dose being 4 to 8 times lower than that of the parent drug. Similar results were obtained in another antitumor test system (Table II).

An interesting feature of 4-demethoxydaunorubicin is its activity by the oral route (*16*). Whereas daunorubicin showed a more than 10-fold lower potency when administered orally in comparison with the standard iv treatment in mouse Gross leukemia (doxorubicin displayed no activity or toxicity at oral doses of 200 mg/kg), **11b** exhibited an optimal oral dose between 1.7 and 2.55 mg/kg with up to 100% increase in average survival time as compared with the 0.75 mg/kg value found for the iv treatment in the same system. In solid sarcoma 180 tumor, three oral daily doses of 2 mg/kg afforded a more than 50% reduction of tumor growth together with a remarkable increase of average survival time of treated animals, being even more potent than doxorubicin given iv. As for the antitumor activity, oral acute toxicity in mice was detected at doses approximately 4 times higher than the parenteral ones, major necroptic findings being the strong reduction in spleen size and hemorrhagic appearence of small intestine and lungs.

Formelli *et al.* (*17*) have studied the cell uptake of 4-demethoxydaunorubicin in mouse embryo fibroblast cultures *in vitro* and in adult mice bearing solid sarcoma 180. The analogue is more lipophilic than the parent drug, as the partition coefficients of the two compounds between *n*-butanol and Tris

Table II

Comparison of 4-Demethoxydaunorubicin with Daunorubicin and Doxorubicin in Murine P 388 Lymphoctic Leukemia[a]

Experiment	Treatment schedule	4-Demethoxydaunorubicin		Daunorubicin		Doxorubicin	
		O.D.[b]	T/C[c]	O.D.[b]	T/C[c]	O.D.[b]	T/C[c]
3445	QD 1–9	0.2	171	—	—	1	192
3566	QD 1–9	0.4	205	—	—	1	223
3842	QD 1–9	0.2	183	1	174	1	23
4905	Q4D 5,9,13	2.4	174	16	154	8	166
5099	Q4D 5,9,13	2.4	152	8	133	16	169

[a] The drugs were administered ip. Experiments performed under the auspices of NCI, screener A.D. Little.
[b] Optimal nontoxic doses, mg/kg.
[c] Average survival time of treated animals expressed as percent of untreated controls.

buffer were, respectively, 27.7 and 15.3. The analytical evaluation of drug concentrations was carried out fluorometrically after extraction with *n*-butanol from cultured cells and plasma samples and with isoamyl alcohol according to Schwartz (*18*) from tissues.

The rate of uptake of 4-demethoxydaunorubicin was faster than that of daunorubicin and a fourfold intracellular concentration of the analogue with respect to the parent was found *in vitro*, in agreement with the higher cytotoxycity displayed by the analogue on HeLa cells.

4-Demethoxydaunorubicin appeared to be retained longer than daunorubicin in mice tissues and showed a higher concentration in kidney, lung, spleen, tumor and small intestine 6 hr after treatment. Equitoxic doses of daunorubicin given iv resulted in higher concentrations of fluorescence in all tissues examined in comparison with the analogue. TLC analysis of tissue extracts indicated the presence of metabolite patterns similar to that shown after daunorubicin treatment.

In chronically treated rabbits, 4-demethoxydaunorubicin exhibited a small incidence of cardiac lesion even at doses causing marked hematological disturbances and 40% mortality. A similar behavior was found in mice under different schedules of treatment, as the compound induced cardiac damage only at doses causing death in a high percentage of the animals. In contrast, cardiac lesions were present to a large extent in animals treated with doxorubicin at doses causing no other toxic manifestations in the animals (*19*). In Zbinden's rat cardiotoxicity model (*20*), the compound showed marked cardiotoxicity, the MCCD value being 1.75 mg/kg by the ip and 7.5 mg/kg by the oral route.

Oncogenicity in different experimental systems is a known property of antitumor anthracyclines. 4-Demethoxydaunorubicin did not induce mutations to 8-azaguanine resistance in Chinese hamster cells, although chromosomal alterations were observed, and exhibited only minimal activity in inducing malignant transformation of mouse fibroblasts (*21*). On the other hand, the same authors found that single iv doses (1.8 mg/kg) induced mammary tumors in female rats within 1 year from treatment and that the compound was a mutagen in the *S. typhimurium* bacterial mutagenesis test.

4-Demethoxydoxorubicin and Its 4'-Epi Analogue

The 4-demethoxy derivative (**28**) of doxorubicin was obtained from **11b** via the corresponding 14-bromo derivative (*22*). The related analogue **29c**, in which the aminosugar, daunosamine, was substituted with acosamine, was prepared by coupling **20** with 2,3,6-trideoxy-3-trifluoroacetamido-4-*O*-trifluoroacetyl-α-L-*arabino*-hexopyranosyl chloride in methylene chloride and in the presence of silver trifluoromethanesulfonate to give, after a chromatographic separation, 4-demethoxy-*N*-trifluoroacetyl-4′-epidaunorubicin (**29a**). Removal of the protecting group with a mild alkaline treatment afforded 4-demethoxy-4′-epidaunorubicin (**29b**), which was converted into the corresponding doxorubicin analog as above (*23*).

Both compounds **28** and **29c** were found endowed with a greater biological activity, on a weight basis, when compared with the parent drug, doxorubi-

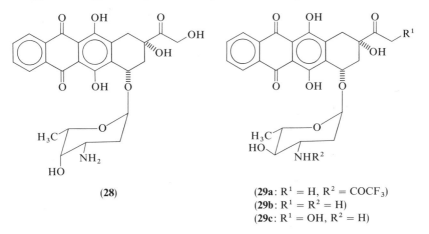

(**28**)

(**29a**: R¹ = H, R² = COCF₃)
(**29b**: R¹ = R² = H)
(**29c**: R¹ = OH, R² = H)

cin. The new analogues displayed IC_{50} lower than 1 nM on the colony-forming capacity of exponentially growing, cultured HeLa cells after 8 and 24 hr of exposure, corresponding to a 100 to 500 times higher potency compared with doxorubicin, and were at least 10 times more effective than the parent drug in inhibiting [³H]thymidine incorporation in cultures of mouse embryo fibroblasts stimulated with fresh calf serum. The latter result was in agreement with the higher uptake (almost four-fold) of **28** as compared with doxorubicin in the cultured fibroblasts (*12*). The two analogues exerted a remarkable antitumor effect on different experimental tumors in mice (Tables III and IV). Active doses were generally 5 to 10 times lower than those of doxorubicin, the antitumor activity being, however, very similar in L 1210 and P 388 leukemia, Gross leukemia, and B 16 melanoma. These results are of particular relevance when account is taken of the toxicity data reported for **28**. In a chronic test in mice, the compound induced considerable cardiac damage only at dose levels higher than one-fifth of the acute DL_{50} value, whereas the reference drugs daunorubicin and doxorubicin exhibited noticeable cardiotoxicity at correspondingly lower fractions of the DL_{50} dose. When a "therapeutic ratio" was deduced from the minimal cumulative dose in mice treated iv 2 times a week for 5 weeks and the optimal cumulative

Table III

Comparison of 4-Demethoxydoxorubicin, 4-Demethoxy-4'-epidoxorubicin, and Doxorubicin on Experimental Leukemia in Mice[a]

Leukemia	Experiment	Treatment	4-Demethoxy		4-Demethoxy-4'-epi		Doxorubicin	
			O.D.[b]	T/C	O.D.	T/C	O.D.	T/C
L1210	1	ip, day 1	0.75	189	0.75	189	5	161
	2	ip, day 1	0.5	166	0.5	166	5	166
P388	1	ip, day 1	0.5	162	0.5	162	10	200
	2	ip, day 1	0.5	200	0.75	195	10	254
Gross	1	iv, day 1, 2, 3	0.45	228	0.65	207	4.5	178
	2	iv, day 1, 2, 3	0.35	228	0.45	221	4.5	186

[a] From Di Marco et al. (24).
[b] Optimal non toxic ($\leq LD_{10}$) dose.

Table IV

Activity of 4-Demethoxydoxorubicin on Experimental Tumors in Mice[a]

Tumor	Experiment (number)	Treatment	4-Demethoxydaunorubicin		Doxorubicin	
			O.D.	T/C	O.D.	T/C
P 388 leukemia	3410[b]	ip, day 1	1.3	216	10	245
,,	3847[b]	ip, day 1	1.05	233	10	221
,,	3445[b]	ip, QD 1–9	0.2	221	1	192
,,	3602[b]	ip, QD 1–9	0.2	261	1	207
,,	4776[b]	ip, Q4D 5,9,13	1	183	8	168
,,	5101[b]	ip, Q4D 5,9,13	1	167	16	144
,,	0069[c]	ip, Q4D 1,5,9	0.6	166	4	174
L 1210 leukemia	P994[b]	ip, QD 1–9	0.25	175	4	176
,,	R072[b]	ip, QD 1–9	0.5	161	2	138
B 16 melanoma	0833[b]	ip, day 1	1.5	250	4	250
,,	0866[b]	ip, day 1	3	307	8	309
,,	0861[b]	ip, day 5	0.75	124	8	147
,,	0026[c]	ip, Q4D 1,5,9	0.6	283	4.8	285
,,	0027[c]	ip, Q4D 5,9,13	1	154	4.8	197
Colon 38	41710[d]	sc, days 3,10	2.2	184	8.0	220

[a] NCI data.
[b] Screener A.D. Little.
[c] Screener Assoc. Chief Lab. Res.
[d] Screener: Southern Research Institute.

antitumor dose in mice bearing Gross leukemia and treated iv at days 1, 2, and 3, compound **28** was found to be the best analogue within a series of highly active daunorubicin and doxorubicin derivatives. The said ratio was in fact 4.95 for 4-demethoxydoxorubicin, compared with 0.73 for doxorubicin. Other compounds ranked in the following order: 4-demethoxydaunorubicin, 3.11; 4'-O-methyldoxorubicin, 2.29; 4'-deoxydoxorubicin, >1.57; 2,3-dimethyl-4-demethoxydoxorubicin, 1.28; daunorubicin, 1.1; and 4'-epidoxorubicin, 0.93 (*19*). According to Zbinden, the compound was clearly cardiotoxic in the rat, the minimal ip cumulative cardiotoxic dose being 3 mg/kg (*20*), which is 3 to 4 times lower than that shown by doxorubicin (10–12 mg/kg).

OTHER SYNTHETIC APPROACHES TO
4-DEMETHOXY ANALOGUES

Important studies concerned with the development of efficient methods for the synthesis of 4-demethoxydaunomycinone have been reported in the last 3 years. As for the problem of the total synthesis of doxorubicin presented in Chapter 2, quite a few experienced investigators with well-known expertise in the chemistry of natural products have taken this opportunity for the exercise of their imaginative capabilities and for the application of up-to-date methodologies of modern organic chemistry. As a matter of fact, the synthesis of 4-demethoxy analogues has represented a simplified model for the preparation of the related biosynthetic compounds, owing to the absence of the regioselectivity problems connected with the latter, that show unsymmetrical substitution of ring A. On the other hand, the high intrinsic bioactivity of 4-demethoxydaunorubicin and of 4-demethoxydoxorubicin have recently made this objective an important one, independent of the concurrent problem of the synthesis of daunomycinone itself.

The different approaches outlined below, although each displaying original features in the choice of reactants and in the solution of important details related with functionalization and stereochemistry, can be grouped in two basic types. The former involves the preparation of a tetraline derivative representing final rings BA and its condensation, either by a Diels–Alder reaction or by acylation with a phthalic acid derivative, to the eight-carbon-atom fragment corresponding to rings DC in the tetracyclic product. The second is based on the preparation of a tricyclic DCB intermediate on which ring A is built either by ring closure of a suitable side chain (in one instance) or by performing a Diels–Alder condensation with a properly substituted diene.

Diels–Alder Condensations of 6-Acetyl-6-acetoxy- (or Hydroxy-) Tetrahydronaphthoquinone

Kende's isobenzofuran route to anthracyclinones has already been shown in Chapter 2 with regard to its application to the synthesis of 7-deoxydaunomycinone. In the original paper (25), the synthesis of 4-demethoxydaunomycinone (**20**) was also described. According to this approach, tetrahydronaphthaquinone derivative **30a**, obtained in three steps (ethynylation, mercuric acetate catalyzed hydration, and oxidative demethylation) from 1,4-dimethoxy-6-tetralone (**31**) (26), was heated at 140°C in diglyme with **32**, a compound prepared by condensation of α-pyrone with the benzyne–furan adduct and known to give rise to isobenzofuran by thermolysis. The resulting mixture of adducts (**33**) was aromatized, by heating with sodium acetate in acetic acid, to **34a**, whose reduction with zinc dust in acetic anhydride to **35** followed by oxidation of the latter with chromic anhydride in acetic acid gave quinone **36** in 40% yield from **30a**. Racemic 4-demethoxy-7-deoxydaunomycinone (**24**), obtained from **36** by acid hydrolysis, was converted to **20** by bromination at C-7 followed by reaction with silver trifluoroacetate, hydrolysis, equilibration of the C-7 epimeric mixture in trifluoroacetic acid, and subsequent methanolysis in 45% yield. Transformation

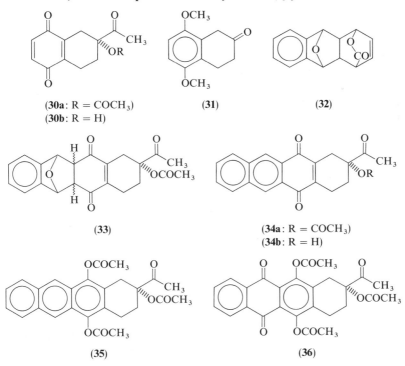

(**30a**: R = COCH$_3$)   (**31**)   (**32**)
(**30b**: R = H)

(**33**)   (**34a**: R = COCH$_3$)
                           (**34b**: R = H)

(**35**)   (**36**)

of **20** to 4-demethoxyadriamycinone was performed in 55% yield by C-14 bromination followed by alkaline treatment.

The same starting material, **31**, was used by Wiseman *et al.* (*27*) for the synthesis of **30b** by reaction of **31** with methoxyvinyl lithium to give **37**, the yield being 87% provided that the treatment were repeated 4 times on the crude reaction product, followed by acid hydrolysis to **2** and oxidation of the latter to **30b** with argentic oxide. Overall yield of **30b** from **31** was 85%.

The four-ring skeleton of the anthracyclinone was built by reaction of **30b** with *o*-quinone dimethane (**38**), generated from tetrabromoxylene (**39**), to form an adduct that spontaneously lost hydrogen bromide giving rise to **34b** in 33% yield after a chromatographic separation step. Reduction and concomitant acetylation of **34b** with zinc, acetic anhydride, and triethylamine gave 94% yield of **35**, whose oxidation to **36** with chromic acid at room temperature followed by acid hydrolysis afforded racemic **24** in 69% yield.

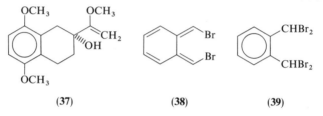

            (37)   (38)   (39)

Acylation of Substituted Tetralins

Tetralin (**42b**) was the key intermediate in the synthetic approach to 4-demethoxy analogues reported by Alexander and Mitscher (*28*). The compound was prepared starting from the Diels–Alder adduct of *p*-benzoquinone and butadiene (**40**), which was transformed into **41** and the latter into **42a** by hydroboration followed by peroxide oxidation. Conversion of **42a** to **42b** was carried out with isobutylene under borotrifluoride etherate catalysis. The overall yield of **42b** from **40** was nearly 90%.

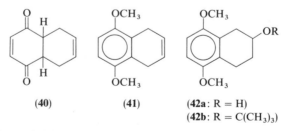

        (40)   (41)   (42a: R = H)
                                                   (42b: R = C(CH$_3$)$_3$)

Bromination of **42b** gave a regioisomeric mixture of bromoderivatives **43a** which were condensed with dimethyl phthalate in tetrahydrofuran and in the presence of *n*-butyllithium at $-80°$C. Resulting regioisomeric mixture

43b was cyclized to **44** in 96% yield with boron trichloride in dichloromethane at room temperature. Oxidation of alcohol **44** to the corresponding ketone had already been described in the literature (*29*).

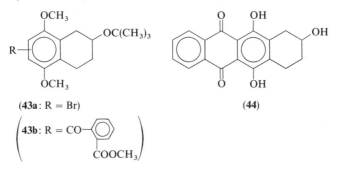

(**43a**: R = Br)

(**43b**: R = CO—⟨⟩—COOCH₃)

(**44**)

The work of Terashima *et al.* (*30*) is the only available study aimed at a stereoselective synthesis of 4-demethoxydaunomycinone not involving enantiomeric separation of racemic intermediates. Although the attempt to build the C-9 asymmetric center directly on a tetracyclic intermediate has been unsuccessful so far, the work provides a stereoselective synthesis of optically active tetralin **12**, a key intermediate in anthracycline synthesis (see Chapter 2).

Diels–Alder Reactions of Quinizarinequinone

The first synthesis of 4-demethoxydaunomycinone utilizing quinizarinequinone (**47**) as the DCB fragment in a condensation reaction with a substituted butadiene in order to form ring A, and therefore the tetracyclic system of the anthracyclinones, is that of Kende *et al.* (*31*). According to these investigators, 1,4-dimethoxyanthraquinone (**46a**), prepared by Friedel–Crafts acylation of *p*-dimethoxybenzene with phthalic anhydride and treatment of the resulting 2-(2′,5′-dimethoxybenzoyl)benzoic acid (**45**) with sulfuric acid, was oxidized to anthradiquinone **47** with argentic oxide and nitric acid. The same compound was obtained upon lead tetraacetate oxidation of 1,4-dihydroxyanthraquinone **46b** in 81% yield.

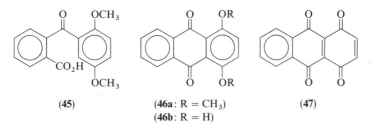

(**45**)

(**46a**: R = CH₃)
(**46b**: R = H)

(**47**)

Condensation of **47** with 2-acetoxybutadiene in acetic acid and at room temperature afforded **48** in 81% yield. Heating of the latter with anhydrous sodium acetate in glacial acetic acid allowed aromatization to **49** in 82%

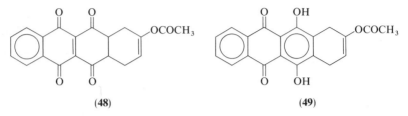

(48)   (49)

yield. Ketone **50**, obtained upon acid hydrolysis of enolacetate **49** in almost quantitative (96%) yield, was allowed to react with a large excess of ethinyl-magnesium bromide in tetrahydrofuran to give, after a chromatographic purification, compound **51** in 91% yield. Mercuric acetate catalyzed hydra-

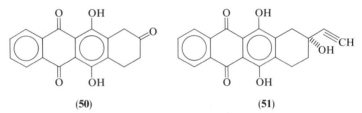

(50)   (51)

tion of **51** afforded 62% yield of 4-demethoxy-7-deoxydaunomycinone-9-acetate (**52**), which was quantitatively hydrolyzed to **24** with dilute sodium hydroxide. Conversion of **24** to racemic **20** was carried out by bromination in carbon tetrachloride under light irradiation followed by hydrolytic work-up to give mixture of **20** and **21**, the latter being epimerized to the former via formation of the 7-*O*-trifluoroacetate.

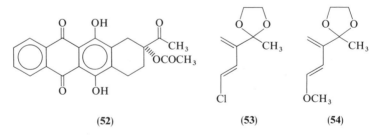

(52)   (53)   (54)

The synthetic approach to 4-demethoxydaunorubicin investigated by Kelly and Tsang (*32*) was based on the favorable course of the cycloaddition of chlorodiene **53** to **47**, affording 88% yield of desired adduct **55**. On the contrary, diene **54** gave internal adduct **56** as the major product. When **55** was submitted to a four-step reaction sequence (*p*-methylthiophenol, *m*-

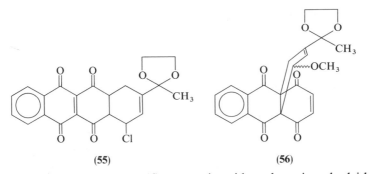

(55)   (56)

chlorobenzoic acid, aqueous trifluoroacetic acid, and acetic anhydride and pyridine), compound **60a** was obtained via intermediate formation of **57**, **58**, and **59** and in 40% overall yield from **47**. Were the hydrolytic step omitted, the yield of ketal **60b** was 51% from **47**. However, conversion of **60a** or **60b**

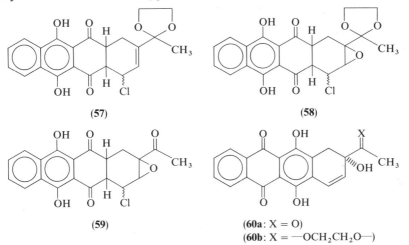

(57)   (58)

(59)   (60a: X = O)
                                          (60b: X = —OCH$_2$CH$_2$O—)

to 4-demethoxydaunomycinone, although different methods were explored, remained unsuccessful, complete aromatization of ring A being the principal outcome of most attempts. On the other hand, catalytic hydrogenation of **60a** afforded **24**, as expected, thus confirming the structure assigned to **60a**.

A remarkable synthetic approach to racemic 4-demethoxydaunomycinone (**20**) in which a trimethylsilyl group was used as the precursor of the C-7 hydroxyl group, thus avoiding the usual bromination–methanolysis (or hydrolysis) steps for introducing the said function, has been developed by Pappo and his co-workers at Searle Laboratories (*33*). Reaction of quinizarinquinone (**47**) with *trans*-4-(trimethylsilyl)-2-acetoxy-1,3-butadiene (**61**), prepared from *trans*-4-(trimethylsilyl)-3-buten-2-one and isopropenyl acetate, gave **62** in 77% yield, from which anthraquinone derivative **63** was

obtained upon mild alkaline treatment. Catalytic hydrogenation of **62** afforded **64**, which was converted to the dimethyl ketal **65** and then, by hydrolysis of the latter, to triketone **66**.

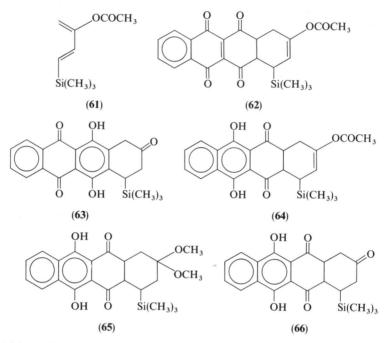

(61)   (62)

(63)   (64)

(65)   (66)

Although compound **63** did not undergo reaction with ethinyl magnesium
bromide, compound **66** reacted selectively with the same reagent to give **67a**
in 86% yield, together with a small amount (11%) of the corresponding 9-
epimer. Reentry into the anthraquinone series was provided by conversion of
the acetate **67b** to the naphthoquinone derivative **68**, followed by isomerization to **69**, the overall yield of **69** from **47** (eight steps) being approximately
48%. Oxidation of **69** with lead tetraacetate to the corresponding anthradiquinone was followed by a displacement of the silyl group (accelerated by the
addition of sodium fluoride) to afford, after reduction with sodium bisulfite,
70 in 79% yield. It was also found that acetylation of the C-6 phenolic group

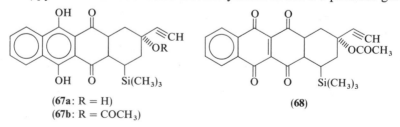

(67a: R = H)   (68)
(67b: R = COCH₃)

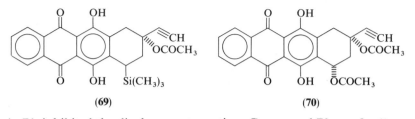

(69)   (70)

as in **71**, inhibited the displacement reaction. Compound **70** was finally converted to **72** in 92% yield by hydration catalyzed by mercuric chloride, and
72 was hydrolyzed to **20** in 85% yield, the latter being obtained in excellent
overall yield (30%) from **47**.

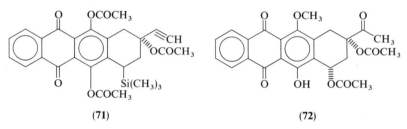

(71)   (72)

The *o*-Quinodimethane Approach

A new synthetic sequence leading to the 4-demethoxy aglycones, developed
by Kerdesky and Cava (*34*) consists in the reaction of dibromide **73** with zinc
dust in dimethylformamide at room temperature and in the presence of
excess methyl vinyl ketone to give, via a Diels–Alder addition of the α,β-
unsaturated ketone to the reactive *o*-quinonedimethane intermediate **74**,
4-demethoxy-7,9-dideoxy-6,11-dimethyldaunomycinone (**75a**). Compound

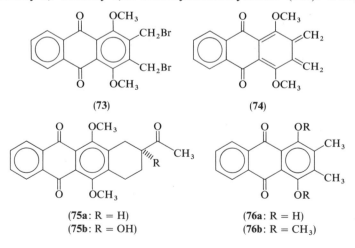

(73)   (74)

(75a: R = H)   (76a: R = H)
(75b: R = OH)   (76b: R = CH₃)

73 was prepared in 73% yield and in three steps, starting from the readily available 2,3-dimethylhydroquinone which was condensed with phthalic anhydride by a Friedel–Crafts reaction to give **76a**. Conversion of the latter to **76b** with dimethyl sulfate and potassium carbonate followed by bromination with *N*-bromosuccinimide afforded **73**. Hydroxylation of **75a** to **75b** was carried out by oxidation with potassium *tert*-butoxide and oxygen in dimethylformamide at −20°C, subsequent reduction with triethylphosphite, and mild acid hydrolysis in 55% yield.

Cycloaddition Reactions Starting from Naphthazarin

Naphthazarin (**77**) was the starting material used by Krohn and Tolkien (*35*) for the synthesis of 4-demethoxydaunomycinone (**20**). The German authors allowed **77** to react with 1,3-substituted butadiene (**78**) to give **79**, directly hydrolyzed by a mild acid treatment to **80a**, the yield being 90% from **77**. Prolonged acid treatment afforded **80b** (yield 85%), which was ethinylated using a 40-fold excess of ethinyl magnesium bromide and alkaline work-up, in 50–55% yield, to an epimeric mixture of cis and trans derivatives **81**. Diels–Alder condensation of the latter in the tautomeric form (**82**) with 1-acetoxybutadiene followed by air oxidation in alkaline conditions

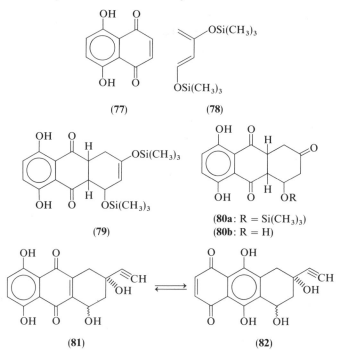

resulted in the quantitative formation of **83**. Kende's procedure for the hydration of the side-chain triple bond was modified as **83** was treated with mercuric sulfate and acetone containing sulfuric acid to give, after acid work up, racemic **20** as the main product in 84% yield, the epimer **21** being recovered in 4% yield.

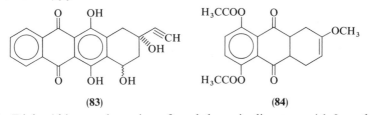

(83)   (84)

The Diels–Alder condensation of naphthazarin diacetate with 2-methoxy-1,3-butadiene was the first step of the synthetic approach reported by Fariña and Prados (36). The product of the reaction, **84**, was treated with acetic anhydride and sodium acetate to give **85** in 78% yield. Acid hydrolysis of **85**, followed by ketalization of the resulting ketone, gave **86**, which was subjected to air oxidation in alkaline conditions to afford **87** in 43% overall yield. A further Diels–Alder reaction on **88**, the less stable tautomeric form of **87**, with (E)-1-methoxy-1,3-butadiene, gave after aromatization, tetracyclic compound **89**, in 90% yield from **87**. The latter was converted by acid hydrolysis almost quantitatively to ketone **90**.

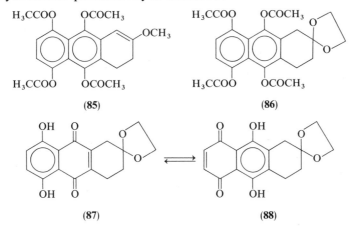

(85)   (86)

(87)   (88)

A further development of this synthetic scheme was represented by the condensation of naphthazarin diacetate with (E)-1-methoxy-3-trimethylsilyloxy-1,3-butadiene to give **91** in 73% yield. The latter was converted into dimethylene ketal **92** in 60% yield upon treatment with ethylene glycol and concentrated hydrogen chloride. Alkaline hydrolysis of **92** followed by acid treatment gave **93** which, as above, was allowed to react in the less stable

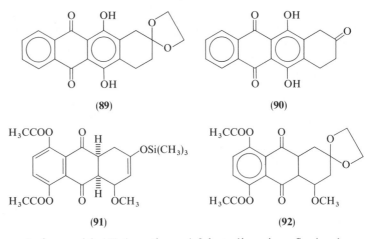

(89)   (90)

(91)   (92)

tautomeric form with (E)-1-methoxy-1,3-butadiene in refluxing benzene to give a mixture of two adducts leading to **94** by aromatization with a mild alkaline treatment.

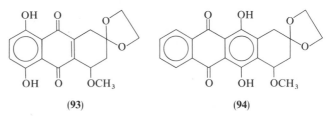

(93)   (94)

The use of naphthazarin (**47**) as starting material was also a feature of the already-mentioned (Chapter 2) study reported by Chandler and Stoodley (*37*) allowing the exploitation of the Diels–Alder route for the preparation of new anthracyclinones bearing different substitutions.

Intramolecular Cyclization of an Anthraquinone Derivative

The synthetic approach developed by Sih and co-workers (*38*) and based on an intramolecular base-catalyzed cyclization was already reported in Chapter 2 as regards its application to daunomycinone synthesis. In the version concerning the synthesis of the 4-demethoxy analogues, key intermediate **95** was obtained by condensation of phthalic anhydride with methylhydroquinone to give a 79% yield of 1,4-dihydroxy-2-methyl-anthraquinone **96a**, which was methylated to **96b**, the latter being then brominated to afford **97**. Alkylation of **97** with ethyl 3-acetyllevulinate gave **98** which was treated with alkalis, followed by esterification with diazomethane, demethylation with phosphorus tribromide at −78°C, and ketalization to give **95** in 23%

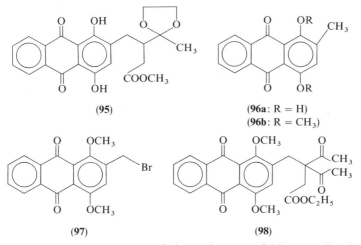

(95)

(96a: R = H)
(96b: R = CH₃)

(97)

(98)

overall yield from **96a**. Because of the resistance of **95** to cyclization in a variety of basic and acidic conditions and of the rather rigid experimental conditions required for intramolecular Claisen cyclization of **99**, **95** was converted into the aldehyde **100** in 35% yield by a five-reaction sequence, namely (a) benzylation of the phenolic hydroxyls, (b) saponification of the ester group, (c) diborane reduction, (d) debenzylation, and (e) oxidation of the resulting primary alcohol to give **100**. Cyclization of **100** to **102** in 50% yield was carried out by converting it into the leuco form with sodium dithionite in the presence of dilute sodium hydroxide, a process equivalent

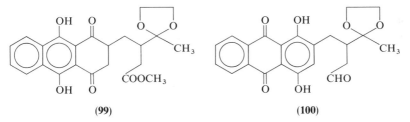

(99)

(100)

to the known Marchalk reaction giving rise to unstable compound **101** which upon dehydration afforded **102**, also deketalized with acid to the corresponding ketone, 4-demethoxy-7,9-dideoxydaunomycinone, in 92% yield.

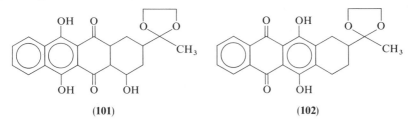

(101)

(102)

NEW RING-D-SUBSTITUTED 4-DEMETHOXYDAUNORUBICINS AND 4-DEMETHOXYDOXORUBICINS

By a procedure similar to that used for the synthesis of 4-demethoxydauno-rubicin, structural analogues **103a** and **103b**, **104a** and **104b**, and **105** were prepared starting from (R)-$(-)$-6-acetyl-1,4-dimethoxy-6-hydroxytetralin (**2**) upon condensation with the corresponding substituted phthalic acid anhydride, followed by introduction of the C-7 hydroxyl and glycosidation (**9**).

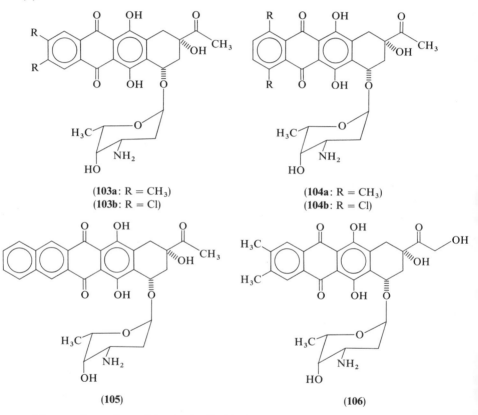

(**103a**: R = CH$_3$)
(**103b**: R = Cl)

(**104a**: R = CH$_3$)
(**104b**: R = Cl)

(**105**)

(**106**)

The condensation of the sterically hindered 3,6-dimethyl and 3,6-dichloro-phthalic acid anhydrides with **2** in the aluminum chloride–sodium chloride melt required higher temperature and longer time so that a small amount of racemic material was found. The latter could be eliminated by crystallization; or, alternatively, separation of 7(R),9(R)- from the 7(S),9(S)-N-trifluoro-acetyldaunosaminides could be performed without difficulty by silica gel chromatography after the glycosidation step. Doxorubicin analogue **106** was eventually obtained from **103a** via bromination at C-14 followed by nucleophilic substitution of the halogen with an hydroxyl group (22).

With all substituted 4-demethoxydaunorubicins described above, a reduction of cytotoxic activity in cultured HeLa cells as compared with **11b** was observed (9). As a matter of fact, the concentrations required for 50% inhibition were in the range of 0.5–3 times that of daunorubicin (Table V).

Table V

Inhibition of Colony-Forming Ability of Cultured Hela Cells after 24 hr Exposure to Daunorubicin, Doxorubicin, and the Analogues Modified in Ring D Substitution

Compound	EC_{50} (ng/ml)
Daunorubicin	10.00
4-Demethoxydaunorubicin	0.15
2,3-Dimethyl-4-demethoxydaunorubicin	5.80
2,3-Dichloro-4-demethoxydaunorubicin	25.00
1,4-Dimethyl-4-demethoxydaunorubicin	10.05
1,4-Dichloro-4-demethoxydaunorubicin	7.15
2,3-Benzo-4-demethoxydaunorubicin	27.00
Doxorubicin	15.00
4-Demethoxydoxorubicin	0.10
2,3-Dimethyl-4-demethoxydoxorubicin	7.00

Similarly, compound **106** was twice as potent as doxorubicin but 70 times less effective than **28** on a weight basis. The reasons for the different behavior are not known, partly because the DNA binding properties of this group of analogues has not yet been investigated, and data of cell uptake are not available. A similar lower potency with respect to the corresponding 4-demethoxy parent compounds was also observed in the animal tests in which, however, the 2,3-dimethyl derivatives displayed outstanding antitumor activity (Tables VI and VII). In fact, compound **103a** was twice as potent as daunorubicin on L 1210 and P 388 leukemias, the much higher effectiveness after oral treatment in Gross leukemia being in agreement with the behavior of 4-demethoxydaunorubicin in this test. Noticeable activity was also shown by the other derivatives, although at higher dosages than daunorubicin, with the exception of **103b** which appeared practically devoid of antitumor effects *in vivo* in the dose range tested. Outstanding antitumor properties were recorded for compound **106** which, although less active on a weight basis than the very potent **28**, was more effective than doxorubicin in the two test systems used. Interestingly, doxorubicin analogue **106** was found not cardiotoxic in chronically treated mice at doses lower than one-fifth of

Table VI

Comparison of Substituted 4-Demethoxydaunorubicins with 4-Demethoxydaunorubicin and Daunorubicin in Experimental Leukemias of the Mouse[a]

Compound	L 1210[b] O.D.[d]	L 1210[b] T/C[e]	P 388[b] O.D.[d]	P 388[b] T/C[e]	Gross leukemia[c] O.D.[d]	Gross leukemia[c] T/C[e]
Daunorubicin	4	150	4	205	50	150
4-Demethoxydaunorubicin	1	150	0.7	200	2.55	200
2,3-Dimethyl-4-demethoxydaunorubicin	2.5	168	2	230	8.6	223
2,3-Dichloro-4-demethoxydaunorubicin	33.7	111	—	—	65.1[f]	100
1,4-Dimethyl-4-demethoxydaunorubicin	6.6	147	10	165	—	—
1,4-Dichloro-4-demethoxydaunorubicin	4.4	125	22.5[f]	140	—	—
2,3-Benzo-4-demethoxydaunorubicin	20	140	—	—	—	—

Optimal doses and activity

[a] From Di Marco et al. (40).
[b] Treatment ip on day 1.
[c] Oral treatment on days 1–3.
[d] Optimal nontoxic dose ($\leq LD_{10}$), mg/kg body weight.
[e] Mean survival time expressed as percent of controls.
[f] Highest dose tested.

Table VII

Comparison of 2,3-Dimethyl-4-demethoxydoxorubicin with 4-Demethoxydoxorubicin and Doxorubicin in Experimental Leukemias of the Mouse[a]

Compound	L 1210[b] O.D.[d]	L 1210[b] T/C[e]	Gross leukemia[c] O.D.[d]	Gross leukemia[c] T/C[e]
Doxorubicin	6.6	159	6.5	208
4-Demethoxydoxorubicin	0.5	166	—	—
2,3-Dimethyl-4-demethoxydoxorubicin	4.4	173	2.6	216

Optimal doses and activity

[a] From Di Marco et al. (40).
[b] Treatment ip on day 1.
[c] Treatment iv on days 1–3.
[d] Optimal nontoxic dose ($\leq LD_{10}$), mg/kg body weight
[e] Mean survival time expressed as percent of controls.

the DL_{50}. Ventricular lesions were, however, observed in 100% of animals at doses equal to one-third of the DL_{50}, the type of lesions being qualitatively different from dose given by doxorubicin (*19*). According to Zbinden (*39*), the compound shows MCCD value of 20 mg/kg (treatment ip with 6×4 mg/kg).

REPLACEMENT OF 4-*O*-METHYL WITH OTHER ALKYL GROUPS

The importance of the C-4 methoxyl substitution in the antitumor anthra-cyclines is certainly an argument worth of consideration in the attempt to fully understand the molecular requirements for biological action and selec-tivity. On the one hand, its exclusive presence in the compounds belonging to the daunorubicin–doxorubicin group that includes the two clinically used antitumor agents would indicate the 4-*O*-methyl substitution as a structural feature of natural derivation endowed with special contribution to the expression of bioactivity. On the other hand, the remarkable antitumor activity of the 4-demethoxyderivatives seems to deny the importance of the 4-methoxyl group as a determinant of biological selectivity of action. However, the replacement of the 4-*O*-methyl group with other alkyl groups was also considered of interest in order to extend our knowledge about the compatibilities of ring D substitutions with antitumor activity, and work in this direction was performed in the author's laboratory.

The key intermediate of the synthetic sequence to this series of analogues was 4-demethoxy-4-hydroxy-6,7,11-triethoxycarbonyldaunomycinone (**107b**), obtained in 42% overall yield upon treatment of daunomycinone with ethoxycarbonyl chloride in pyridine to give **107a**, which was *O*-demeth-ylated with aluminium tribromide in methylene chloride under a nitrogen atmosphere at room temperature (*41*). Alkylation of **107b** with the proper alkyl halide in the presence of silver oxide afforded compounds **107c, 107d–i** and **107l** in variable (43–86%) yields (*42*). Treatment of compounds **107c–107l** with morpholine in anhydrous methanol at room temperature resulted in the methanolysis of the phenolic protecting groups to give compounds **108a–108h**, which were hydrolyzed with dilute alkali in water–acetone at room temperature allowing the isolation of aglycones **109a–109h** after a chromatographic purification step. The yield of the two-step deblocking was in the range 32–57%, a direct alkaline hydrolysis of **107c–107i** resulting in a lower yield because of the concomitant formation of bisanhydro compounds. Condensation of the aglycones **109a–109h** with *N*,*O*-ditrifluoroacetyl-α-daunosaminyl chloride in the presence of silver triflate followed by metha-nolysis of the *O*-trifluoroacetyl group gave the *N*-trifluoroacetyl derivatives

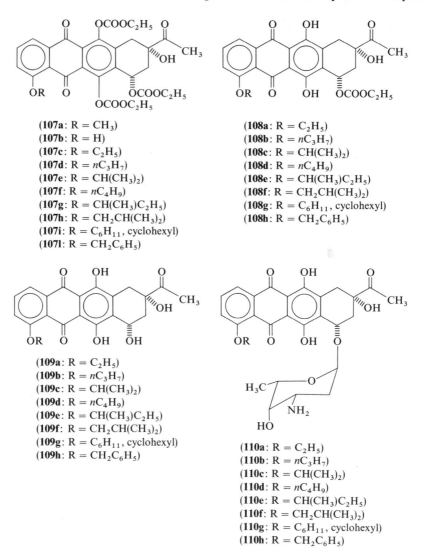

(107a: R = CH₃)
(107b: R = H)
(107c: R = C₂H₅)
(107d: R = nC₃H₇)
(107e: R = CH(CH₃)₂)
(107f: R = nC₄H₉)
(107g: R = CH(CH₃)C₂H₅)
(107h: R = CH₂CH(CH₃)₂)
(107i: R = C₆H₁₁, cyclohexyl)
(107l: R = CH₂C₆H₅)

(108a: R = C₂H₅)
(108b: R = nC₃H₇)
(108c: R = CH(CH₃)₂)
(108d: R = nC₄H₉)
(108e: R = CH(CH₃)C₂H₅)
(108f: R = CH₂CH(CH₃)₂)
(108g: R = C₆H₁₁, cyclohexyl)
(108h: R = CH₂C₆H₅)

(109a: R = C₂H₅)
(109b: R = nC₃H₇)
(109c: R = CH(CH₃)₂)
(109d: R = nC₄H₉)
(109e: R = CH(CH₃)C₂H₅)
(109f: R = CH₂CH(CH₃)₂)
(109g: R = C₆H₁₁, cyclohexyl)
(109h: R = CH₂C₆H₅)

(110a: R = C₂H₅)
(110b: R = nC₃H₇)
(110c: R = CH(CH₃)₂)
(110d: R = nC₄H₉)
(110e: R = CH(CH₃)C₂H₅)
(110f: R = CH₂CH(CH₃)₂)
(110g: R = C₆H₁₁, cyclohexyl)
(110h: R = CH₂C₆H₅)

of glycosides **110a–110h**, the latter being obtained upon hydrolysis with dilute alkali. The overall yield of the glycosidation and deblocking steps was in the range 11–31%.

Antitumor activity of this series of 4-*O*-alkyl analogues in a mouse experimental system is presented in Table VIII. All compounds gave a positive response in the test, but the activity appeared at higher doses in comparison with daunorubicin. One exception is represented by the propoxy analogue, which is more active than the parent drug at 50% higher dosage.

Table VIII

Comparison of 4-Demethoxy-4-alkoxydaunorubicins with Daunorubicin on P 388 Lymphocytic Leukemia in Mice[a]

Experiment[b]	4-Alkoxy group	O.D.[c]	T/C[d]	Daunorubicin O.D.[c]	T/C[d]
5500	4-Ethoxy (**110a**)	25	136	8	133
6522	4-Propoxy (**110b**)	25	149	4	128
5422	4-Isopropoxy (**110c**)	12.5	162	8	133
6795	4-*n*-Butoxy (**110d**)	25	141	4	113
6795	4-*n*-Isobutoxy (**110f**)	12.5	128	4	113
5621	4-Cyclohexyloxy (**110g**)	50	122	8	144
5620	4-Benzyloxy (**110h**)	50	155	8	131

[a] Treatment ip on days 5,9,13.
[b] NCI data, screener A.D. Little.
[c] Optimal nontoxic dose (mg/kg).
[d] Average survival time of treated animals expressed as percent of controls.

THE 6-*O*-METHYL AND 11-*O*-METHYL DERIVATIVES

Methylation of both phenolic groups at C-6 and C-11 in daunorubicin resulted in a marked reduction of activity as regards to inhibition of mucleic acid synthesis in cultured L 1210 cells (*43*). 6,11-Di-*O*-methyldaunorubicin (**111**) had been obtained by reaction of *N*-trifluoroacetyldaunorubicin with methyl sulfate followed by treatment with dilute sodium hydroxide, and was found not to affect the T_m of DNA. Independently, Zunino *et al.* (*44*) also reported about the lack of the DNA binding properties of the same derivative. An important feature of compound **111** is the absence of the chelated quinone carbonyls typical of daunorubicin structure, which is accompanied by a modification in the electronic properties of the anthraquinone chromophore, clearly discernible by the remarkable changes in the ultraviolet and visible spectra. For this reason it appeared of interest to synthesize *O*-methylated derivatives still possessing the hydrogen-bonded quinone function as in **112a** and **113a**. Another point of interest in the biological evaluation of such compounds is related to the suggested mechanism according to which cellular damage induced by the antitumor anthracyclines is the result of the intermediate formation of semiquinone radicals (see Chapter 3). As a matter of fact, both the ring C quinone and ring B hydroquinone could be involved in this mechanism. For instance, no mutagenic properties have been claimed for aclacinomycin, a biosynthetic anthracycline showing only one chelated quinone carbonyl group (see Chapter 8).

Moreover, the possibility that a methoxyl group at C-6 would modify the property of the anthracycline to act as a substrate of the reductive glycosidase, which is responsible for the *in vivo* inactivation of the compounds,

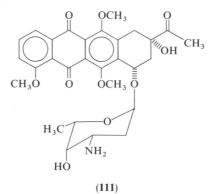

(111)

was also taken into consideration (*45*).

Starting material for the synthesis of **112a** and **113a** was triethoxycarbonyl-daunomycinone **107a**, as it was found that treatment of the latter with

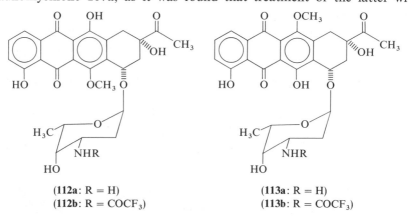

(**112a**: R = H)   (**113a**: R = H)
(**112b**: R = COCF₃)   (**113b**: R = COCF₃)

aluminum chloride in chloroform resulted in a 50% yield of diphenolic compound **114a**, not showing the nonchelated quinone carbonyl band at 1680 cm⁻¹ exhibited, for example by **107a**, and expected for the alternative structure corresponding to a 7,11-diethoxycarbonyl derivative. Compound **114a** was benzylated to **114b** (yield 90%), and the latter transformed to **115a** in 73% yield upon treatment with an anionic ion exchange resin as the free base in methanol, compound **115a** showing quinone carbonyl bands at 1680, 1629, and 1587 cm⁻¹.

Alkylation of **115a** with methyl iodide in the presence of silver oxide gave almost quantitatively **115b**, whose treatment with trifluoracetic acid at room

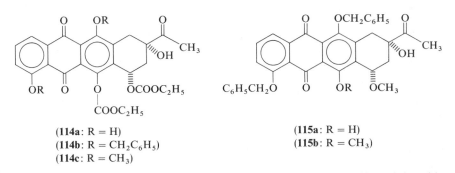

(114a: R = H)
(114b: R = CH₂C₆H₅)
(114c: R = CH₃)

(115a: R = H)
(115b: R = CH₃)

temperature gave **116a**. The 7-methoxyl group was not affected by this treatment, a notable difference from the behaviour shown in the 6-hydroxy series. However, when the solution of **116a** in trifluoroacetic acid was refluxed for 2 hr and followed by aqueous work-up including a chromatographic purification step, 4-demethoxy-4-hydroxy-6-O-methyldaunomycinone (**116b**) was obtained. The overall yield of the latter from **115b** was approximately 60%, and that from **107a**, 19%. Condensation of **116b** with N,O-ditrifluoroacetyl-α-daunosaminyl chloride in the presence of silver triflate, followed by chromatography, gave **112b** in 46% yield. Daunorubicin isomer **112a** (6-O-methylcarminomycin) was obtained in 47% yield upon alkaline deblocking of the latter.

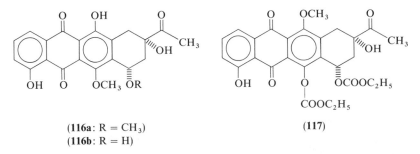

(116a: R = CH₃)
(116b: R = H)

(117)

For the preparation of the 11-O-methyl analogue, intermediate **114a** was heated at the reflux temperature with methyl iodide and silver oxide in dichloromethane for 2 hr. The reaction afforded two methylated compounds, monomethyl ether **117** and dimethyl ether **114c**, the former being the major product obtained in 18% yield after a chromatographic separation. The position of the O-methyl group in **117** was established on the basis of the infrared spectrum of the product of alkaline hydrolysis. In fact compound **118a**, formed in 66% yield upon treatment of a methanolic solution of **117** with an anionic exchange resin in the free base form, displayed one nonhydrogen-bonded quinone band at 1670 cm⁻¹ that should not have been present were the compound methylated at C-4. Treatment of **118a** with trifluoroacetic acid at room temperature afforded 56% of daunomycinone isomer **118b**. In this step, as well as in the other mentioned above for the analogous O-demethylation of **116a**, a small amount of the 7-epimer was also isolated, the latter being present largely in the intramolecular hemiketal form **119**. Glycosidation of **118b** as above gave **113b** in 35% yield after a chromatographic purification, and 11-*O*-methylcarminomycin (**113a**) was finally obtained in almost 50% yield upon mild alkaline treatment of **113b**.

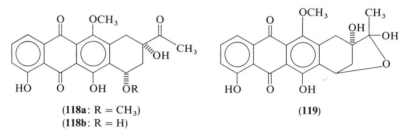

(**118a**: R = CH₃)
(**118b**: R = H)

(**119**)

The 11-*O*-methyl ether of daunorubicin was also prepared starting from intermediate **114a**, which was treated with an excess of methyl iodide and silver oxide to give the diether **120**. Alkaline deblocking of the esterified hydroxyl groups and concomitant nucleophilic displacement at C-7 similarly afforded 7,11-di-*O*-methyldaunomycinone (**121a**), readily converted into 11-*O*-methyldaunomycinone (**121b**) by trifluoroacetic acid treatment. Glycosidation to 11-*O*-methyldaunorubicin (**122a**) was performed in the usual manner (*45*).

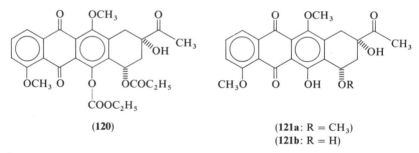

(**120**)

(**121a**: R = CH₃)
(**121b**: R = H)

Compounds **112a**, **113a**, and **122a** were tested on murine P 388 lympho-cytic leukemia in comparison with daunorubicin. The results (Table IX) indicated that methylation of one of the phenolic groups in ring B did not abolish the antitumor properties of the compounds, although the same appeared to be less effective than the parent compound in this experimental system. As regards **112a** and **113a**, the unfavorable effect of ring B mono-methylation appears even more clearly when the high potency shown by carminomycin (**122b**) is considered.

Table IX

Comparison of 6- and 11-O-Methylcarminomycin, and of Carminomycin, with Daunorubicin on P 388 Leukemia in Mice[a]

Experiment[b]	Compound	O.D.[c]	T/C[d]	Daunorubicin O.D.[c]	T/C[d]
5893	Carminomycin, 6-O-methyl (**112a**)	12.5	129	16	148
6210	Carminomycin, 11-O-methyl (**113a**)	50[e]	125	4	134
4751	Carminomycin (**122b**)[f]	3.13	179	8	126
4931	Carminomycin (**122b**)[f]	0.78	140	16	136
5129	Carminomycin (**122b**)[f]	3.13	149	16	139

[a] Treatment ip on days 5,9,13.
[b] NCI data, screener A.D. Little.
[c] Optimal nontoxic dose (mg/kg).
[d] Average survival time of treated animals expressed as percent of controls.
[e] Highest dose tested.
[f] Semisynthetic carminomycin (*46*).

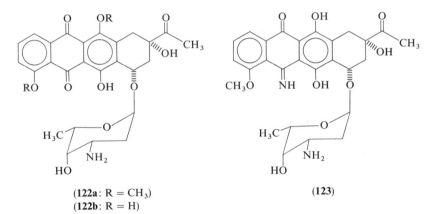

(**122a**: R = CH₃)
(**122b**: R = H)

(**123**)

5-IMINODAUNORUBICIN

When daunorubicin hydrochloride was treated with methanolic ammonia at 0–5°C, formation of a blue-violet product was obtained. The product, isolated in 57% yield after a chromatographic purification on a silica gel column, possessed structure **123**. This assignment was based on NMR spectroscopical observations. Three chelated protons were shown by the PMR spectrum, and their presence could be explained only by assuming the presence of a weak hydrogen bond between the aminohydrogen and the methoxyl oxygen. Substitution of one of the quinone oxygens in daunorubicin with an imino group was also supported by the ^{13}C-NMR spectrum (*47*).

5-Iminodaunorubicin appeared to retain the antitumor activity of the parent compound in murine P 388 leukemia in two different schedules of treatment. Interestingly, the compound was found to be 4.5 times less cardiotoxic than daunorubicin in the rat. Moreover, it displayed no mutagenic activity in a bacterial system, but was as mutagenic as doxorubicin in V 79 Chinese hamster cells. Compound **123** also showed a lower effect when compared with daunorubicin on the stabilization of DNA double helix against thermal denaturation, the potency of the two compounds as inhibitors of nucleic acid synthesis in L 1210 leukemia cells being, however, almost similar. In a recent paper, Lown *et al.* (*48*) reported that iminodaunorubicin was less effective than the parent drug in producing strand scission in a closed circular DNA preparation after reductive activation with sodium borohydride, a process which is thought to proceed by a mechanism involving the intermediate formation of a semiquinone and consequently of superoxide anion (see Chapter 3). This result was related by the authors to the stability of the reduced form of **123** to reoxidation, as shown by electrochemical and chemical methods, apparently a consequence of the stabilization induced by the additional hydrogen bonding due to the imino hydrogen.

RECENT DEVELOPMENTS

The synthesis of daunomycinone-related compounds modified in ring D substitution has been recently reported by Krohn and Tolkien (*49*). The reaction sequence is similar to that already applied by the same authors for the preparation of 4-demethoxydaunomycinone, and is the result of a detailed investigation on the synthetic approach based on the building of the tetracylic ring system by performing successive cycloadditions on naphthazarin (*77*). In a first part of their study, these authors had realized that intermediates of the type **124a** and **124b** did not withstand reaction with ethinylmagnesium bromide, sodium cyanide, or trimethylsilyl cyanide because of the tendency to undergo full aromatization. Such intermediates had been obtained upon reaction of naphthazarin with 1-methoxy-3-trimethylsilyloxy-1,3-butadiene giving rise, after an acid treatment of the adduct, to **125**; or with **78**, in which case the product was **80b**. Compounds **125** and **80b** were converted to **124a** and **124b** via monoketalization, followed by oxidation to **126a** and **126b**, Diels–Alder reaction with 1-acetoxy-1,3-butadiene, alkaline treatment of the unstable adduct and deketalization. Reaction of **126a** with

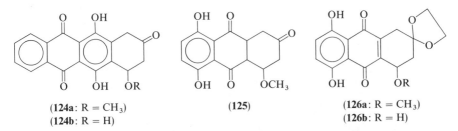

(124a: R = CH₃)
(124b: R = H)

(125)

(126a: R = CH₃)
(126b: R = H)

1-methoxy-3-trimethylsilyoxy-1,3-butadiene followed by alkaline treatment afforded the 1:1 mixture of regioisomers **127a** and **127b**, also characterized as the corresponding methyl ethers **127c** and **127d**.

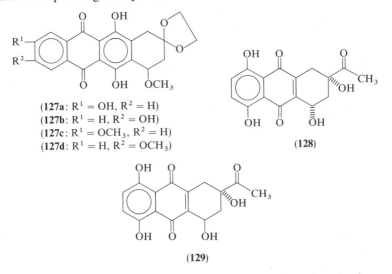

(127a: R¹ = OH, R² = H)
(127b: R¹ = H, R² = OH)
(127c: R¹ = OCH₃, R² = H)
(127d: R¹ = H, R² = OCH₃)

(128)

(129)

The above-mentioned difficulty was circumvented as already shown on page 282 by performing the Grignard reaction on **80b**. In this study, however, the mixture of cis and trans compounds (**81**) was directly subjected to mercuric salt catalyzed hydration to give, after a chromatographic separation, the two epimers **128** and **129** in 50% yield, **128** being the main reaction product. 4-Demethoxydaunomycinone could be obtained upon reaction of **128** with 1-methoxy-1,3-butadiene in almost quantitative yield, 7-epi-4-demethoxydaunomycinone being similarly prepared from **129**. On the other hand, reaction of **128** with 1-methoxy-1,3-cyclohexadiene followed by alkaline air oxidation of the resulting adduct **130** to **131** and pyrolysis of the latter afforded, after a thin-layer chromatographic separation, daunomycinone and its regioisomer "isodaunomycinone" (**132**) in respectively 17 and 32% yield. Similarly, **129** afforded the 7-epi-analogues of daunomycinone and of **132** in 23 and 28% yield respectively. The interesting new daunomycinone

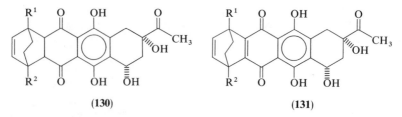

(130)   (131)

regioisomers **133a** and **133b** were eventually prepared in comparable yield from **128** using 1,3-bistrimethylsilyloxy-1,3-butadiene as the diene reagent and methylating with diazomethane, the phenols arising on alkaline treatment of the adducts mixture. Compounds **133a** and **133b** were identified on the basis of the comparison of chemical shifts of the corresponding phenol protons with those of synthetic model compounds.

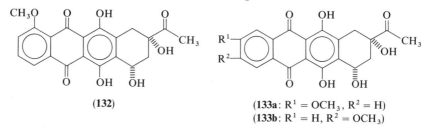

(132)   (133a: $R^1 = OCH_3$, $R^2 = H$)
                                (133b: $R^1 = H$, $R^2 = OCH_3$)

REFERENCES

1. F. Arcamone, L. Bernardi, P. Giardino, B. Patelli, A. Di Marco, A. M. Casazza, G. Pratesi, and P. Reggiani, *Cancer Treat. Rep.* **60**, 829 (1976).
2. C. M. Wong, D. Popien, R. Schwenk, and T. Raa, *Can. J. Chem.* **49**, 2712 (1971).
3. G. Schroeter, *Chem. Ber.* **54**, 2242 (1921).
4. C. Dufraisse and R. Horclos, *Bull. Soc. Chim. Fr.* **3**, 1880 (1936).
5. J. P. Marsh, R. H. Iwamoto, and L. Goodman, *Chem. Commun.* p. 589 (1968).
6. B. Patelli, L. Bernardi, F. Arcamone, and A. Di Marco, Ger. Patent 2,525,633 (Jan. 2, 1976).
7. F. Arcamone, L. Bernardi, B. Patelli, and A. Di Marco, Ger. Patent 2,601,785 (July 29, 1976).
8. T. R. Kelly, *Annu. Rep. Med. Chem.* **14**, 288 (1979).
9. F. Arcamone, L. Bernardi, B. Patelli, P. Giardino, A. Di Marco, A. M. Casazza, C. Soranzo, and G. Pratesi, *Experientia* **34**, 1255 (1978).
10. F. Arcamone, L. Bernardi, B. Patelli, and S. Penco, Belg. Patent 842,930 (Oct. 1, 1976); *C.A.* **87**, 85201 (1977).
11. L. Bernardi, P. Giardino, B. Patelli, and F. Arcamone, Ger. Patent 2,727,341 (Dec. 22, 1977); *C.A.* **88**, 120871 (1978).
12. R. Supino, A. Necco, T. Dasdia, A. M. Casazza, and A. Di Marco, *Cancer Res.* **37**, 4523 (1977).
13. F. Zunino, R. Gambetta, A. Di Marco, G. Luoni, and A. Zaccara, *Biochem. Biophys. Res Commun.* **69**, 744 (1976).

14. T. W. Plumbridge and J. R. Brown, *Biochem. Pharmacol.* **27**, 1881 (1978).
15. T. W. Plumbridge and J. R. Brown, *Biochim. Biophys. Acta* **563**, 181 (1979).
16. A. Di Marco, A. M. Casazza, and G. Pratesi, *Cancer Treat. Rep.* **61**, 893 (1977).
17. F. Formelli, A. Di Marco, A. M. Casazza, G. Pratesi, R. Supino, and A. Mariani, *Curr. Chemother., Proc. Int. Congr. Chemother. 10th* p. 1240 (1978).
18. H. S. Schwartz, *Biochem. Med.* **7**, 369 (1973).
19. A. M. Casazza, A. Di Marco, G. Bonadonna, V. Bonfante, C. Bertazzoli, O. Bellini, G. Pratesi, L. Sala, and L. Ballerini, in "Anthracycline Workshop," Norfolk (Virginia), June 14-15, 1979. by Academic Press, New York, in press (1980).
20. G. Zbinden, Fed. Inst. of Technol., Zurich, personal communication (Mar. 8, 1978).
21. H. Marquardt, F. S. Philips, H. Marquardt, and S. S. Sternberg, *Proc. Annu. Meet. Clin. Oncol. 15th, New Orleans, La.* **20**, 45 (1979).
22. F. Arcamone, L. Bernardi, P. Giardino, and A. Di Marco, Ger. Patent 2,652,391 (May 26, 1977); *C.A.* **87**, 152522 (1977).
23. F. Arcamone, A. Bargiotti, A. Di Marco, and S. Penco, Ger. Patent 2,618,822 (Nov. 11, 1976); *C.A.* **86**, 140416 (1977).
24. A. Di Marco, A. M. Casazza, F. Giuliani, G. Pratesi, F. Arcamone, L. Bernardi, G. Franchi, P. Giardino, B. Patelli, and S. Penco, *Cancer Treat. Rep.* **62**, 375 (1978).
25. A. S. Kende, D. P. Curran Y. Tsay, and J. E. Mills, *Tetrahedron Lett.* No. 40, 3537 (1977).
26. T. R. Lewis, W. B. Dickinson, and S. J. Archer, *J. Am. Chem. Soc.* **74**, 5321 (1952).
27. J. R. Wiseman, N. Iroff French, R. K. Hallmark, and K. G. Chiong, *Tetrahedron Lett.* No. 40, 3765 (1978).
28. J. Alexander and D. A. Mitscher, *Tetrahedron Lett.* No. 37, 3403 (1978).
29. W. W. Lee, A. P. Martinez, T. H. Smith, and D. W. Henry, *J. Org. Chem.* **41**, 2296 (1976).
30. S. Terashima, S. Jew, and K. Koga, *Tetrahedron Lett.* No. 49, 4937 (1978).
31. A. S. Kende, J. E. Mills, and Y. Tsay, U.S. Patent 4,021,427 (May 3, 1977).
32. T. R. Kelly and W. Tsang, *Tetrahedron Lett.* No. 46, 4457 (1978).
33. R. B. Garland, J. R. Palmer, J. A. Schulz, P. B. Sollman, and R. Pappo, *Tetrahedron Lett.* No. 39, 3669 (1978).
34. F. A. J. Kerdesky and M. P. Cava, *J. Am. Chem. Soc.* **100**, 3635 (1978).
35. K. Krohn and K. Tolkien, *Tetrahedron Lett.* No. 42, 4023 (1978).
36. G. Fariña and P. Prados, *Tetrahedron Lett.* No. 5, 477 (1979).
37. M. Chandler and R. J. Stoodley, *J.C.S. Chem. Commun.* p. 997 (1978).
38. F. Suzuki, S. Trenbeath, R. D. Gleim, and C. J. Sih, *J. Org. Chem.* **43**, 4159 (1978).
39. G. Zbinden, personal communication (June 1, 1978).
40. A. Di Marco, A. M. Casazza, C. Soranzo, and G. Pratesi, *Cancer Chemother. Pharmacol.* **1**, 249 (1978).
41. L. Bernardi, P. Masi, O. Sapini, A. Suarato, and F. Arcamone, *Farmaco, Ed. Sci.* **34**, 884 (1979).
42. L. Bernardi, P. Masi, A. Suarato, and F. Arcamone, Ger. Patent 2,750,812 (May 18, 1978).
43. D. W. Henry, G. Tong, A. N. Fujiwara, and W. W. Lee, *Am. Chem. Soc., Natl. Meet., 172nd* Medi 90 (1976).
44. F. Zunino, A. Di Marco, and A. Zaccara, *Chem. Biol. Interact.* **24**, 217 (1979).
45. P. Masi, A. Suarato, P. Giardino, G. Iraci, L. Bernardi, and F. Arcamone, *Farmaco, Ed. Sci.* **35**, 347 (1980).
46. G. Cassinelli, A. Grein, P. Masi, A. Suarato, L. Bernardi, F. Arcamone, A. Di Marco, A. M. Casazza, G. Pratesi, and C. Soranzo, *J. Antibiot.* **31**, 178 (1978).
47. L. Tong, D. W. Henry, and E. M. Acton, *J. Med. Chem.* **22**, 36 (1979).
48. J. W. Lown, H.-H. Chen, and J. A. Plambeck, *Biochem. Pharmacol.* **27**, 1 (1979).
49. K. Krohn and K. Tolkien, *Chem. Ber.* **112**, 3453 (1979).

8

New Developments in Biosynthetic Anthracyclines

In the first chapter of this book, the classical studies on the chemistry of anthracyclines were reviewed up to 1963. These studies were concerned with the rhodomycins, pyrromycins, aklavins, and cinerubins. This field has been further investigated, also, because of the interest aroused by the successful therapeutical applications of doxorubicin, and new related compounds have been isolated and identified in cultures of different *Streptomyces* species. Among the new anthracyclines, aclacinomycin A has recently received considerable attention because of its antitumor properties. In fact, the compound is presently under clinical evaluation as a chemotherapeutic agent of potential usefulness in the treatment of human cancer. New daunorubicin-related compounds have been described such as carminomycin, the baumycins, and a group of 11-deoxy analogues, including 11-deoxydoxorubicin, and the interest for the further pharmacological evaluation of these new derivatives is easily understandable. Other anthracyclines, namely steffimycin and nogalamycin, and especially the latter and some of its derivatives, appear to be important additions to the anthracycline family of antibiotics. At the end of this chapter, a short description of present knowledge on biosynthesis and microbial transformation of the anthracyclines will be provided, mainly with the aim of allowing the reader to set these compounds in the ever-expanding frame of natural products and of microbial metabolism in general.

THE RHODOMYCINS AND RELATED COMPOUNDS

New Anthracyclinone Derivatives from *S. purpurascens*

As was shown in Chapter 1, the glycosides produced by *Streptomyces purpurascens* were the first anthracycline compounds to be isolated and studied. In his review published in 1963 (*1*) Brockmann described seven glycosides belonging to the rhodomycin–isorhodomycin family, namely rhodomycin A and B, whose aglycone component was β-rhodomycinone (**1a**); γ-rhodomycins I to IV, having γ-rhodomycinone (**1b**) as the nonsugar moiety; and isorhodomycin A, differing from rhodomycin A because of the presence of β-isorhodomycinone (**2**). In addition to these, the mycetins and violarins, antibiotics isolated in Russia, were also mentioned as glycosides

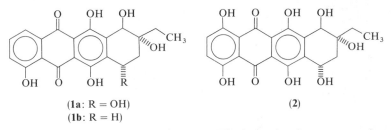

(**1a**: R = OH)
(**1b**: R = H)

(**2**)

belonging to the same structural group. The investigations concerning the rhodomycins were actively pursued in the following years (1963–1973), mainly by Brockmann and co-workers in Göttingen, Germany. A number of studies were concerned with the elucidation of structure of the different aglycones produced by strains of *Streptomyces purpurascens*. The chemical investigation leading to the formulation of β- and γ-rhodomycinones as respectively either **1a** and **1b** or the corresponding structures with the hydroxyl group at C-1 instead of C-4 were reported in detail in 1963 (*2*). Ring D substitution was, however, clarified by comparison of the electronic spectrum of bisanhydro-β-rhodomycinone with that of synthetic 1,6,7,11- and 1,6,10,11-tetrahydroxy-(5,12)-tetracenquinones, the result being extended not only to γ-rhodomycinone, but also to ε- and ζ-rhodomycinone (**4a** and **4b**) on the basis of the fact that all these aglycones could be converted to the same product, descarbomethoxy-bis-anhydro-ε-rhodomycinone (**3**) (*3*). We now know that position 4 is always substituted by a hydroxyl (or a methoxyl in the daunorubicin–doxorubicin group of antibiotics) in the biosynthetic anthraquinones, the 4-deoxy analogues being only accessible by total synthesis (see Chapter 7). Three new aglycones, namely α-rhodomycinone, β_1-rhodomycinone, and 10-deoxy-γ-rhodomycinone, were isolated as minor

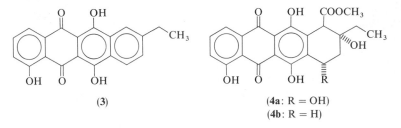

(**3**)

(**4a**: R = OH)
(**4b**: R = H)

components, together with the main pigment, γ-rhodomycinone, in the acid hydrolysate of the raw rhodomycin produced by a strain of *S. purpurascens*, and their structure was elucidated (*4*). The first compound was characterized as 7-epi-β-rhodomycinone (**5**) on the basis of *inter alia*, the formation of γ-rhodomycinone (**1b**) upon catalytic hydrogenolysis. For the second aglycone, showing one carbon atom less than γ-rhodomycinone, the mass spectrum indicated structure **6**, corresponding to the first anthracyclinone possessing a methyl group instead of an ethyl group at C-9. Similarly, the third compound was identified on the basis of its mass and PMR spectra and of its formation upon catalytic hydrogenation of γ-rhodomycinone. In a subsequent paper, Brockmann and Niemeyer (*5*) compared the behavior of **1a** and **5** toward the reaction sequence represented by 7-*O*-trifluoroacetylation followed by saponification or methanolysis of the ester. In brief, the results

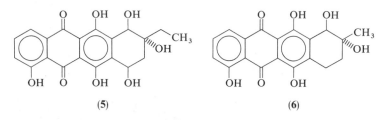

(5)   (6)

showed that both esterification and subsequent methanolysis of the 7(*S*) compound **1a** occurred with retention of configuration at the C-7 center, but aqueous sodium bicarbonate hydrolysis of 7-*O*-trifluoroacetyl-β-rhodomycinone resulted in the formation of both **1a** and **5**, apparently because of the polarization and solvation effect of the solvent (enhancing that due to the resonance of the anthraquinone chromophore and the inductive effect of the fluorine atoms) leading to S_N1-type displacement. On the other hand, esterification of **5** with trifluoroacetic acid followed by either methanolysis or alkaline hydrolysis gave the mixture of the C-7 epimers, indicating the importance of C-7 configuration for the steric outcome of 7-*O*-trifluoroacetate formation and/or solvolysis. In the same study, the configuration of γ-rhodomycinone (**1b**), that is, the trans relationship of C-9 and C-10 hydroxyl groups, was established by comparison of the slower rate of periodate oxidation of the compound when compared with the 10-epimer and extended to **1a** and **5** by analysis of the circular dichroism and rotatory dispersion spectra of the compounds. Ring A conformation of **1a** and **5** was investigated by 100 Hz NMR spectroscopy, ABX system represented by the C-7 and C-8 protons being examined in detail. The conclusion was that the half-chair conformation showing an equatorial orientation of the ethyl sidechain was the most stable one in both anthracyclinones.

Five other new anthracyclinones were obtained upon acid hydrolysis of a glycosidic fraction from *S. purpurascens*, namely α_1-, α_2-, and α_3-rhodomycinone, and α- and γ-citromycinone. The structure of α_2-rhodomycinone was established to be **7** because it afforded, upon heating with hydrogen bromide in acetic acid, a bisanhydro derivative **8** whose electronic and mass spectra indicated the presence of a 1,4,6-trihydroxynaphthacene-5,12-quinone system and which, although isomeric with demethoxy carbonyl-η-pyrromycinone, was clearly different from the latter (IR spectrum). Rotatory dispersion curves indicated that **7** possessed the same configuration in ring A as β-rhodomycinone. The new anthracyclinone, which was found therefore

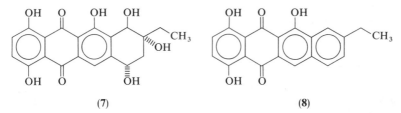

(7)   (8)

to represent a new structural variant among 10-hydroxy derivatives produced by strains belonging to *S. purpurascens* (note the relationship with δ-rhodomycinone which instead has a carbomethoxy group at C-10), also differed from the other compounds exhibiting a hydroxyl group at C-7 in the behavior toward catalytic hydrogenation. In fact, in contrast with the latter compounds which are known to undergo hydrogenolysis at C-7 when hydrogenated with palladium in ethanol and in the presence of triethanolamine, α_2-rhodomycinone failed to give the corresponding 7-deoxy derivative in the same conditions, two yellow products being instead produced, the more polar one being identical to the cometabolite, α-citromycinone. In fact, the citromycinones displayed a 1,5-dihydroxy-anthraquinone chromophore and appeared to belong to a new group of anthracyclinones, as this pattern of hydroxylation of the aromatic system was still unknown among this family of biosynthetic compounds. On the basis of mass spectra and of the chemical derivation from α_2-rhodomycinone mentioned above, structure **9a** was established for α-citromycinone, structure **9b** being proposed for the related pigment, γ-citromycinone (6).

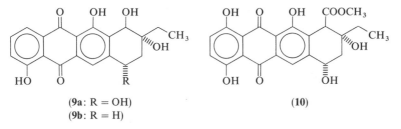

(9a: R = OH)   (10)
(9b: R = H)

The complete structure elucidation of the related δ-rhodomycinone (**10**) had been reported by Brockmann and Brockmann (*7*). This compound could not be converted to the corresponding 7-deoxy analogue by catalytic hydrogenolysis, a behavior similar to that of **7** and of **9a**. Isomeric with ε-rhodomycinone (and with ε-pyrromycinone), this aglycone was a derivative of 9-ethyl-1,4,11-trihydroxynaphthacene-5,12-quinone, still possessing however the C-11 phenolic group typical of all *S. purpurascens*-derived anthracyclinones.

The structure of rhodomycins A and B, of isorhodomycin A, and of other aminoglycosides has been also clarified by Brockmann *et al.* (*8*). Rhodomycin A (*9*), for which the new denomination β-rhodomycin II was proposed (this denomination indicates the aglycone type with the Greek letter and the number of sugar residues with the Roman numeral) gave rhodomycin B (β-rhodomycin I) and rhodosamine upon mild acid hydrolysis (0.1 *N* sulfuric acid and 40°C for 2 hr), the former being in turn catalytically hydrogenolyzed to give γ-rhodomycinone (**1b**) and another rhodosamine molecule. On the other hand, catalytic hydrogenolysis of rhodomycin B afforded a mixture of 10-rhodosaminyl-γ-rhodomycinone and 10-deoxy-γ-rhodomycinone. Structures **11a** and **12** were therefore established for rhodomycins A and B respectively, the α orientation of the glycoside bonds being revealed by the small values of the coupling constants of the anomeric protons indicating the same to be equatorial. Incidentally, **11a** was more active than **12** as an antibiotic, as the lowest dose causing inhibition of growth of test bacterial cultures was recorded as corresponding to a 1 to 5 × 10⁶ dilution for the former and 1 to

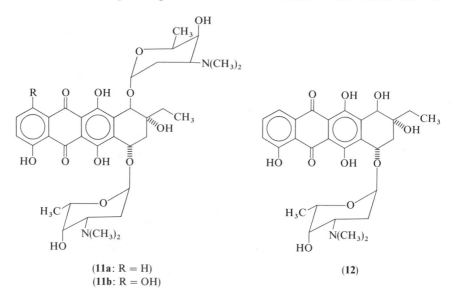

(**11a**: R = H)   (**12**)
(**11b**: R = OH)

2×10^5 dilution for the latter glycoside. The structure of another β-rhodo-mycinone glycoside, β-rhodomycin IV, was also elucidated and found to be **13**, the two additional sugar residues of 2-deoxy-L-fucose and rhodinose being ordered in analogy with the sequence found in γ-rhodomycin IV (*10*). Isorhodomycin A was identified as **11b**. Finally, the glycoside of α_2-rhodo-mycinone (see above) was characterized as an α_2-rhodomycin II and was

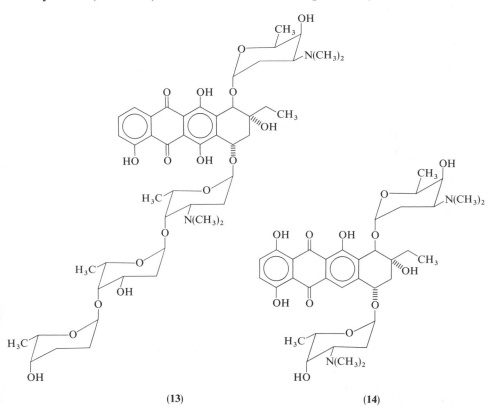

(13)   (14)

assumed to be **14**, by analogy with the coproduced metabolite rhodomycin A which also showed identical chromatographic behavior.

A new anthracycline was isolated by Shoji et al. (*11*) from a *Streptomyces* strain belonging to the species *S. purpurascens* and also producing rhodo-mycins A and B. The new glycoside appeared to contain β-rhodomycinone and probably three sugar residues, none of which was 2-deoxy-L-fucose as proved by GLC of the trimethylsilyl derivatives of the products derived by acid hydrolysis of the new antibiotic. A *Streptomyces* strain, characterized as *S. bobiliae* and belonging to the series "Ruber" according to Waksman, was instead found to produce a number of rhodomycin-type glycosides, out of which two rhodomycins, X and Y, were identified as trisaccharide derivatives of β-rhodomycinone and of γ-rhodomycinone respectively, the sugar moieties (rhodosamine, 2-deoxy-L-fucose, and rhodinose) being linked to the C-10 hydroxyl as depicted in **15a** and **15b** (*12*). The glycoside, rhodomycin X, displayed antibiotic activity against Gram positive bacteria and some protozoa.

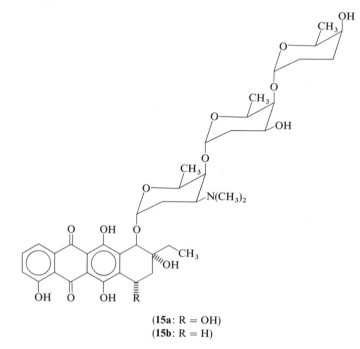

(**15a**: R = OH)
(**15b**: R = H)

The structure of new glycosides isolated after different separation steps (including countercurrent distribution and thin-layer chromatography) from a complex rhodomycin mixture derived from *S. purpurascens* (*13*) was elucidated by Brockmann and Greve (*14*). These glycosides were also endowed with exceptionally strong inhibitory properties against *B. subtilis* and *Mycoplasma*. Stepwise acid hydrolysis and benzylic hydrogenolysis coupled with spectrophotometric and osmometric molecular weight determinations and with other chromatographic and spectroscopic techniques allowed the determination of structure corresponding to the following rhodomycines: β-iso-rhodomycin-S-1a (**16a**), β-rhodomycin S-1b (**16b**), S-2 (**16c**), S-3 (**16d**), and S-4 (**17**). All new glycosides appear therefore to be derivatives of rhodomycin A (**11a**) and isorhodomycin A (**11b**) in which one or two rhodinosyl (or 2-deoxy-L-fucosyl) residues are added to both ends of the molecule. A five-hexose chain has been found in roseorubicin A, a γ-rhodomycinone

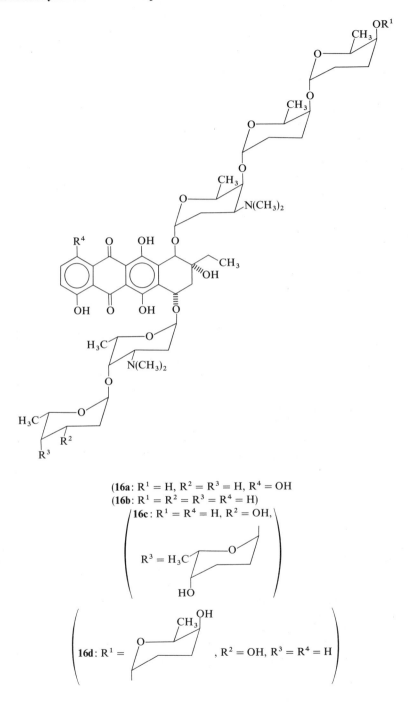

(**16a**: R^1 = H, R^2 = R^3 = H, R^4 = OH
(**16b**: R^1 = R^2 = R^3 = R^4 = H)
16c: R^1 = R^4 = H, R^2 = OH,

R^3 = H$_3$C

16d: R^1 = , R^2 = OH, R^3 = R^4 = H

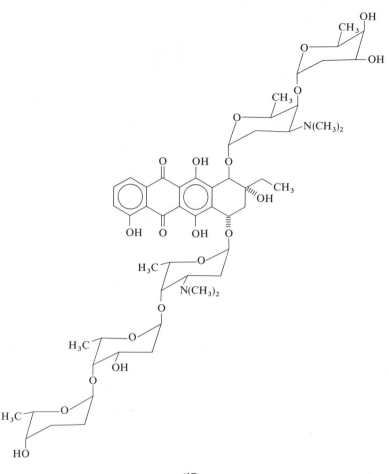

(17)

glycoside recently described by Matsuzawa *et al.* (*15*) and produced, together with roseorubicin B (presumably identical to γ-rhodomycin II) by strains belonging to different *Streptomyces* species, including *S. purpurascens*. The structure of the compound was established, on the basis of partial acid hydrolysis experiments and of the ^{13}C-NMR spectrum (all the 54 carbon atoms of the compound could be revealed by the latter method), to be **18**. Roseorubicin A was markedly active on different Gram positive bacteria *in vitro*, the related roseorubicin B being 10-fold less active in the same test. The violamycin complex isolated from cultures of *S. violaceus* was found to be a mixture of glycosides of α_2- and β-rhodomycinone and ε-isorhodomycinone (*16*). On the basis of optical rotatory dispersion spectra, all known rhodomycinones were related stereochemically to daunomycinone, whose absolute configuration was known, and asymmetric centers on ring A were established as already indicated in structural formulas drawn in Chapter 1 and in the present chapter (*17*).

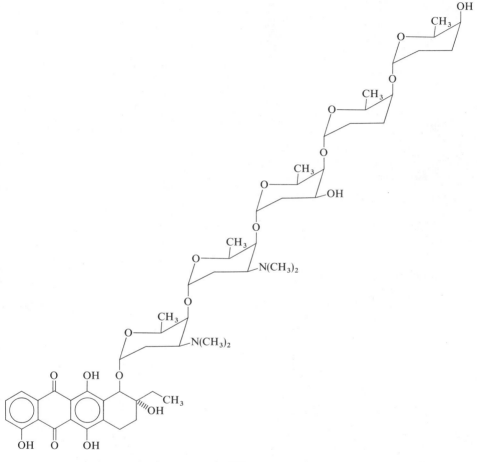

(18)

Other studies concerning the application of physicochemical techniques to the structural analysis of the anthracyclinones have been published. In 1963, Reed and Reid (*18*) reported on the electron impact-induced fragmentation of rhodomycinones, isorhodomycinones, and pyrromycinones. The assignment of structure to the main fragments is however due to Brockmann *et al.* (*19*). Fragments **19a** and **19b**, corresponding to the loss of 50 and 68 mass units respectively, were identified (*inter alia*) in the mass spectrum of

ε-rhodomycinone (**4a**), a similar behavior being shown by δ- and ζ-rhodomy-
cinones and ε- and ζ-isorhodomycinone, which also possess a hydroxyl group
at C-11. In α-rhodomycinone (**5**), the main fragmentation process is a retro

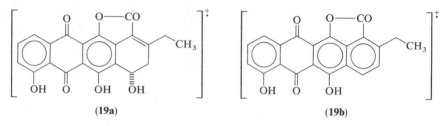

(19a)   (19b)

Diels–Alder reaction giving arise to **20a**, from which both **21** and **22a** are
derived upon loss of water and of carbon monoxide, respectively. Similarly,
γ-rhodomycinone afforded the radical ions **20b** and **22b**. In 10-deoxy-γ-rho-
domycinone, the retro Diels–Alder product **23** appeared not to undergo
further dissociation.

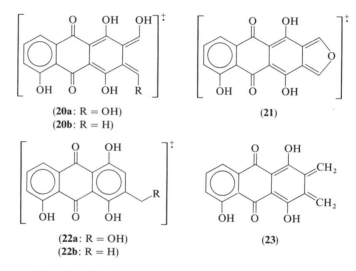

(**20a**: R = OH)   (**21**)
(**20b**: R = H)

(**22a**: R = OH)   (**23**)
(**22b**: R = H)

The crystal and molecular structure of γ-rhodomycinone (**1b**) were investigated by the X-ray diffraction method (*20*). In the crystals, the molecules
appeared ordered in parallel layers, the distance between these being 3.35 Å,
and in each layer the single units being represented by dimeric elements constituted by the association of two molecules linked through hydrogen bonds
(Fig. 1). The α-hydroxyquinone groups are involved in the bifurcated hydrogen bonding, each hydrogen atom being linked with two oxygen atoms giving
rise to one intramolecular and one intermolecular bond, the latter responsible for the dimerization. Ring A alcoholic hydroxyl groups also participate

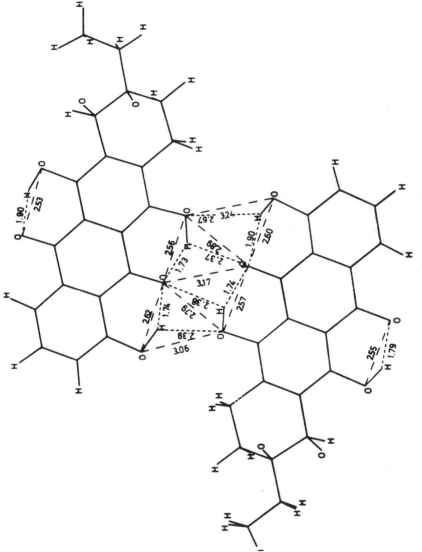

Fig. 1. Hydrogen bonds between two γ-rhodomycinone molecules of one asymmetric unit. Reproduced from Röhrl and Hoppe (20).

in hydrogen bonds, namely those intervening between molecules of different layers.

Synthetic Studies on Rhodomycinones

Although Brockmann and co-workers had already investigated the synthesis of bisanhydro derivatives with the aim of establishing the position of the ring D hydroxyl group in α-, β-, γ-, ε-, and ζ-rhodomycinone, definitely confirmed to be at C-4 (*21*), the first synthesis of a rhodomycin aglycone appeared in 1977 and was carried out by Kende and Tsay (*22*) on the wave of the interest aroused in the anthracyclines by the development of doxorubicin and of its analogues. The synthesis started from intermediate **24a**, itself obtained in 25% yield and in a three-step reaction sequence involving a cycloaddition of a substituted butadiene to 1,4,5-trimethoxyanthraquinone (see Chapter 2, p. 69). Compound **24a** was demethylated with aluminum chloride in methylene chloride to **24b** and the latter allowed to react with vinyl magnesium bromide to give **25** in 50% yield. Diimide reduction of **25** afforded

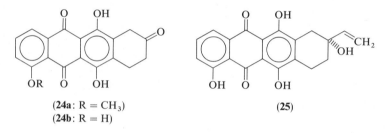

(**24a**: R = CH$_3$)
(**24b**: R = H)

(**25**)

racemic 10-deoxy-γ-rhodomycinone (**26a**) in excellent yield, while a similar reaction sequence starting from **24a** afforded **26b** in 73% yield. Treatment of the latter with aluminum chloride afforded **27**, which gave ($\pm$)-γ-rhodomycinone (**1b**) upon transhydroxylation with *O*-sulphoperbenzoic acid in ace-

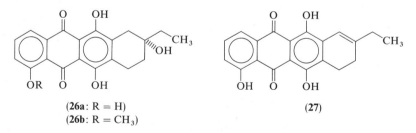

(**26a**: R = H)
(**26b**: R = CH$_3$)

(**27**)

tone. On the other hand, epoxidation of **27** to **28**, followed by treatment of the epoxide with acetic acid and sodium acetate, afforded mainly the 9,10-trans product, **29**. Bromination of **29** and subsequent treatment of the C-7

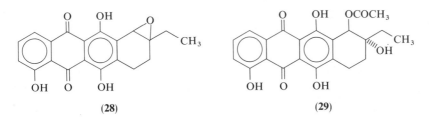

(28)(29)

bromination product with silver trifluoroacetate gave, after hydrolysis and chromatographic separation, $(\pm)$-α-rhodomycinone-10-acetate (30) and $(\pm)$-β-rhodomycinone-10-acetate (31), from which 5 and 1a were obtained upon O-deacetylation.

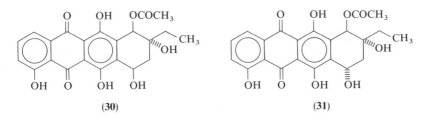

(30)(31)

More recent investigations on the total synthesis of the rhodomycinones have been carried out by Krohn and co-workers at the University of Hamburg. In a first publication, Krohn and Rösner (23) reported the synthesis of 4-deoxy-γ-rhodomycinone from naphthazarin, outlined in Scheme 1. Reaction of 32 with ethylbutadiene furnished 33, whose oxidation with air in alkaline solution gave 34a. This compound reacted with 1-acetoxybutadiene via the tautomeric form 34b, affording the mixture of 35a and 35b which was converted into 36 by an alkaline treatment and air oxidation. The 9,10-unsaturated isomer 37 was then obtained in high yield upon treatment of 36 with aluminium trichloride in dichloromethane or from the diacetate of the latter with acid. Hydroxylation of 36 and of 37 with osmium tetroxide furnished the cis diols 38 and 39 respectively, while reaction of the same olefins with m-chloroperbenzoic acid to the corresponding epoxides, followed by acid opening of the oxirane ring, resulted in the formation of 40 and of racemic 4-deoxy-γ-rhodomycinone (41), the overall yield of the latter from naphthazarin being 63%.

A stereoselective synthesis of new anthracyclinones possessing a substitution pattern similar to ε-rhodomycinone, with the exception of a methyl instead of an ethyl group at C-9 and no hydroxyl at C-4, has been developed by Krohn and Radeloff (24). After the exploration of other reactions, the authors obtained conversion of leukoquinizarine (42) to (3-hydroxy-n-butyl)quinizarine (43) in 94% yield by treatment of the former with freshly

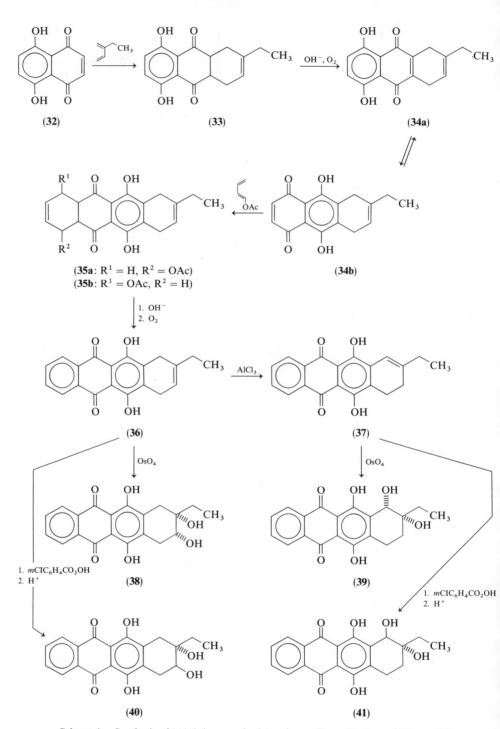

Scheme 1. Synthesis of (±)-4-deoxy-γ-rhodomycinone. From Krohn and Rösner (23).

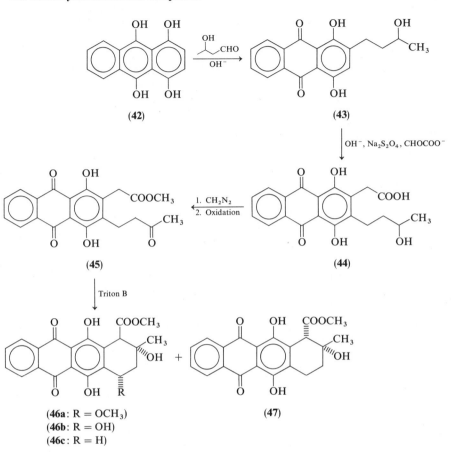

Scheme 2. Synthesis of new anthracyclinones related to ε-rhodomycinone. From Krohn and Radeloff (24).

distilled 3-hydroxybutyraldehyde in alkaline methanol followed by heating at reflux temperature for 15 min (Scheme 2). The acid **44** was obtained (67% yield) using glyoxylic acid as the precursor of the second substituent. Formation of ring A of the anthracyclinone system by intramolecular aldol addition in **45**, prepared from **44** by esterification and subsequent oxidation with pyridinium chlorochromate in 82% yield, afforded 24% yield of **46a**, 21% yield of **46b**, and 11% yield of **46c**, together with the corresponding epimer at C-10, **47**. The authors underlined the interest of the direct functionalization at C-7 occurring during the formation of **46a** and **46b**. The reaction was explained taking account of the two mesomeric forms **48** and **49** of the trianion of **46c** which on reaction with a nucleophilic species would be in equilibrium with **50**. Air oxidation would than convert **50** to **46b**.

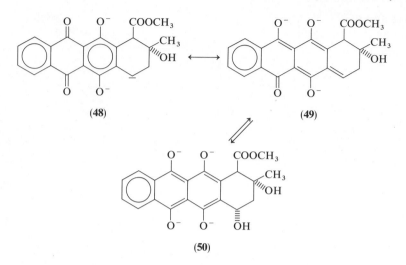

(48) ⟷ (49)

(50)

In another publication (*25*), the construction of ring A of 4-deoxy-ε-rhodo-mycinone analogues was achieved be reaction of the easily available anthra-quinone derivative **51a** with α,β-unsaturated aldehydes, such as 2-butenal or 2-pentenal. The reaction consisted in a two-step process, the former being a Michael-type addition in the presence of sodium hydride and the second an acid-catalyzed cyclization to give 40–50% yield of **52a** or **52b**, and **53a** or **53b**. The cyclized products differed only in the configuration at C-9, and the es-

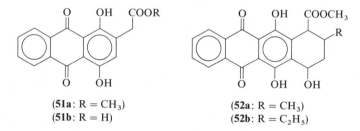

(**51a**: R = CH₃)
(**51b**: R = H)

(**52a**: R = CH₃)
(**52b**: R = C₂H₅)

tablishment of their relative stereochemistry was made on the basis of the results of dithionite reductions furnishing the corresponding 7-deoxy deriva-

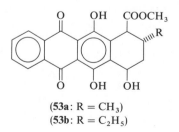

(**53a**: R = CH₃)
(**53b**: R = C₂H₅)

tives and of 270-MHz PMR spectra of **52a** and **52b**, and **53a** and **53b**. Continuing in the studies along the above-mentioned lines, and with the aim of identifying appropriate precursors for the synthesis of the anthracyclinones, Krohn and Hemme (*26*) undertook a careful investigation on the reaction of leucoquinizarin (**42**) with formaldehyde, a reaction previously studied by Marschalk *et al.* (*27*), and more recently by Bredereck *et al.* (*28*). The preparation of **54a**, **54b**, and **54c** was optimized by carrying out the alkylation of quinizarin in the presence of methanolic potassium hydroxide and sodium dithionite under a nitrogen atmosphere, the amount of formaldehyde, the temperature, and the duration of the reaction being the factors influencing the yields and the nature of the products. The study was also extended to higher aldehydes such as acetaldehyde, propionaldehyde, and butyraldehyde, and the formation of the hydroxy compounds **55a**, **55b**, and **55c** together with the corresponding deoxy derivatives **56a**, **56b**, and **56c** was recorded. In view of further transformations, the protection of the phenolic groups as benzyl ethers and the derivatization of the side chain in **54a** and in **55a–c** by substitution of the alcoholic hydroxyl group with a chlorine atom or the oxidation of the same group to a benzylic ketone function were also investigated. Finally, the reaction of **42** with glyoxylic acid to give **51b** and with levulinic acid to give **57** and **58** were examined and proposed as useful approaches for the exploration of new synthetic routes in the field of the anthracyclinones.

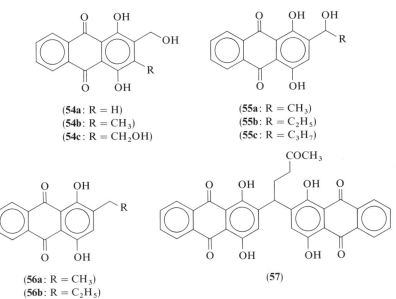

(**54a**: R = H)
(**54b**: R = CH$_3$)
(**54c**: R = CH$_2$OH)

(**55a**: R = CH$_3$)
(**55b**: R = C$_2$H$_5$)
(**55c**: R = C$_3$H$_7$)

(**56a**: R = CH$_3$)
(**56b**: R = C$_2$H$_5$)
(**56c**: R = C$_3$H$_7$)

(**57**)

Intermediate **51a**, when allowed to react with methylvinylketone in dimethylformamide and in the presence of sodium hydride, gave two products, **59** and **60**, the formation of the latter being rationalized by the authors (*29*) by suggesting the participation of the quinone function as indicated in inter-

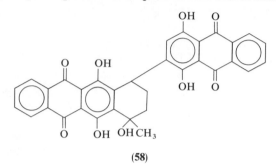

(58)

mediate **61**, (resulting from a 1,3-dipolar cycloaddition of the reagent to the trianion of **51a**, whose air oxidation would afford **60**). In the same study, *inter alia*, the reaction of formaldehyde with the free acid **51b** in the presence of methanolic potassium hydroxide and sodium dithionite was investigated and found to give, after air oxidation and esterification, lactone **62** as the

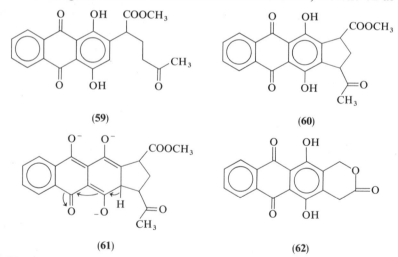

(59)   (60)

(61)   (62)

main product (52% yield), together with 34% of **63**, both compounds being of general interest for the preparative chemistry of the anthracyclinones.

The principles outlined above were further developed in a more recent study, according to which leuco compound **64**, when treated with formaldehyde and alcoholic potassium hydroxide, furnished **65a** regioselectively in 18–21% yield, about 60% of 1,4,5-trihydroxy-9,10-anthraquinone being re-

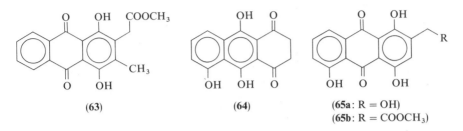

(63) (64) (65a: R = OH)
(65b: R = COOCH₃)

covered. Additionally, similar treatment of **64** with glyoxylic acid, followed by sodium dithionite reduction, air reoxidation, and esterification, afforded **65b** in 33% overall yield. The synthesis of 9-deoxy-ε-rhodomycinone from **65b** in only two steps was also announced (*30*).

As far as the rhodomycinone glycosides are concerned, the only published reports on the synthesis of the glycosidic linkage in this series are those of El Khadem *et al.* (*31*) and of Smith *et al.* (*31a*). The former authors prepared 26 ε-rhodomycinone glycosides by allowing ε-rhodomycinone to react with a large excess of the O-acetylated sugar halide in the presence of mercuric bromide, mercuric cyanide, and molecular sieves in tetrahydrofuran at reflux temperature. Yields of the 16 described protected glycosides resulting from this reaction were in the range from 0.5–83%. The following sugar moieties were present in the 10 described unblocked glycosides: D-glucopyranosyl, 2-deoxy-L-fucopyranosyl, 2-deoxy-L-rhamnopyranosyl, 2-deoxy-D-ribopyranosyl, L-fucopyranosyl, L-arabinopyranosyl, D-ribofuranosyl, D-xylofuranosyl, L-lyxofuranosyl, and 2-deoxy-D-ribofuranosyl. The deblocked glycosides displayed practically no antitumor activity in the P 388 mouse test. In the second publication, the synthesis of 7-*O*-daunosaminyl-ε-rhodomycinone was described. The compound was clearly less active and less potent than daunorubicin in the murine P 388 assay system.

The synthesis of the enantiomorph of rhodinose has been accomplished by Stevens *et al.* (*32*), thus confirming the L-threo configuration of this sugar.

PYRROMYCINONE AND AKLAVINONE GLYCOSIDES

The Anthracyclines of *S. galilaeus*

Conclusive evidence for the assignment of structures **66a** and **67a** to cinerubins A and B respectively was presented by Keller-Schierlein and Richle (*33,34*) and by Richle *et al.* (*35*). Besides pyrromycin (7-*O*-α-rhodosaminyl-ε-pyrromycinone), mild acid hydrolysis of cinerubin A afforded a disaccharide that by methanolysis gave methyl 2-deoxy-α-L-fucoside. The second sugar component was identified as a 2,3,6-trideoxy-4-hexulose (cinerulose A), whose configuration was deduced from the isolation of the known sugar L-amicetose on lithium aluminum reduction of the disaccharide followed by hydrolysis. Cinerubin B differed from cinerubin A in that an anhydrodisaccharide, $C_{12}H_{18}O_6$, was obtained, together with pyrromycin, on mild acid hydrolysis. A PMR study of the monoacetyl derivative and of the methyl glycoside of the $C_{12}H_{18}O_6$ fragment, coupled with the results of an X-ray study on the product obtained upon lithium aluminum hydride reduction of the said methyl glycoside, allowed the establishment of structure **67a** for cinerubin B. The name of cinerulose B was given to the new ketosugar present

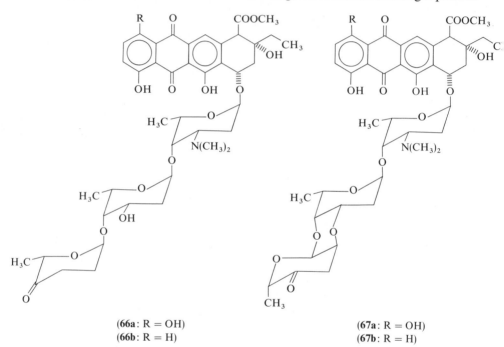

(**66a**: R = OH)
(**66b**: R = H)

(**67a**: R = OH)
(**67b**: R = H)

in cinerubin B. The synthesis of the corresponding D-enantiomorph has been reported by Stevens *et al.* (*36*).

The pigmented compounds produced by a strain belonging to the species *S. galilaeus* were investigated by Eckardt (*37*). Four nonglycosidic pigments (galirubinones B_1, B_2, C, and D) were identified as bisanhydroaklavinone, η-pyrromycinone, ζ-pyrromycinone, and 7-deoxyaklavinone respectively. Two glycosides were also isolated, namely galirubins A and B, whose aglycones were identified with ε-pyrromycinone and aklavinone respectively. Two new aglycones were characterized as aklavinone I and II as they possessed the same structure as aklavinone but differed in the configuration of at least one asymmetric center (*38*). The PMR spectrum of aklavinone II indi-

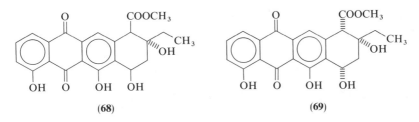

(68)   (69)

cated the axial orientation of H-7 and, as the values of the coupling constants and of the chemical shifts were comparable to those of α-rhodomycinone (5), formula **68** was attributed to the new compound. This conclusion was also in agreement with circular dichroism measurements. On the other hand, aklavinone I showed a quasiequatorial orientation (small values of the H-7,H-8e and H-7,H-8a coupling constants) of H-7, a half-chair conformation of ring A, and a reversed CD curve in respect to aklavinone, although of lower amplitude. This latter result and conformational arguments ruled out the possibility that aklavinone I was a 9-epiaklavinone or its enantiomorph, leaving only formula **69** (or its mirror image) available for aklavinone I (*39*).

Of greater importance were the anthracyclines named aclacinomycins A and B, isolated by Oki *et al.* (*40*) from a strain also characterized as belonging to the species *S. galilaeus*. Both glycosides furnished aklavinone on acid hydrolysis. Partial methanolysis of aclacinomycin A resulted in 1-deoxypyrromycin and a methylated disaccharide identical to that already obtained in similar conditions from cinerubin A. Analogous results were recorded for aclacinomycin B, which was found to be the 1-deoxy derivative of cinerubin B. Structures **66b** and **67b** were therefore proposed for the new anthracyclines, whose antitumor activity in mice bearing L 1210 leukemia was remarkable. In a subsequent paper, Oki *et al.* (*41*) reported the isolation and structure elucidation of 17 other anthracyclinone derivatives produced by the same strain of *S. galilaeus*. Hydrolysis and methanolysis experiments, carried out on each purified glycoside (six compounds were of the aglycone type, namely bisanhydroaklavinone, aklavinone, 7-deoxyaklavinone, a dimeric condensation product derived from aklavinone indicated as component E₁, ζ-pyrromycinone, and ε-pyrromycinone), afforded the identification of pyrromycin, cinerubin A and B, and of eight new aklavinone-derived or ε-pyrromycinone-derived anthracyclines. Among the former, the following glycosides were described: 1-deoxypyrromycin or 7-*O*-(α-rhodosaminyl)aklavinone, *N*-monodemethylaclacinomycin A (containing *N*-methyldaunosamine as the aminosugar moiety), 4′-(2-deoxy-α-L-fucosyl)-1-deoxypyrromycin (**70**), the two epimeric 4‴-dihydro derivatives of aclacinomycin A (**71a** and **71c**), and a compound 5‴-epiaclacinomycin A, possessing D-cinerulose, instead of L-cinerulose as in the parent compound. Two new ε-pyrromycinone glycosides were reported, namely 4′-(2-deoxy-α-L-fucosyl)pyrromycin (**72a**) and

the L-amicetose-containing glycoside **71b**. In a report by Oki (*42*), two additional glycosides were cited: *N*-didemethylaclacinomycin A, possessing daunosamine instead of rhodosamine as in **70**, and aclacinomycin Y, a new
derivative differing from **70** because of the presence of L-aculose (2,3-dehy-
drocinerulose A) in the place of L-cinerulose A as the third sugar residue.

When tested against the L 1210 leukemia in mice, aclacinomycin A, injected ip once daily for 10 days at the dose of 1.5 mg/kg, afforded a survival
period equal to 300% that of the control untreated animals. The acute LD_{50}
value in mice was 22.6 mg/kg ip and 33.7 mg/kg iv, aclacinomycin B appearing less active but more toxic. Aclacinomycin A at the dose level of 50 mg/kg
ip, did not cause ECG changes in the hamster, whereas doxorubicin induced
such modifications at 3 mg/kg, single injection, by the same route (*40*).

All aclacinomycins as well as the cinerubins and related glycosides exhibited antimicrobial and antitumor properties, the ε-pyrromycinone-derived
compounds being generally more active on a weight basis than the aklavinone
derived ones (*42*). An exception was aclacinomycin Y, which was the most
potent compound in the *in vitro* tests based on the inhibition of microbial
(*S. aureus, B. subtilis, S. cerevisiae*) growth and of the DNA and RNA synthesis in cultured L 1210 cells. In mice bearing L 1210 leukemia, ip daily treatment on days 1–9 with the optimal dose of aclacinomycin A afforded 103%

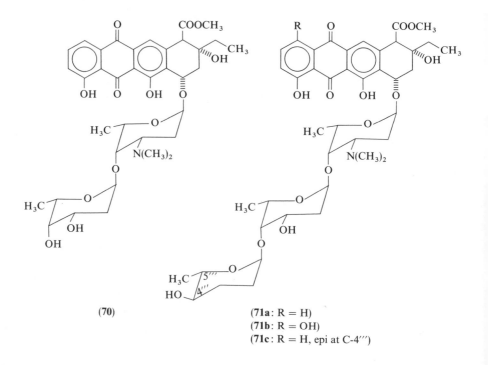

(**70**)

(**71a**: R = H)
(**71b**: R = OH)
(**71c**: R = H, epi at C-4''')

increase of median survival time in respect to controls, the other compounds, with the exception of **70**, being less effective (the figure for cinerubin A was 63%).

ε-Pyrromycinone-related compounds have been isolated from unidentified streptomycetes or from species different from *S. galilaeus*. Among these are bisanhydro-ε-pyrromycinone (η-pyrromycinone), from *S. capoamus* n. sp. (*43*), and N_1-pyrromycinone, differing from η-pyrromycinone in having a methyl instead of an ethyl sidechain (*44*). However, the most important were the pigmented antibiotics that will be dealt with in the following section.

The Bohemic Acid Complex and the Rhodirubins

An unexpected relationship between the late nineteenth century musical opera and the anthracycline antibiotics was established with the discovery of the bohemic acid complex, an anthracycline mixture isolated from cultures of *Actinosporangium* sp. by Nettleton *et al.* (*45*). Besides η-pyrromycinone, two biologically active ε-pyrromycinone glycosides were purified and studied, musettamycin and marcellomycin, the former being 4'-*O*-(2-deoxy-α-L-fucosyl)pyrromycin (**72a**) and the latter the corresponding 4''-*O*-(2-deoxy-α-L-fucosyl) derivative **73a**. The two glycosides exhibited an antimicrobial spectrum similar to that shown by pyrromycin, but a more marked antitumor activity than the latter compound in mice bearing the L 1210 leukemia. More precisely, animals treated ip on day 1 after tumor inoculation showed 50% increase of survival time with musettamycin, 12.8 mg/kg, and 57% with marcellomycin, 3.2 mg/kg (optimal doses). Comparable results were obtained using a QD 1–5 schedule at one-fourth the said dosages (*46*). Another new anthracycline, rudolfomycin, also derived from the bohemic acid complex, has been reported to have a unique aminosugar residue as in **72b**.

Another family of new ε-pyrromycinone glycosides was obtained from an unidentified *Streptomyces* strain by Kitamura *et al.* (*47*). Six glycosides were isolated and named rhodirubin A, B, C, D, E, and G. All components of this family gave ε-pyrromycinone on acid hydrolysis and appeared to be of the trisaccharide type as the cinerubins and the components of bohemic acid complex. The structure of rhodirubins A and B was deduced from the formation of pyrromycin on mild methanolysis and of ε-pyrromycinone, rhodosamine, and, respectively, 2-deoxy-L-fucose and L-rhodinose or two L-rhodinose residues on total acid hydrolysis. Therefore structure **73b** was proposed for rhodirubin A and **73c** for rhodirubin B. Rhodirubins C, D, and E were respectively identical to cinerubin A, musettamycin, and marcellomycin, while rhodirubin G, the most lipophilic component of the

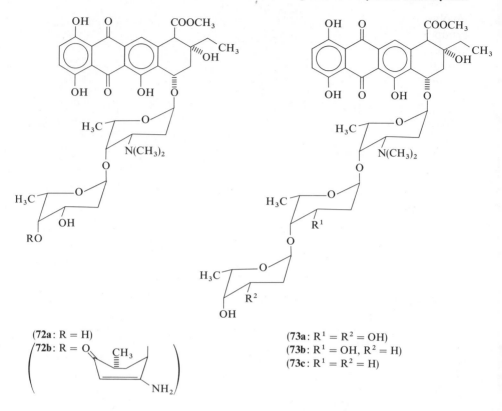

(**72a**: R = H)
(**72b**: R = O⟍CH₃...NH₂)

(**73a**: R¹ = R² = OH)
(**73b**: R¹ = OH, R² = H)
(**73c**: R¹ = R² = H)

rhodirubin family, was also a new anthracycline which, possessing D-cineru-lose A as the third sugar residue, should be considered as 5‴-epicinerubin A (*42*). Rhodirubins A and B displayed marked antimicrobial activity and were effective inhibitors of nucleic acid synthesis in cultured L 1210 leukemia cells (*42*).

Other Studies on the Chemistry of ε-Pyrromycinone Derivatives

The mass spectra of ε-pyrromycinone and of aklavinone, as well as of their 7-deoxy derivatives, were analyzed by Brockmann *et al.* (*19*) The former compound showed, as expected, the peak corresponding to the bisanhydro derivative as the most intense one, together with those corresponding to the subsequent loss of a methyl radical (arising from the ethyl side chain) or to the fragmentation of the carbomethoxy group ($-CH_3O$, $-CH_3OH$, $-CO_2CH_3$, $-HCO_2CH_3$). In addition, the loss of a single water molecule gave the radical ion at m/e 410(**74**), whose further fragmentations involved the loss of the ethyl side chain to give **75**, or of the carbomethoxy group as in fragment **76**. From the latter, the two fragments **77a** and **77b** arose, resulting in important peaks at m/e 333 and 322. Aklavinon exhibited a similar behavior, taking account of the absence of an oxygen atom with respect to ε-pyrromycinone.

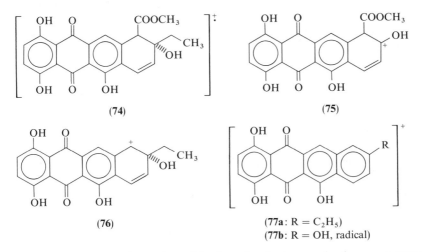

(74)   (75)

(76)

(**77a**: R = C$_2$H$_5$)
(**77b**: R = OH, radical)

A synthetic approach to cinerubin A and aclacinomycin A was reported (*48*) in Chapter 2. Semisynthetic glycosides of ε-pyrromycinone have been prepared by El Khadem and Swartz (*49*). Condensation of the aglycone with di-*O*-acetyl-2-deoxy-L-fucosyl bromide under Koenigs–Knorr conditions (using the mercuric bromide and mercuric cyanide mixture as catalyst and acid acceptor) and two molar equivalents of the sugar halide gave **78a**.

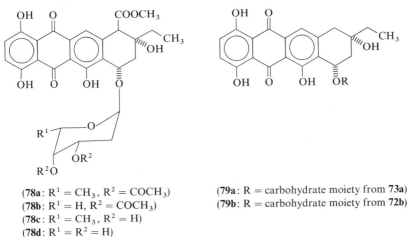

(**78a**: R^1 = CH$_3$, R^2 = COCH$_3$)
(**78b**: R^1 = H, R^2 = COCH$_3$)
(**78c**: R^1 = CH$_3$, R^2 = H)
(**78d**: R^1 = R^2 = H)

(**79a**: R = carbohydrate moiety from **73a**)
(**79b**: R = carbohydrate moiety from **72b**)

Similarly, reaction of ε-pyrromycinone with di-*O*-acetyl-2-deoxy-D-*erythro*-pentopyranosyl bromide furnished **78b**. Yields of the acetylated glycosides were approximately 80%. Deacetylation was achieved by treatment with an excess of sodium methoxide in absolute methanol and at room temperature. Biological activity of resulting glycosides **78c** and **78d** was not reported.

Descarbomethoxy derivatives of marcellomycin, of **79a**, and of rudolfomycin (**79b**) were obtained by Du Vernay *et al.* (*50*) upon saponification of the biosynthetic antibiotics with dilute aqueous potassium hydroxide at room temperature followed by storing the solution of the free acid in dimethylformamide at room temperature and recovery of the products by repeated chromatographic steps. The reported yields were 6 and 24% for the decarbomethoxylation of **73a** and **72b** respectively.

Structure–Activity Relationships

The ability of anthracyclines other than daunorubicin or doxorubicin and their derivatives to bind to DNA is a generally recognized property of this class of compounds. Cinerubins were found to form complexes with DNA and to inhibit DNA-dependent RNA and DNA synthesis *in vitro*, behaving, in this respect, similarly to daunorubicin (*51–53*). The rhodomycins and the violamycins also displayed this property which, as in the case of the galirubins A and B, appeared restricted to the glycosylated derivatives, the aglycones being devoid of DNA binding capability (*52, 54–56*). Incorporation of radioactive precursors into RNA and DNA of isolated mitochondria derived from normal and tumor tissues was inhibited by cinerubin A (*57,58*).

An interesting finding concerning cinerubin A is its activity in doxorubicin-resistant P 388 experimental leukemia. According to Johnson *et al.* (*59*), who compared the effect of different anthracyclines on mice bearing a sensitive or a doxorubicin-resistant P 388 subline, essentially complete cross resistance was exhibited by daunorubicin, carminomycin, doxorubicin 14-octanoate, rubidazone, and even by nogalamycin, but not by cinerubin A. The latter antibiotic was, however, clearly inferior to doxorubicin in other transplanted tumors of the mouse such as L 1210 leukemia, Lewis lung carcinoma, and B16 melanoma. A difference in the uptake mechanism between the trisaccharide derivative cinerubin A and the other anthracyclines could explain the lack of complete cross resistance mentioned above. In agreement to this study, Wilkoff and Dolmadge (*60*) reported that cultured P 388 leukemia cells derived from cells with *in vivo* developed resistance to vincristine were also resistant to doxorubicin, daunorubicin, actinomycin D, and *N*-trifluoroacetyldoxorubicin 14-valerate, but not to cinerubin A.

Aclacinomycin A prevented RNA synthesis more markedly than DNA synthesis in cultured mouse lymphoblastoma cells, as [³H]uridine incorporation into the cold TCA-insoluble fraction was 50% inhibited at an antibiotic concentration of 0.07 μg/ml, whereas the IC_{50} for [^{3}H]thymidine uptake was 1.0 μg/ml in the same experimental conditions (incubation of the cells with radiolabeled precursors and with the drug for 60 min at 37°C. On the other hand, doxorubicin afforded 50% inhibition of RNA synthesis at 1.2 μg/ml and of DNA synthesis at 6.6 μg/ml. The *in vitro* reaction catalyzed by RNA polymerase II isolated from Ehrlich mouse carcinoma was sensitive to aclacinomycin A (IC_{50} was approximately 1 μg/ml) when either calf thymus DNA or poly(dAdT), but not poly(dIdC), were used as the template, and the inhibition was competitively reversed by increasing concentrations of the template. Growth and nucleic acid synthesis of *E. coli* were rather resistant to aclacinomycin A, and the RNA polymerase reaction catalyzed by the *E. coli* enzyme was blocked by 50% at 10 μg/ml of the drug, DNA polymerase I reaction not being affected (*61*).

The relative effect on cellular RNA and DNA synthesis of different anthracyclines was investigated by Crooke *et al.* (*62*) in cultured Novikoff hepatoma cells. When whole-cell RNA and DNA synthesis was measured by the incorporation rate of labeled uridine or thimidine into high-molecular-weight components in the presence of the drugs during a 2-hr incubation period, inhibition of both processes was recorded. However, the 50% inhibitory concentrations of doxorubicin, carminomycin, and pyrromycin for DNA synthesis were less than twice those found for RNA synthesis, whereas in the case of marcellomycin, musettamycin, and aclacinomycin, the concentrations resulting in 50% inhibition of DNA synthesis were about seven times greater than those affecting RNA synthesis to the same extent (Table I). The difference between the two groups of compounds was more

Table I

Comparison of Different Anthracyclines as Inhibitors of Nucleic Acid Synthesis in Novikoff Hepatoma Ascites Cells

Antibiotic	IC_{50} (μM)		
	Total DNA	Total RNA	Nucleolar RNA
Doxorubicin	6.1	3.2	6.0
Carminomycin	14.7	8.9	13.06
Pyrromycin	5.7	4.5	6.15
Marcellomycin	11.3	1.7	0.009
Musettamycin	10.0	1.5	0.014
Aclacinomycin A	6.3	0.85	0.037

[a] From Crooke *et al.* (*62*).

striking when the inhibition of nucleolar RNA was considered. The latter was determined by exposure of the cells (prelabeled with [^{3}H]uridine) to the drugs and to [^{32}P]phosphate, followed by extraction of RNA and sedimentation of the same in a linear sucrose gradient. Incorporation of ^{32}P into newly synthesized 45S preribosomal RNA was inhibited more effectively by the second group of antibiotics, in comparison with that group including doxorubicin. The presence of the second or of the third sugar moiety was suggested as the critical structural feature determining the observed differences in pharmacological behavior at the cell level. Electron microscopic examination of nucleolar modifications induced by the above-mentioned drugs in the same cells were in agreement with these conclusions, suggesting the hypothesis of a higher specificity of binding to nucleolar DNA of marcellomycin in respect to doxorubicin and carminomycin (*63*). In another study, marcellomycin and rudolfomycin were compared with the corresponding 10-descarbomethoxy analogues in the same systems. The result was that the latter analogues had lost the selectivity towards the inhibition of nucleolar RNA already demonstrated for marcellomycin and also found, although at higher IC_{50} values, for rudolfomycin. When the four compounds were tested for cytotoxicity on cultured Novikoff hepatoma cells or in mice bearing ascitic L 1210 leukemia, a clear correlation was found between the nucleolar RNA inhibiting capacity *in vitro* and the inhibition of colony-forming ability of cultured cells or of tumor growth *in vivo*. In the animal system, the correlation was expressed both in terms of potency and of activity, as the optimal dose exhibited by the biosynthetic antibiotics was 0.8 mg/kg in a QD 1–5 schedule with an almost 50% increase of mean survival time, whereas the optimal doses of **79a** and **79b** were 4.0 and 32.0 mg/kg respectively with approximately 30% prolongation of the mean lifespan of treated mice with respect to controls (*50*). These results are of interest as they suggest a role for the carbomethoxy group at C-10 in the ε-pyrromycinone-derived anthracyclines, but, along with those concerning the different behavior towards nucleolar RNA synthesis and the corresponding structure–activity relationships, the results should be verified in other systems for a more substantiated generalization and correlation with the antitumor effects of the anthracyclines.

Variation in chemical structure of the anthracyclines seems to have an importance in the exhibition of cross resistance among this group of compounds. The activity displayed by cinerubin A on a doxorubicin-resistant P 388 subline *in vivo* has already been mentioned. More recently, Nishimura *et al.* (*64*) have found that daunorubicin and the baumycins A$_1$ and A$_2$ showed complete cross resistance in cultured cells of a doxorubicin-resistant mutant subline of mouse lymphoblastoma, but pyrromycin, 1-deoxypyrromycin, the aclacinomycins A, B, and Y, musettamycin, and cinerubin exhibited only partial cross resistance. However, the mechanism of drug resistance of the mutant subline was not established.

Aclacinomycin A and 1-deoxypyrromycin, in contrast to daunorubicin (and doxorubicin), were nonmutagenic in the *S. typhimurium* test, and so were their *N*-monodemethyl derivatives. The corresponding *N*-dimethyl analogues exhibited instead a high degree of mutagenic properties, whereas *N*-dimethyldaunorubicin appeared devoid of such properties (65). These results suggested a role for the substitution at the aminosugar nitrogen atom for the expression of mutagenicity, at least in the conditions of the Ames test. When tested on *B. subtilis* mutant strains with or without recombination–repair system, the aclacinomycins, cinerubin A, and the rhodirubins showed little differential inhibiting effects, whereas daunorubicin, doxorubicin, and their related compounds carminomycin and the baumycins displayed a potency index in the range 3.6–4.2, the latter being expressed by the rec$^+$/rec$^-$ ratio of concentrations which produced a 15 mm growth inhibition zone against rec$^-$ and rec$^+$ strains. Rec$^-$ mutants were reported to be more sensitive to mutagenic and carcinogenic compounds than rec$^+$ strains (66).

The Development of Aclacinomycin A

Aclacinomycin A behaved similarly to doxorubicin with regard to the DNA binding properties when these were monitored by the stabilization of the double-strand structure of the biopolymer to heat denaturation, by the changes in antibiotic visible spectrum upon reaction with DNA, and by equilibrium dialysis experiments aimed to measure the apparent association constant of the drug–DNA complex. Scatchard plot evaluation of the binding constant afforded the value $1.2 \times 10^6 \ M^{-1}$ indicating an affinity of the same order of magnitude as that of daunorubicin and doxorubicin (67). In the same study, it was found that more molecules of the antibiotic were bound to poly(dAdT) than to native calf thymus DNA or to poly(dIdC), and that aclacinomycin A was able to bind to tubulin in a manner similar to that observed for daunorubicin by Na and Timasheff (68).

Reductive cleavage of the glycosidic bond at C-7 is an important biochemical reaction in the metabolism of all anthracyclines studied so far, and of aclacinomycin A as well. Oki *et al.* (41) have demonstrated that the enzyme in rat liver microsomes catalyzing this reaction is identical to the known microsomal NADPH–cytochrome C reductase. The enzyme was isolated in purified form, and the ratio of anthracycline glycoside reductase to cytochrome C reductase activity remained constant throughout the purification process (69). The reaction (leading, in the case of aclacinomycin A, to 7-deoxyaklavinone and to a 7-deoxyaklavinone dimer) required anaerobic conditions, whereas in the presence of oxygen anthracycline antibiotics were found to stimulate the NADPH oxidase activity of the enzyme and the production of hydrogen peroxide.

A nondegradative reduction of aclacinomycin A was also detected from *in vivo* experiments, as the two compounds **71a** and **71c** were identified in plasma, urine, and tissues of laboratory animals treated with the antibiotic. A microsomal NADH-dependent cinerulose reductase from rat liver was characterized by Komiyama *et al.* (*70*). The possibly new enzyme catalyzed the conversion of the L-cinerulose residue of aclacinomycin A to an L-rhodinose residue (thus giving rise to **71c**), was very sensitive to the action of detergents, and displayed a low K_m value for the antibiotic, 2.1×10^{-5} M.

In a subsequent paper, Komiyama *et al.* (*71*) described the separation of the microsomal enzyme from a cinerulose reductase activity which was recovered in the soluble fraction of rat liver homogenate and was dependent on NADPH. As both compounds **71a** and **71c** were produced from aclacinomycin A by this fraction, at least two enzymes, soluble cinerulose reductase I and soluble cinerulose reductase II, were present in the soluble preparation, the former responsible for the formation of the equatorial alcohol (L-amicetose) and the latter for the formation of the axial epimer (L-rhodinose). The two enzymes were similar to the aldo–keto reductase (Chapter 4) catalyzing the conversion of daunorubicin and doxorubicin to daunorubicinol and doxorubicinol respectively, but differed as regards to the sensitivity of different inhibitors.

The quantitative analysis of aclacinomycin A and its metabolites in plasma and blood cells of rabbits was carried out by Kitamura *et al.* (*72*). The procedure used by these authors included extraction of the drug and metabolites into a chloroform–methanol mixture followed by thin-layer chromatography using a multiple development technique starting from chloroform alone to chloroform containing increasing amounts of methanol. This method allowed the separation of endogenous fluorescent materials and the determination of the drug-derived components by a fluorescence scanning device. Both **71a** and **71c** were detected, together with aclacinomycin A, in the samples from rabbits treated intravenously with the antibiotic. Fall of the latter in the plasma below 0.1 μg/ml occurred after 1 hr after treatment. Interestingly, a peak appearing at 8 hr in the concentration-versus-time curve suggested the presence of an enterohepatic circulation of the drug. An HPLC method for the separation of aclacinomycin A from its metabolites and their spectrofluorometric quantitation has been recently reported by Peters and Murray (*73*). An excellent linear regression was obtained extracting aclacinomycin A from control rabbit plasma over a concentration range of 0.05–1.0 μg/ml of plasma.

Phase I clinical studies carried out in Japan have allowed the conclusion that aclacinomycin A would deserve further testing in man as a potentially less toxic analogue of doxorubicin (74). The results of a phase II clinical trial in 22 patients with hematological malignancies indicated an oncostatic efficiency of aclacinomycin A in acute lymphoid leukemia and in lymphosarcoma, together with no incidence of alopecia and one case of cardiac intolerance (75). The dose regimen used (10–20 mg/m^2 per day up to a total dose in the range 42–600 mg/m^2) induced haematologic toxicity in 75% of the patients. No response was achieved with aclacinomycin A in two patients who had already shown no improvement with a four-drug combination including doxorubicin. The activity against acute myeloblastic leukemia suggested by the report concerning a successful case by Suzuki et al. (76) was not confirmed by Mathé et al. (77).

BIOSYNTHETIC GLYCOSIDES RELATED TO DAUNORUBICIN

Daunorubicin (**80a**) is a well-known compound to the readers of this book. This antibiotic, extensively studied both at the preclinical and clinical stages, has presently found a definite place in cancer chemotherapy. Only a brief mention of such developments will be made in this chapter. On the other hand, various new daunorubicin-related compounds have been isolated from microbial sources and represent important additions to the family of the anthracyclines. Among these are carminomycin, a compound that has also reached the clinical stage, the baumycins, and finally other new derivatives obtained during a study of mutant strains of S. peucetius, the daunorubicin- (and doxorubicin-) producing organism.

Daunorubicin and Derivatives

According to the studies carried out in the 1960s and summarized by Di Marco (78) and by Di Marco et al. (79), daunorubicin was the first anthracycline whose cytotoxic effects were related to its ability to bind to DNA and to inhibit nucleic acid synthesis in cultured cells as well as the DNA and RNA polymerase reactions in vitro. Most of the preclinical studies have preceded or accompanied those already described for doxorubicin, and they have already been presented in the preceding chapters. As already mentioned, the lower therapeutic effects shown by daunorubicin with respect to doxorubicin in certain transplantable tumor systems have been related to a less marked inhibitory effect against nucleic acid polymerases (80), or to the higher immunosuppressive properties of the former when compared with the latter (*81–84*), or to a slower metabolism in the experimental animal (*85*).

An updated analysis of preclinical and clinical data which have been accumulated up to the year 1978 on daunorubicin has been carefully performed by Von Hoff *et al.* (*86*). Starting from the early clinical studies that were also reported in the proceedings of an international symposium held in Paris in 1967 (*87*), evidence has been accumulated (records concerning 5613 patients were mentioned in the above-cited review) showing that daunorubicin is effective as a single agent in children with acute lymphocytic leukemia (ALL) affording a 17–66% rate of complete remissions, the frequency of the latter being improved when the combinations daunorubicin plus prednisone or daunorubicin plus prednisone plus vincristine were used. Chemotherapeutic combinations including daunorubicin were also active in adult ALL. The antibiotic is cleary effective in childhood and adult acute myelocytic leukemia, and different combinations have been used; among the most popular are daunorubicin plus cytosine arabinoside alone or also accompanied by vincristine and prednisone. Daunorubicin has been used alone and in combination for treating the less common leukemias and in pediatric solid tumors with favorable results. The lack of promising activity in adult solid tumors may be partially due to inadequate trials. Toxic side-effects of daunorubicin therapy are similar to those recorded for doxorubicin, cardiotoxicity being a major factor of total cumulative dose limitation (*86*).

Duborimycin (13-dihydrodaunorubicin, **81a**) has also received consideration in France as a clinically useful anticancer agent. A report concerning a study in 151 patients has been published by Chauvergne (*88*). Administration of 200 or 300 mg/m^2 iv doses every 15 days up to total doses in the range 0.3–10 g for 2–52 weeks revealed cardiac intolerance as the major toxicity, whereas hematological reactions were moderate in most cases. However, objective responses were recorded, including 56 tumor regressions (two of which were complete: a squamous-cell carcinoma and an embryonal testicular tumor).

The group of anthracycline antibiotics isolated by Fleck and Strauss (*89*) from cultures of *Streptomyces griseus* was resolved into a lipophilic fraction, leukaemomycin A, consisting of a mixture of daunomycinone-related aglycones; and three biologically active components, leukaemomycins B, C, and D. Both components B and C were shown to possess cytostatic properties and, whereas leukaemomycin B was more effective against Ehrlich ascites carcinoma cells *in vitro*, leukaemomycin C afforded a higher activity in the L 1210 leukemia test. Comparative chromatographic studies of the antibiotics and of the products derived by acid hydrolysis indicated that leukaemomycin B$_1$ was identical to rubomycin B (4′-rhodinosyldaunorubicin), leukaemomycin C to daunorubicin, and leukaemomycin D to dihydrodaunorubicin, and suggested the identity of leukaemomycin B$_2$ with daunosaminyldaunorubicin (90).

Carminomycin

The carminomycins are a family of anthracycline type glycosides isolated from a culture of *Actinomadura carminata* (91). The most important component was carminomycin 1, thereafter indicated as carminomycin in many publications, a compound showing antitumor activity in animal tests. Acid hydrolysis of carminomycin furnished carminomycinone (82), differing from daunomycinone because of the absence of the C-4 *O*-methyl group. Mainly on the bases of physicochemical analysis and of the identification of daunosamine as the sugar moiety, structure 80 (aside from stereochemistry) was attributed to the antibiotic (92). Characterization of the different carminomycins was reported in a subsequent paper. Carminomycin 2 and 3 gave carminomycin upon mild acid hydrolysis, whereas carminomycins 4 and 5 remained unchanged. Carminomycin 6 was identified as the aglycone, carminomycinone. Carminomycins 1, 2, and 3 showed the same electronic spectrum and dissociation constant (pK_a = 8.00) (93). Carminomycinone acetate and methyl ether were prepared and compared with the same derivatives of daunomycinone.

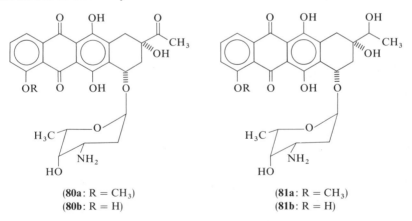

(80a: R = CH$_3$)
(80b: R = H)

(81a: R = CH$_3$)
(81b: R = H)

Carminomycin was also isolated from a different source, *Streptosporangium* sp., by Wani *et al.* (94). These authors confirmed the conclusions of the Russian group and also established the absolute configuration of the antibiotic by direct single-crystal X-ray crystallographic analysis of carminomycin hydrochloride monohydrate. The same conclusions were reached by Pettit *et al.* (95), who independently performed the X-ray crystal structure determination of the compound. Additional details of the crystal structure

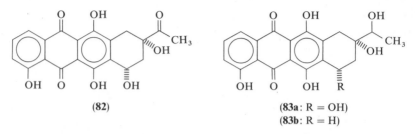

(82)

(83a: R = OH)
(83b: R = H)

and molecular conformation of carminomycin hydrochloride have been reported by Von Dreele and Einck (96). Comparative circular dichroism measurements were, as expected, in agreement with the assignment of the same stereochemistry to **82** and daunomycinone (97).

13-Dihydrocarminomycin (**81b**) has been obtained by chemical (98) and microbiological (99) reduction of carminomycin. The compound was, however, also obtained from the cultures of a mutant strain of *S. peucetius* by Cassinelli *et al.* (100). In the latter study, in addition to physicochemical and degradative investigations that allowed the attribution of structure **81b** to the new biosynthetic antibiotic, a comparison of the corresponding aglycone with a sample of 4-*O*-demethyl-13-dihydrodaunomycinone (**83a**), prepared from daunomycinone by 4-*O*-demethylation with anhydrous aluminum chloride in methylene chloride to give 4-*O*-demethyldaunomycinone (carminomycinone) and reduction of the latter with sodium borohydride, afforded the direct chemical correlation of **81b** with daunorubicin. Conversion of daunorubicin to carminomycin was completed by glycosidation of 4-*O*-demethyldaunomycinone with *N,O*-ditrifluoroacetyl-α-daunosaminyl chloride in ethyl ether and in the presence of silver triflate followed by deblocking of the sugar moiety. Moreover, the infrared and mass spectra of **83b**, obtained by catalytic hydrogenolysis of **81b**, were identical to those of demethyldeoxydaunorubicinol aglycone described by Takanashi and Bachur (101). In mice bearing L 1210 leukemia, compound **81b** displayed an antitumor activity similar to that of **80b**, both compounds showing optimal doses approximately 5 times lower than daunorubicin in the same test system (100). When directly compared with daunorubicin and doxorubicin in the murine P 388 system (Table II), carminomycin appeared more potent than both reference antibiotics, the antitumor activity, as measured by the effect on survival, being intermediate between the activities of daunorubicin and doxorubicin. The remarkable efficacy of *N*-trifluoroacetylcarminomycin at high dosage is also an interesting finding to which the same considerations as those made for doxorubicin *N*-trifluoroacetate (Chapter 6) should apply.

Carminomycin, similarly to doxorubicin, binds to DNA and strongly inhibits DNA and RNA polymerase reactions. Russian investigators have

Table II

Comparative Activity of Carminomycin[a] and of *N*-Trifluoroacetylcarminomycin[a] against P 388 Experimental Leukemia in Mice[b]

Compound	O.D.[c]	T/C[d]	Daunorubicin		Doxorubicin	
			O.D.[c]	T/C[d]	O.D[c]	T/C[d]
Carminomycin	3.13	179	8	126	8	185
Carminomycin	0.78	140	16	136	16	139
Carminomycin	3.13	149	4	155	8	198
N-Trifluoroacetylcarminomycin	200	214	8	132	8	197

[a] Semisynthetic compounds.

[b] NCI data, screener A. D. Little, experiments 4751, 4929, 4931, 5129.

[c] Optimal doses, mg/kg.

[d] Median increase of survival time as percent of controls.

demonstrated its antitumor activity in a range of transplantable tumors of mice including a "prestomach cancer," a bronchogenic carcinoma, and L 1210 ascitic leukemia, and have shown it to be superior to daunorubicin (rubomycin) both in terms of activity and potency in the last system. The drug is also absorbed orally and mainly excreted in the bile. The LD_{50} values in the mouse were 1.7 mg/kg (ip), 3.7 mg/kg (iv) and 7.3 mg/kg (po). Toxic manifestations in dogs included myelosuppression, inhibition of erythropoiesis, and liver damage. In the Zbinden rat model, the EKG changes induced by carminomycin treatment were not so marked as those following equipotent doses of doxorubicin. Electron microscopic examination of myocardium from rats treated with toxic doses indicated a prevalence of mitochondrial damage, instead of nucleolar alterations as after doxorubicin treatment (*102*).

Clinical trials carried out in Russia with carminomycin administered twice weekly (total dose 10–50 mg/m²), daily, or every other day (total dose 15–30 mg/m²) indicated leukopenia, thrombocytopenia, nausea and vomiting, and EKG changes as major toxicities. Activity in soft tissue sarcomas, lymphomas, acute leukemias, and breast cancer was reported (*102,103*). The phase I results have been confirmed in preliminary investigations carried out in the United States (*104*).

Methylation of the 11-hydroxyl of carminomycin to give 11-*O*-methyl-carminomycin (**84**) has been recently reported by Essery and Doyle (*105*). This synthesis (yields were not given) was based on the selective hydrolysis of the 11-*O*-acetate in a fully acetylated anthracyclinone derivative, such as ε-rhodomycinone tetraacetate (**85a**) and 4,6,11,4′-tetraacetylcarminomycin (**86a**). It was found that when the solution of **85a** in an acetone–pH 7.5

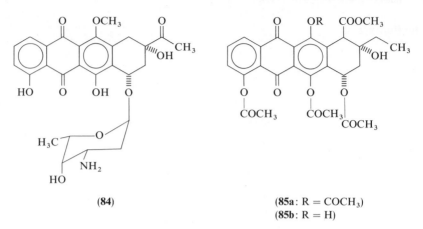

(84)

(85a: R = COCH₃)
(85b: R = H)

phosphate buffer mixture (4:3) was left for 64 hr at 22°C, only one acetyl group was removed and **85b** was obtained. Compound **85b** was identified as 4,6,7-triacetyl-ε-rhodomycinone on the basis of the infrared spectrum of the product resulting from the treatment with methyl iodide and potassium carbonate in refluxing acetone followed by hydrolysis of the acetyl groups, showing absorptions at 1670 cm⁻¹ and 1620 cm⁻¹, similarly to those exhibited by aklavinone, and as expected for structure **87**. Similarly, hydrolysis

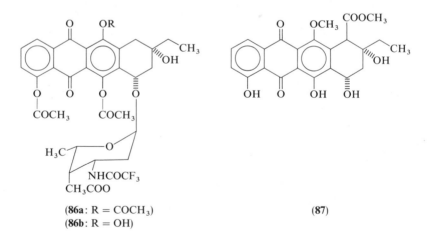

(86a: R = COCH₃)
(86b: R = OH)

(87)

of **86a** in the mixture of acetone with 5% aqueous sodium bicarbonate for 1.5 hr at 22°C, gave **86b**, which was methylated as above and hydrolysed with diluted sodium hydroxide to **84**. The monomethylated carminomycin **84** showed a T/C value of 136% at 16 mg/kg in mice bearing L 1210 Leukemia, thus being clearly less active than carminomycin (T/C 157% at 0.8 mg/kg).

The Baumycins

Six new daunorubicin derivatives were isolated, together with daunorubicin itself, *N*-acetyldaunorubicin, and *N*-acetyl-13-dihydrodaunorubicin,
from cultures of a strain belonging to the species *Streptomyces caeruleorubidus* (*106,107*). The new compounds, which gave daunorubicin on mild
acid treatment, were named baumycin A1, A2, B1, B2, C1 and C2. Four
aglycones were also isolated, namely ε-rhodomycinone, 7-deoxydihydro-
daunomycinone, dihydrodaunomycinone, and its 7-epimer. The structure
of baumycins A1 and A2 was established mainly on the basis of PMR data
concerning the glycosides, their peracetylated derivatives, and the tetraacetate of the sugar moiety obtained, together with 7-deoxydaunomycinone,
on catalytic hydrogenolysis of the glycosides. Baumycins A1 and A2 were
found to have the acetal structure **88a** and were considered to be epimers at
C-1″ or C-3″. Similarly, structure **88b** was attributed to baumycins B1 and
B2 from PMR and mass spectroscopic analysis of the corresponding methyl
esters. Baumycins C1 and C2 were identified as *N*-formyldaunorubicin and
N-formyl-13-dihydrodaunorubicin, the former being directly compared with
a authentic sample prepared by *N*-formylation of daunorubicin.

When tested for their ability to inhibit DNA and RNA synthesis in
cultured leukemia cells (effect on incorporation of labeled uridine or thymidine at 37°C into acid-insoluble material), the baumycins, as well as
doxorubicin, daunorubicin, pyrromycin, and 1-deoxypyrromycin, inhibited

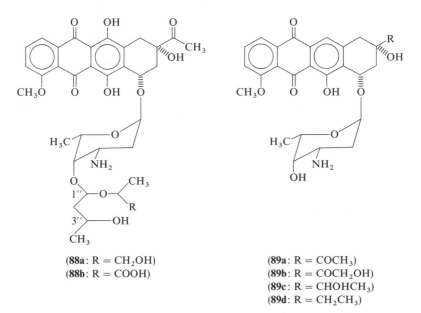

(**88a**: R = CH₂OH)
(**88b**: R = COOH)

(**89a**: R = COCH₃)
(**89b**: R = COCH₂OH)
(**89c**: R = CHOHCH₃)
(**89d**: R = CH₂CH₃)

both processes at approximately equivalent concentrations (IC_{50} values), whereas cinerubins, aclacinomycins, and rhodirubins inhibited RNA synthesis at 9 to 19 times lower concentrations than those required for DNA synthesis (*42*). The differential effect seems therefore to be related to the presence of more than one sugar moiety. Baumycin Al was more potent than, but equiactive to, daunorubicin in the L 1210 test *in vivo*, while baumycins Bl and Cl showed a lower activity at the optimal doses (*42*).

The 11-Deoxy Glycosides

A mutant strain derived from *S. peucetius* and characterized as *Micromonospora peucetica* was found to produce four new yellow anthracyclines displaying antimicrobial and antitumor activity (*108*). Isolation and structural elucidation of these compounds allowed assignement of formulas **89a**, **89b**, **89c**, and **89d** to the compounds, all showing the same UV and visible spectra and the presence of one hydrogen-bonded and one nonbonded quinone carbonyl in the infrared (1625 and 1670 cm^{-1}). Acid hydrolysis afforded daunosamine and four different aglycones. The PMR and ^{13}C-NMR spectra of the aglycone **90a** and of its triacetate indicated a close relationship with daunomycinone. Demethylation of the same aglycone with aluminum chloride in dichloromethane afforded compound **90b**, still possessing one hydrogen-bonded and one nonbonded quinone carbonyl, indicating that the methoxy and the hydroxy substituents on the aromatic chromophore were

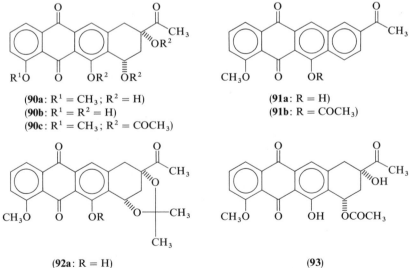

(**90a**: R^1 = CH$_3$; R^2 = H)
(**90b**: R^1 = R^2 = H)
(**90c**: R^1 = CH$_3$; R^2 = COCH$_3$)

(**91a**: R = H)
(**91b**: R = COCH$_3$)

(**92a**: R = H)
(**92b**: R = COCH$_3$)

(**93**)

both peri to the same quinone carbonyl group. Similarly to daunomycinone, the aglycone **90a** furnished the totally aromatic bisanhydro derivative **91a** both derivatives being characterized also through their monoacetates **91b** and **92b**. Formation of **93** on mild acid hydrolysis of **92b**, involving the acetate 6,7-shift, allowed assignment of positions 4 and 6 to the methoxyl and the phenolic hydroxyl group respectively.

Assignment of the α configuration to the glycosidic linkage in **89a** on the basis of PMR and ^{13}C-NMR signals of the C-1' H group defined the new glycoside as 11-deoxydaunorubicin. Direct chemical transformation of the latter to **89b**, **89c**, and **89d** clarified the structures of the latter compounds as 11-deoxydoxorubicin, 11-deoxy-13-dihydrodaunorubicin, and 11-deoxy-13-deoxodaunorubicin. The X-ray analysis of **90c** confirmed unequivocally the assigned structures as well as the absolute stereochemistry of the new glycosides (*109*).

OTHER ANTHRACYCLINE ANTIBIOTICS

In addition to the families of anthracycline antibiotics derived from rhodomycinones, pyrromycinones, aklavinone, and daunomycinone, different structural types are known that exhibit interesting biological properties. Among these are nogalamycin, steffimycin, and isoquinocycline A, and a brief account of their discovery and properties is the subject of this section.

Nogalamycin and Derivatives

Nogalamycin was first described by Wiley *et al.* (*110*) in 1968. Analytical and degradation studies showed it to be related to the anthracyclines, and possibly identical with reticulomycin A (*111*), and to possess a glycosidic structure, with one neutral sugar, nogalose, being easily split by acid treatment with formation of nogalarol (or of *O*-methylnogalarol after methanolysis). A second dimethylaminosugar residue was instead resistant to hydrolytic cleavage and could not be isolated intact. Partial structures **94a**,

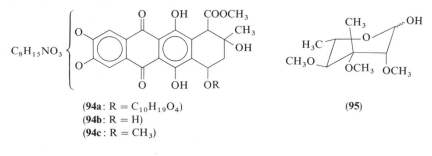

(**94a**: R = C$_{10}$H$_{19}$O$_4$)
(**94b**: R = H)
(**94c**: R = CH$_3$)

(**95**)

94b, and **94c** were derived for nogalamycin and its degradation products. The elucidation of complete structure and stereochemistry of nogalose was eventually achieved three years later (*112*). On the basis of chemical reactions of nogalose and of PMR data as well as of X-ray crystallographic analysis of amide **96**, formula **95** was attributed to this new sugar belonging to the L series and possessing a C-methyl group and three methoxyl groups. The synthesis of nogalose has been performed recently (*113*).

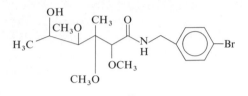

(96)

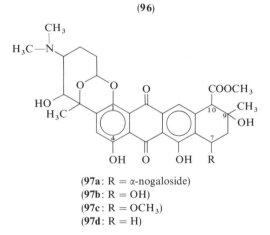

(97a: R = α-nogaloside)
(97b: R = OH)
(97c: R = OCH₃)
(97d: R = H)

The structure of nogalamycin was reported by Wiley *et al.* (*114*) as **97a**. Acid hydrolysis of the antibiotic gave **97b**, nogalose, and the bisanhydro derivative **98**, whereas to 7-*O*-methylnogalarol, the product obtained by

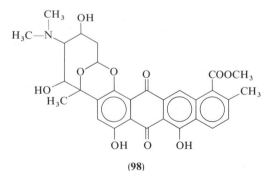

(98)

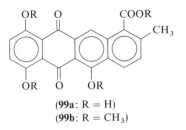

(**99a**: R = H)
(**99b**: R = CH$_3$)

methanolysis, structure **97c** was ascribed. Catalytic hydrogenolysis of **97a** afforded **97d**, and boiling of the latter with sodium acetate and acetic anhydride resulted in the pentaacetate of the corresponding 9,10-anhydro derivative. Treatment of **97a**, **97b**, **97c**, or **98** with sodium hydroxide furnished **99a**, which was methylated to **99b**.

The DNA binding properties of nogalamycin were demonstrated by its ability to displace methyl green from a methyl green–DNA complex and to inhibit pancreatic deoxyribonuclease (*115*); by polarographic (*54*) and circular dichroism (*116*) measurements; by spectral titration (*117*); by the nitrocellulose filter retention technique (*118*); by equilibrium dialysis, spectrophotometry and viscosimetry (*119*); and by flow-dichroism studies (*120*). The main binding mode was considered to be of the intercalative type, as also confirmed by Sinha *et al.* (*121*) on the basis of, *inter alia*, electron microscopic observations. Nogalamycin at low concentrations inhibited both *E. coli* DNA and RNA polymerase systems (*122*) and primed synthesis of polyd(A–T)·polyd(T–A) catalyzed by purified *E. coli* DNA polymerase (*123*). Treatment of human chromosome preparations with the antibiotic did not produce fluorescent banding as instead observed with doxorubicin (*124*).

Inhibition of nucleic acid synthesis was also observed in isolated mithochondria (*125*) and it explained the morphological changes in amphibian embryonic cells exposed to nogalamycin (*126*). In HeLa cells, a marked selectivity for DNA-dependent RNA synthesis was recorded by Ellem and Rhodes (*127*). Nogalamycin was most cytotoxic to a sinchronous cell population when the latter was exposed to the drug while at the G$_1$–S border region (*128*). Similarly to daunorubicin, it induced metaphase chromosome crossbanding in cultured mammalian cells (*129*) and did not cause breakdown of pulselabeled RNA in *B. megatherium*, the anthracyclines behaving therefore differently than actinomycin D, mithramycin, and chromomycin A (*130*). Also similarly to daunorubicin, nogalamycin selectively inhibited viral but not cellular protein synthesis (*131*), and inhibited endogenous respiration of Ehrlich tumor cells only at high concentrations (100 μg/ml).

A marked selective inhibition of RNA synthesis by nogalamycin was recorded in both normal and regenerating liver of rats treated with 1–10 mg/kg of the drug. At the same dose level, hydrocortisone induction of tryptophan pyrrolase was also blocked (*132*). Regression of experimental tumors in rats upon nogalamycin treatment was reported by Bempong (*133*). Nogalamycin showed essentially complete cross resistance to doxorubicin when tested against doxorubicin-resistant P 388 leukemia (*59*). Nogalamycin was not a good substrate for microsomal reductive glycosidase (*134*).

Nogalamycin and its derivatives **97b**, **97c**, and **97d** inhibited the incorporation of labeled precursors into RNA by 69–80% and into DNA by 30–40% when added for a period of 2 hr to the incubation medium of K B cells. However, the said derivatives were much less effective in stabilizing the double-helical DNA towards heat denaturation and appeared to have a lower affinity for this biopolymer when compared with the parent drug. Although less cytotoxic in cultured cells than nogalamycin, 7-*O*-methyl-nogalarol (**97c**) was more active than **97a** in the L 1210 test in mice, optimal dose being however 40 times higher (*135*).

Additional information on the synthesis of **97c** and of 10-descarbomethoxynogalamycin (*136*), on the differential effects of nogalamycin and its derivatives on nucleic acid synthesis in L 1210 cells (*137*), and on antitumor activity of the said derivatives (*138*), has been reported. The most interesting compound within this series seems to be **97c**, which has been confirmed to have poor DNA complexing ability but to be, in contrast with the parent, relatively more effective as an inhibitor of DNA synthesis rather than of RNA synthesis and as an antitumor agent in P 388 and L 1210 murine leukemias. In the latter tests, the compound was equal or even superior to doxorubicin. In a recently published work, Egorin *et al.* (*139*) demonstrated that **97c** was taken up into both L 1210 and P 388 cultured cells to a greater extent than was daunorubicin, the concentration dependency and the effect of inhibitors on uptake suggesting a different mechanism regulating the intracellular accumulation of the two compounds. Intracellular distribution of **97c** indicated a preferential cytoplasmic accumulation. On the other hand, this derivative produced, similarly to daunorubicin, a dose-dependent inhibition of [^{3}H]thymidine incorporation in the said cell systems, and showed cross resistance with daunorubicin and doxorubicin when tested on P 388 cells resistant to doxorubicin.

Other biosynthetic anthracyclines whose structures have not been determined but which have been related to nogalamycin are the cytotetrins (*140*) and the beromycins (*141*).

Steffimycin

Steffimycin (U-20661) and steffimycin B are anthracycline antibiotics isolated from *S. steffisburgensis* (*142*) and from *S. elgreteus* (*143*) respectively.

The structure of steffimycin has been established to be **100a** on the basis of chemical degradation and physicochemical analysis (*144*). The 1,8-dihydroxyanthraquinone chromophore was shown by the ultraviolet spectrum, and the presence of three carbonyl groups was shown by the infrared bands at 1620 (hydrogen-bonded quinone), 1672 (nonbonded quinone), and 1710 cm^{-1} (ketone). Acidic methanolysis afforded the corresponding aglycone, steffimycinone, and methyl 2-*O*-methyl-α-L-rhamnoside. Catalytic reduction of steffimycin furnished 7-deoxysteffimycinone. Both ^{13}C- and ^{1}H-NMR spectra of the antibiotic and its degradation products together with sodium borohydride reduction studies of steffimycinone allowed the establishment of the structure of the aglycone moiety. Steffimycin B was found to be the 4'-*O*-methyl derivative **100b** of steffimycin.

Steffimycin was soon recognized to be a strong inhibitor of macromolecular synthesis in bacteria (*122,145,146*). It is noteworthy that the two steffimycins share the property of binding to double-stranded DNA as evidenced by spectroscopic and thermal stabilization measurements (*147,148*), but their effects on DNA-directed RNA and DNA synthesis are remarkably different. Steffimycin, upon interaction with salmon sperm DNA used as the template, inhibited by 50% the reaction catalyzed by *E. coli* RNA polymerase when added to the reaction mixture at 4 μM concentration, whereas a 100 times higher concentration affected the synthetic reaction catalyzed by DNA polymerase I by 15–28%. On the other hand, the presence of the 4'-*O*-methyl group in steffimycin B modified the properties of the drug–DNA complex in such a way that in similar conditions the latter antibiotic inhibited the DNA polymerase I reaction by 50% when present at a contration of 10 μM in the incubation mixture, whereas the RNA polymerase reaction was not significantly affected in the presence of a 10-fold greater concentration of the drug.

As already found for nogalamycin, steffimycin did not appear to be a good substrate for microsomal reduction glycosidase, the liver enzyme responsible for the main inactivating metabolic reaction of the anthracyclines (*134*).

Isoquinocycline A and Trypanomycin

Isoquinocycline A (*101*) was found (*149,150*) to be an inhibitor of DNA-dependent RNA and DNA synthesis catalyzed by enzyme preparations obtained from *E. coli*. The concentrations required for 50% inhibition were, however, 4 to 8 times greater in the case of RNA synthesis and approximately twice in that of DNA synthesis than the IC$_{50}$ values found for daunorubicin, cinerubin, and nogalamycin (*52*).

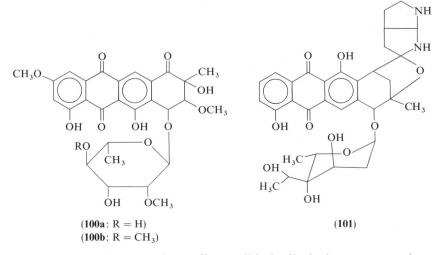

(**100a**: R = H)   (**101**)
(**100b**: R = CH₃)

Trypanomycin is an anthracycline antibiotic displaying strong antiprotozoal activity and cytotoxicity in cultured mammalian cells. The chemical structure of this compound was not investigated (*151*).

THE BIOSYNTHESIS OF THE ANTHRACYCLINES

The presence of the anthracyclines among the metabolic products of actinomycetes rises the question of their mode of formation and of their significance as natural, biologically active compounds. The latter question cannot be answered at present time, as is the case for most "secondary products" of microbes and plants, including the antibiotics, but two considerations can be made. The first is that these compounds seem to be of rather common occurrence in the above-mentioned genus, as is witnessed by the number of species that have been found able to produce them. The second one is that the biogenetic pathways leading to the anthracycline glycosides are now known as a result of radioisotopic tracer investigations indicating the acetate–propionate units and the sugars as the starting biochemical species for their biosynthesis, thus relating the formation of the compounds to that of a number of other products of microbial and plant origin. In 1970, Umezawa and co-workers (*152*) suggested that extrachromosomal genetic material might be involved in the production or biosynthesis of *Streptomyces* antibiotics such as kasugamycin, aureothricin, and thiolutin. This suggestion was based on the observation that the ability to produce these "secondary metabolites" was a property of certain strains belonging to different species, not of the species themselves, and that the ability to produce the said compounds was lost after acriflavine treatment or exposure to high temperatures, known procedures leading to elimination of plasmids in bacterial and fungal cells. The involvement of plasmids in the production of other antibiotics and enzyme inhibitors was subsequently reported by the same and by other investigators, and later Umezawa reported on this aspect as applied to anthracycline formation (153). Acriflavine treatment eliminated the anthracycline-producing ability of the aclacinomycin-producing strain, although this was restored when the aglycone, aklavinone, was added to the cultures. Also, the baumycins-producing organism lost the ability to produce both daunomycinone derivatives and ε-rhodomycinone upon treatment with acriflavin, the latter aglycone appearing to be transformed to daunorubicin when added to the cultures of the nonproducing strain. It was also found that aklavinone was the precursor of ε-rhodomycinone and of daunorubicin. The author concluded suggesting that genetic sets for the biosynthesis of daunorubicin and aclacinomycin were very similar and were concerned with the biosynthesis of aklavinone. The production of anthracycline compounds by different *Streptomyces* strains were related to the distribution of plasmids containing the same genetic set for the biosynthesis of aklavinone whose diverse modification and glycosidation by the single strains would give rise to the different compounds.

Extensive investigations on the genetic and biosynthetic relationships in anthracycline production by *S. caeruleorubidus* and *S. galilaeus* have been carried out by Vanek and co-workers of the Czechoslovak Academy of Sciences. A summary of the results obtained from metabolites idenfication, biotransformation ability, and cosynthetic activity of different mutants has been recently reported (154). The reaction sequences leading to anthracycline biosynthesis as deduced by the said authors are presented in Fig. 2. Different mutants with impaired biosynthetic capabilities were identified in the mutant organisms. Starting from *S. caeruleorubidus*, the following mutants were obtained (biosynthetic steps affected are in parentheses): P_1 (1,2,5); A (1,2,7); B (5,7); C (3,5,7,9); D (3,5); E (1–3,5,6,9). From *S. galilaeus*, the mutants were: P_2 (1,2,10); F (10); G (2,7,8,10–14). The authors concluded suggesting that observed complex changes in the biosynthetic abilities resulting from mutation would favor the hypothesis that the genetic loci which control different steps of the biosynthetic sequence were closely clustered. Vanek and his group have also published detailed studies on the effect of chemical composition of fermentation media and of strain improvement on productivity of *S. caeruleorubidus* and *S. peucetius* (155), of *S. galilaeus* [(156), and references cited therein] and of *S. nogalater* (157). Substantial variations were recorded as a result of qualitative and quantitative modifications of the carbon source, aeration conditions, concentration of some metal ions, and the presence of different inhibitors such as diethylbarbiturate, propanol,

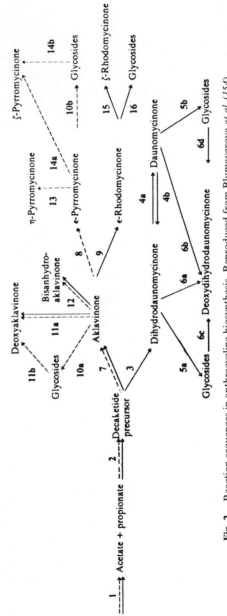

Fig. 2. Reaction sequences in anthracycline biosynthesis. Reproduced from Blumauerova *et al.* (*154*).

and sodium propionate. The importance of cultural conditions for productivity is also easily understood on the basis of the documented transformations that the final products of the fermentation process can undergo as a result of metabolic activity of the producing microorganism. An oxygen-inhibited conversion of daunomycin to 7-deoxydaunomycinone in the fermentation beers was recorded by Kern *et al.* (*158*). Enzymatic conversion of aclacinomycin A to aclacinomycin Y was found to be catalyzed by a specific oxidoreductase which was isolated from the culture filtrates of *S. galilaeus* (*159*).

The acetate–propionate origin of the anthracycline skeleton involving the intermediate formation of an enzyme-bound polyketide has already been mentioned in Chapter 1. The biogenesis of the anthracyclinone has been reviewed by Vanek *et al.* (*160*). The development of ^{13}C-NMR has more recently allowed more detailed and accurate investigations of the biogenetic process when ^{13}C-labeled precursors of high isotopic purity are used. Casey *et al.* (*161*) have grown *S. peucetius* in the presence of [1-^{13}C]acetate or of [2-^{13}C]acetate or of [1,2-^{13}C]acetate and submitted the crude mycelial extract to acid hydrolysis in order to convert all daunorubicin to daunomycinone, which was then purified by reextraction and chromatography. For NMR analysis, daunomycinone was converted to the tetraacetate and enrichment levels of the various carbon atoms of the latter in the absence and in the presence of labeled precursors were recorded. The signals of enriched carbons appeared 2 or 3 times more intense than the natural abundance level. Distribution of incorporation when singly labeled acetate was used is indicated in Fig. 3. The results were in agreement with the previous formulation concerning the pathway of polyketide folding and condensation. The preservation of spin–spin coupling at the expected adjacent positions in the enriched product from doubly labeled acetate, but not at C-10 which appeared as a singlet, allowed firm establishment of the said pathway. This obviously involved the decarboxylation at C-10 and the derivation of the C-9,C-13,C-14 fragment from propionate. The latter postulate was unequivocally demonstrated by [1-^{13}C]propionate incorporation experiments into

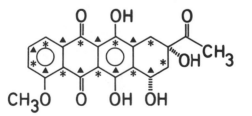

Fig. 3. Distribution of ^{13}C-enrichment in daunomycinone when [1-^{13}C]acetate (▲) or [2-^{13}C]acetate (*) were fed to cultures of *S. peucetius.*

the aglycones of daunorubicin and doxorubicin by cultures of *S. peucetius* var. *caesius* (*162*), leading to a 10-fold enrichment of the quaternary aliphatic ring carbon (C-9). Similarly, by the use of ^{13}C-labeled acetate as precursor, the aglycones of nogalamycin and steffimycin B were shown to be derived from 10 acetate units (*163*). In this study it was also demonstrated that the neutral sugar moieties present in the said antibiotics were originated from D-glucose and the *O*- and *N*-methyl groups from methionine, the precursor of the aminosugar residue of nogalamycin remaining uncertain, as the corresponding carbon atoms, but not carbon C-2′, exhibited ^{13}C-enrichment upon addition of uniformely ^{13}C-labeled D-glucose to the *S. nogalater* fermentations.

MICROBIAL TRANSFORMATIONS

Microbial modifications of the anthracyclines have been investigated with the aim of obtaining new and improved antitumor agents. In the course of these studies, considerable similarity was found between mammalian and bacterial metabolism of these compounds.

The presence of enzymes catalyzing transformation of the anthracyclines in the cultures of the producing microorganisms has already been mentioned above. Anthracycline-producing strains were also found to be able to modify other anthracyclines in addition to those normally produced. Marshall *et al.* (*164*) described a cell-free extract preparation from *S. steffisburgensis* catalyzing the conversion of daunorubicin to 7-deoxydaunomycinone in the presence of NADH as a cofactor. The same preparation transformed 7-deoxydaunomycinone into 7-deoxy-13-dihydrodaunomycinone, NADPH being the preferred cofactor. In a subsequent paper it was also shown that 13-dihydrodaunorubin and doxorubicin were good substrates of the *S. steffisburgensis*-derived crude enzyme, doxorubicin being converted to 7-deoxyadriamycinone and 7-deoxy-13-dihydroadriamycinone (*165*). Cell-free preparations of *S. nogalater* catalyzed the NADH-dependent, oxygen-sensitive hydrogenolysis not only of nogalamycin, 7-*O*-methylnogarol, and 7-*O*-methylnogalarol, but also of doxorubicin, steffimycin, and steffimycin B, to give the corresponding 7-deoxyaglycones (*166*).

Different facultative microorganisms isolated from sewage were able to bring about the benzylic hydrogenolysis of anthracycline glycosides. The microorganisms were identified as *Aeromonas hydrophila*, *Escherichia coli*, and *Citrobacter freundii*, and microaerophilic incubation conditions were essential for the reductive reaction to occur. In this way, steffimycin was converted to 7-deoxysteffimycinone, and a similar transformation was obtained using daunorubicin, nogalamycin, and cinerubin A as substrates.

The requirement of almost anaerobic conditions was interpreted as the consequence of inducer or repressor roles associated with oxygen tension in the growth medium. As for the streptomycete enzyme, NADH was the preferred hydrogen donor when dialyzed cell-free extracts of micro-aerophilically grown *A. hydrophila* were used (*167*).

Reduction of the C-13 carbonyl group of daunorubicin and its derivatives has also been carried out as a distinct microbiological transformation. Reduction of carminomycin to give 13-dihydrocarminomycin was performed with cultures of *S. lavendulae*, *S. roseochromogenes*, *Corynebacterium simplex*, or *Bacterium cyclooxydans* (*99*). The conversion of daunomycinone to 13-dihydrodaunomycinone by washed micelium of *S. aureofaciens* was reported by Karnetová *et al.* (*168*). Many different microbial isolates were found capable of converting daunorubicin and *N*-acetyldaunorubicin to the corresponding 13-dihydro derivatives, by Aszalos *et al.* (*169*). In this study, a strain of *Corynebacterium equi* was used for the preparative experiments. The mold, *Mucor spinosus*, and its cell-free extract both reduced daunorubicin to daunorubicinol (*165*). *N*-Acetyldaunorubicin and *N*-acetyldaunorubicinol were produced upon addition of the corresponding nonacetylated compounds to a growing culture of *Bacillus cereus* var. *mycoides* (*170*).

REFERENCES

1. H. Brockmann, *Fortschr. Chem. Org. Naturst.* **21**, 121 (1963).
2. H. Brockmann, P. Boldt and J. Niemeyer, *Chem. Ber.* **96**, 1356 (1963).
3. H. Brockmann and E. Wimmer, *Chem. Ber.* **98**, 2797 (1965).
4. H. Brockmann, J. Niemeyer, H. Brockmann, Jr., and H. Budzikiewicz, *Chem. Ber.* **98** 3785 (1965).
5. H. Brockmann and J. Niemeyer, *Chem. Ber.* **100**, 3578 (1967).
6. H. Brockmann and J. Niemeyer, *Chem. Ber.* **101**, 1341 (1968).
7. H. Brockmann and H. Brockmann, Jr., *Chem. Ber.* **96** 1771 (1963).
8. H. Brockmann, T. Waehneldt, and J. Niemeyer, *Tetrahedron Lett.* No. 6, 415 (1969).
9. H. Brockmann, and P. Patt, *Chem. Ber.* **88**, 1455 (1955).
10. H. Brockmann and T. Waehneldt, *Naturw.* **48**, 717 (1961).
11. J. Shoji, S. Kozuki, H. Nishimura, M. Mayama, K. Motokawa, Y. Tanaka, and H. Otsuka, *J. Antibiot.* **21**, 643 (1968).
12. E. Biedermann and H. Bräuniger, *Pharmazie* **27**, 782 (1972).
13. H. Brockmann, B. Scheffer, and C. Stein, *Tetrahedron Lett.* No. 38, 3699 (1973).
14. H. Brockmann and H. Greve, *Tetrahedron Lett.* No. 11, 831 (1975).
15. Y. Matsuzawa, A. Yoshimoto, T. Oki, T. Inui, T. Takeuchi, and H. Umezawa, *J. Antibiot.* **32**, 420 (1979).
16. W. Fleck, D. Strauss, A. Koch, and H. Prauser, *Antibiotiki* (*Moscow*) **20**, 966 (1975); *C.A.* **84**, 87877 (1976).
17. H. Brockmann, H. Brockmann, Jr., and J. Niemeyer, *Tetrahedron Lett.* No. 45, 4719 (1968).
18. R. Reed and W. K. Reid, *Tetrahedron* **19**, 1817 (1963).
19. H. Brockmann, Jr., H. Budzikiewicz, C. Djerassi, H. Brockmann, and J. Niemeyer, *Chem. Ber.* **98**, 1260 (1965).

20. M. Röhrl and W. Hoppe, *Chem. Ber.* **103**, 3502 (1970).

21. H. Brockmann and R. Zunker, *Tetrahedron Lett.* No. 1, 45 (1966).

22. A. S. Kende and Y. Tsay, *Chem. Commun.* p. 140 (1977).

23. K. Krohn and A. Rösner, *Tetrahedron Lett.* No. 4, 353 (1978).

24. K. Krohn and M. Radeloff, *Chem. Ber.* **111**, 3823 (1978).

25. K. Krohn, *J. Chem. Res. (S)* p. 394 (1978).

26. K. Krohn and C. Hemme, *Justus Liebigs Ann. Chem.* p. 19 (1979).

27. C. Marschalk, F. König, and N. Ouroussoff, *Bull. Soc. Chim. Fr.* **3**, 1545 (1936).

28. K. Bredereck, H. Kimmich, and G. Sigmund, *Justus Liebigs Ann. Chem.*, 184 (1977).

29. K. Krohn and C. Hemme, *Justus Liebigs Ann. Chem.*, 35 (1979).

30. K. Krohn, *Angew. Chem., Int. Ed. Engl.* **18**, 621 (1979).

31. H. S. El Khadem, D. L. Swartz, and R. R. Cermak, *J. Med. Chem.* **20**, 957 (1977).

31a. T. H. Smith, A. N. Fujiwara, and D. W. Henry, *J. Med. Chem.* **21**, 280 (1978).

32. C. L. Stevens, P. Blumbergs, and D. L. Wood, *J. Am. Chem. Soc.* **86**, 3592 (1964).

33. W. Keller-Schierlein and W. Richle, *Antimicrob. Agents Chemother.*, *1970* p. 68 (1971).

34. W. Keller-Schierlein and W. Richle, *Chimia* **24**, 35 (1970).

35. W. Richle, E. K. Winkler, D. M. Hawley, M. Dobler, and W. Keller-Schierlein, *Helv. Chim. Acta* **55**, 467 (1972).

36. C. L. Stevens, K. W. Schultze, D. J. Smith, and P. M. Pillai, *J. Org. Chem.* **40**, 3704 (1975).

37. K. Eckardt, *Chem. Ber.* **100**, 2561 (1967).

38. K. Eckardt, D. Tresselt, and J. Tax, *Tetrahedron* **30**, 3787 (1974).

39. D. Tresselt, K. Eckardt, and J. Tax, *Tetrahedron* **31**, 613 (1975).

40. T. Oki, Y. Matsuzawa, A. Yoshimoto, K. Numata, I. Kitamura, S. Hori, A. Takamatsu, H. Umezawa, M. Ishizuka, H. Naganawa, H. Suda, M. Hamada, and T. Takeuchi, *J. Antibiot.* **28**, 830 (1975).

41. T. Oki, N. Shibamoto, Y. Matsuzawa, T. Ogasawara, A. Yoshimoto, I. Kitamura, T. Inui, H. Naganawa, T. Takeuchi, and H. Umezawa, *J. Antibiot.* **30**, 683 (1977).

42. T. Oki, *Jpn. J. Antibiotics* **30**, Suppl. 3, S70 (1977).

43. O. Goncalves da Lima, F. Delle Monache, I. L. D'Albuqueque, and G. B. Marino-Bettolo, *Tetrahedron Lett.* No. 4, 471 (1968).

44. J. R. Hegyi and N. N. Gerber, *Tetrahedron Lett.* No. 13, 1587 (1968).

45. D. E. Nettleton, Jr., T. W. Doyle, and W. T. Bradner, *U.S. Patent* 4, 123, 608 (Oct. 31, 1978).

46. W. T. Bradner and M. Misiek, *J. Antibiot.* **30**, 519 (1977).

47. I. Kitamura, N. Shibamoto, T. Oki, T. Inui, H. Naganawa, M. Ishizuta, T. Masuda, T. Takeuchi, and H. Umezawa, *J. Antibiot.* **30**, 616 (1977).

48. M. E. Jung and J. A. Lowe, *Chem. Commun.* p. 95 (1978).

49. H. S. El Khadem and D. L. Swartz, *Carbohydr. Res.* **65**, Cl (1978).

50. V. H. Du Vernay, Jr., J. A. Pachter, and S. T. Crooke, *Biochemistry* **18**, 4024 (1979).

51. W. Kersten and H. Kersten, *Biochem.* **341**, 174 (1965).

52. K. Koschel, G. Hartmann, W. Kersten, and H. Kersten, *Biochem.* **344**, 76 (1966).

53. W. Wehrli, J. Nueesch, F. Knuesel, and M. Staehelin, *Biochim. Biophys. Acta* **157**, 215 (1968).

54. H. Berg and K. Eckardt, *Z. Naturfortsch., Teil* **25** *B*, 362 (1970).

55. G. Löber, V. Kleinwächter, Z. Balcarova, R. Klarner, and W. Fleck, *Stud. Biophy.* **71**, 205 (1978).

56. G. Löber, V. Kleinwächter, Z. Balcarova, H. Fritzsche, and D. G. Strauss, *Stud. Biophys.* **71**, 203 (1978).

57. H. Helge and D. Neubert, *Naunyn-Schmiedebergs Arch. Exp. Pathol. Pharmakol.* **251**, 113 (1965).

58. M. Schmieder and D. Neubert, *Naunyn-Schmiedebergs Arch. Pharmakol. Exp. Pathol.* **255**, 68 (1966).
59. R. K. Johnson, A. A. Ovejera, and A. Goldin, *Cancer Treat. Rep.* **60**, 99 (1976).
60. L. J. Wilkoff and E. A. Dulmadge, *J. Natl. Cancer Inst.* **61**, 1521 (1978).
61. H. Yamaki, H. Suzuki, T. Nishimura, and N. Tanaka, *J. Antibiot.* **31**, 1149 (1978).
62. S. T. Crooke, V. H. Duvernay, L. Galvan, and A. W. Prestayko, *Mol. Pharmacol.* **14**, 290 (1978).
63. Y. Daskal, C. Woodard, S. T. Crooke, and H. Busch, *Cancer Res.* **38**, 467 (1978).
64. T. Nishimura, K. Muto, and N. Tanaka, *J. Antibiot.* **31**, 493 (1978).
65. K. Umezawa, M. Sawamura, T. Matsushima, and T. Sugimura, *Cancer Res.* **38**, 1782 (1978).
66. A. Yoshimoto, T. Oki, and T. Inui, *J. Antibiot.* **31**, 92 (1978).
67. M. Misumi, H. Yamaki, T. Akiyana, and N. Tanaka, *J. Antibiot.* **32**, 48 (1979).
68. C. Na and S. N. Timasheff, *Arch. Biochem. Biophys.* **182**, 147 (1977).
69. T. Komiyama, T. Oki, T. Inui, T. Takeuchi, and H. Umezawa, *Gann* **70**, 403 (1979).
70. T. Komiyama, T. Oki, T. Inui, T. Takeuchi, and H. Umezawa, *Biochem. Biophys. Res. Commun.* **82**, 188 (1978).
71. T. Komiyama, T. Oki, T. Inui, T. Takeuchi, and H. Umezawa, *Gann* **70**, 395 (1979).
72. I. Kitamura, T. Oki, and T. Inui, *J. Antibiot.* **31**, 919 (1978).
73. J. H. Peters and J. F. Murray, *J. Liq. Chromatogr.* **2**, 45 (1979).
74. M. Ogawa, J. Inagaki, N. Horikoshi, K. Inoue, T. Chinen, H. Ueoka, and E. Nagura, *Cancer Treat. Rep.* **63**, 931 (1979).
75. G. Mathe, M. Bayssas, J. Gouveia, D. Dantchev, P. Ribaud, D. Machover, J. L. Misset, L. Schwarzenberg, C. Jasmin, and M. Hayat, *Cancer Chemother. Pharmacol.* **1**, 259 (1978).
76. H. Suzuki, K. Kawashima, and K. Yamada, *Lancet* i, 870 (1979).
77. G. Mathe, F. Gescher, M. A. Gil, M. Byassa, M. Delgado, J. L. Missett, P. Ribaud, D. Machover, and M. Hayat, *Lancet* ii, p. 310 (1979).
78. A. Di Marco, in *"Antibiotics"* (D. Gottlieb and P. D. Shaw, eds.), Vol. 1, p. 190. Springer-Verlag, Berlin and New York, 1967.
79. A. Di Marco, F. Arcamone, and F. Zunino, in *"Antibiotics"* (J. W. Corcoran and F. E. Hahn, eds.), Vol. 3, p. 101. Springer-Verlag, Berlin and New York, 1974.
80. F. Zunino, R. Gambetta, A. Di Marco, and A. Zaccara, *Cancer Res.* **35**, 754 (1975).
81. A. M. Casazza, A. Di Marco, and G. Di Cuonzo, *Cancer Res.* **31**, 1971 (1971).
82. H. S. Schwartz and G. B. Grindey, *Cancer Res.* **33**, 1837 (1973).
83. H. S. Schwartz, *Cancer Chemother. Rep.* **58**, 55 (1974).
84. A. Mantovani, N. Polentarutti, W. Luini, G. Peri, and F. Spreafico, *J. Natl. Cancer Inst.* **63**, 61 (1979).
85. H. Loveless, E. Arena, R. L. Felsted, and N. R. Bachur, *Cancer Res.* **38**, 593 (1978).
86. D. Von Hoff, M. Rozencweig, and M. Slavik, *Adv. Pharmacol. Chemother.* **15**, 2 (1978).
87. J. Bernard, R. Paul, M. Boiron, C. Jaquillat, and R. Maral, *Recent Results Cancer Res.* **20**, (1969).
88. J. Chauvergne, *Bull. Cancer* **63**, 41 (1976).
89. W. Fleck and D. Strauss, *Z. Allg. Mikrobiol.* **15**, 495 (1975).
90. D. Strauss and W. Fleck, *Z. Allg. Mikrobiol.* **15**, 615 (1975).
91. M. G. Brazhnikova, V. B. Zbarskiy, M. K. Kudinova, L. I. Murav'yeva, V. I. Potomarenko, and N. P. Potapova, *Antibiotiki (Moscow)* **18**, 678 (1973).
92. M. G. Brazhnikova, V. B. Zbarskiy, N. P. Potanova, Y. N. Scheinker, T. F. Vlasova, and B. V. Rozynov, *Antibiotiki (Moscow)* **18**, 1059 (1973).
93. M. G. Brazhnikova, V. B. Zbarsky, U. I. Ponomarenko, and N. P. Potapova, *J. Antibiot.* **27**, 254 (1974).

94. M. C. Wani, H. L. Taylor, M. E. Wall, A. T. McPhail, and K. D. Onan, *J. Am. Chem. Soc.* **97**, 5955 (1975).
95. G. R. Pettit, J. J. Einck, C. L. Herald, R. H. Ode, R. B. Von Dreele, P. Brown, M. G. Brazhnikova, and G. F. Gause, *J. Am. Chem. Soc.* **97**, 7387 (1975).
96. R. B. Von Dreele and J. J. Einck, *Acta Crystallogr., Sect. B* **33**, 3283 (1977).
97. M. G. Brazhnikova, V. B. Zbarsky, D. Tresselt, and K. Eckardt, *J. Antibiot.* **29**, 469 (1976).
98. L. S. Povarov, V. A. Shorin, V. S. Bazhanov, and N. G. Shepevtseva, *Antibiotiki (Moscow)* **21**, 1008 (1976).
99. Rhône-Poulenc, Fr. Patent 848219 (May 10, 1977).
100. G. Cassinelli, A. Grein, P. Masi, A. Suarato, L. Bernardi, F. Arcamone, A. Di Marco, A. M. Casazza, G. Pratesi, and C. Soranzo, *J. Antibiot.* **31**, 178 (1978).
101. S. Takanashi and N. R. Bachur, *Drug Metab. Dispos.* **4**, 79 (1976).
102. S. T. Crooke, *J. Med.* **8**, 295 (1977).
103. N. I. Perevodchikova, M. R. Lichinister, and V. A. Gorbunova, *Cancer Treat. Rep.* **61**, 1705 (1977).
104. L. H. Baker, D. H. Kessel, R. L. Comis, S. D. Reich, M. D. De Furia, and S. T. Crooke, *Cancer Treat. Rep.* **63**, 899 (1979).
105. J. M. Essery and T. W. Doyle, *J. Antibiot.* **32**, 247 (1979).
106. T. Komiyama, Y. Matsuzawa, T. Oki, and T. Inui, *J. Antibiot.* **30**, 619 (1977).
107. Y. Takahashi, H. Naganawa, T. Takeuchi, H. Umezawa, T. Komiyama, T. Oki, and T. Inui, *J. Antibiot.* **30**, 622 (1977).
108. A. Grein, G. Cassinelli, F. Di Matteo, S. Forenza, S. Merli, M. C. Ripamonti, and G. Rivola, *Int. Symp. Antibiot., Weimar, D.D.R.* Abstr. A-3 (1979).
109. F. Arcamone, G. Cassinelli, F. Di Matteo, S. Forenza, M. C. Ripamonti, G. Rivola, A. Vigevani, T. McCabe, and J. Clardy, *J. Am. Chem. Soc.* **102**, 1462 (1980).
110. P. F. Wiley, F. A. MacKellar, E. L. Caron, and R. B. Kelly, *Tetrahedron Lett.* No. 4, 663 (1968).
111. L. A. Mitscher, W. McGrae, W. W. Andres, J. A. Lowery, and N. Bohonos, *J. Pharm. Sci.* **53**, 1139 (1964).
112. P. F. Wiley, D. J. Duchamp, V. Hsiung, and C. G. Chidester, *J. Org. Chem.* **36**, 2670 (1971).
113. L. Valente, A. Olesker, R. Rabanal, L. E. S. Baratta, and G. Luckas, *Tetrahedron Lett.* No. 13, 1153 (1979).
114. P. F. Wiley, R. B. Kelly, E. L. Caron, V. H. Wiley, J. H. Johnson, F. A. MacKeller, and S. A. Mizsak, *J. Am. Chem. Soc.* **99**, 542 (1977).
115. L. D. Zeleznick and C. M. Sweeney, *Arch. Biochem. Biophys.* **120**, 292 (1967).
116. G. Fey and H. Kernsten, *Hoppe-Seyler's Z. Physiol. Chem.* **351**, 111 (1970).
117. R. K. Neogy, K. Chowdhury, and G. G. Thakurta, *Biochim. Biophys. Acta* **299**, 241 (1973).
118. R. K. Neogy, K. Chowdhury, and I. Kerr, *Biochim. Biophys. Acta* **374**, 9 (1974).
119. G. C. Das, S. Dasgupta, and N. N. D. Gupta, *Biochim. Biophys. Acta* **353**, 274 (1974).
120. S. Marciani, M. Terbojevich, D. Vedaldi, and G. Rodighiero, *Farmaco, Ed. Sci.* **32**, 248 (1977).
121. R. K. Sinha, P. Talapatra, A. Mitra, and S. Mazumder, *Biochim. Biophys. Acta* **474**, 199 (1977).
122. F. Reusser and B. K. Bhuyan, *J. Bacteriol.* **94**, 576 (1967).
123. K. Olson, D. Luk, and C. L. Harvey, *Biochim. Biophys. Acta* **277**, 269 (1972).
124. C. C. Lin and J. H. Van de Sande, *Science* **190**, 61 (1975).

125. M. Schmieder and D. Neubert, *Naunyn-Schmiedebergs Arch. Pharmakol. Exp. Pathol.* **255**, 68 (1966).
126. A. M. Duprat, M. T. Miquel, J. C. Beetschen, and J. P. Zalta, *C. R. Acad. Sci.* **265**, 2080 (1967).
127. K. A. O. Ellem and S. L. Rhode, *Biochim. Biophys. Acta* **209**, 415 (1970.
128. B. K. Bhuyan, L. G. Scheidt, and T. J. Fraser, *Cancer Res.* **32**, 398 (1972).
129. T. C. Hsu, S. Pathak, and D. A. Shafer, *Exp. Cell Res.* **79**, 484 (1973).
130. J. Fok and M. Waring, *Mol. Pharmacol.* **8**, 65 (1972).
131. P. D. Minor and N. J. Dimmock, *Virology* **78**, 393 (1977).
132. G. D. Gray, G. W. Camiener, and B. K. Bhuyan, *Cancer Res.* **26**, 2419 (1966).
133. M. A. Bempong, *Int. J. Clin. Pharmacol. Biopharmacol.* **14**, 6 (1976).
134. N. R. Bachur and M. Gee, *J. Pharmacol. Exp. Ther.* **197**, 681 (1976).
135. B. K. Bhuyan and F. Reusser, *Cancer Res.* **30**, 984 (1970).
136. P. F. Wiley, J. L. Johnson, and D. J. Houser, *J. Antibiot.* **30**, 628 (1977).
137. B. K. Bhuyan and W. C. Krueger, *Proc. Am. Assoc. Cancer Res.* **18**, 250 (1977).
138. G. L. Neil, C. L. Blowers, D. J. Houser, J. H. Johnson, and P. F. Wiley, *Proc. Am. Assoc. Cancer Res.* **18**, 2 (1977).
139. M. J. Egorin, R. E. Clawson, J. L. Cohen, L. A. Ross, and N. R. Bachur, *J. Pharmacol. Exp. Ther.* **210**, 229 (1979).
140. J. Berdy, J. Zsadanyi, M. Halasz, J. Horvath, and K. Magyar, *J. Antibiot.* **24**, 209 (1971).
141. M. K. Kudinova, V. N. Borisova, N. M. Petukhova, and M. G. Brazhnikova, *Antibiotiki (Moscow)* **17**, 689 (1972).
142. M. E. Bergy and F. Reusser, *Experientia* **23**, 254 (1967).
143. T. F. Brodasky and F. Reusser, *J. Antibiot.* **27**, 809 (1974).
144. R. C. Kelly, I. Schletter, J. M. Koert, F. A. MacKellar, and P. F. Wiley, *J. Org. Chem.* **42**, 3591 (1977).
145. F. Reusser, *Biochem. Pharmacol.* **17**, 2001 (1968).
146. F. Reusser, *Biochem. Pharmacol.* **18**, 287 (1969).
147. F. Reusser, *J. Bacteriol.* **93**, 65 (1967).
148. F. Reuseer, *Biochim. Piophys. Acta* **383**, 266 (1975).
149. A. Tulinsky, *J. Am. Chem. Soc.* **86**, 5368 (1964).
150. D. B. Cosulich, J. H. Mowat, R. W. Broschard, J. B. Patrick, and W. E. Meyer, *Tetrahedron Lett.* No. 13, 750 (1964).
151. W. Fleck, D. Strauss, C. Schönfeld, W. Jungstand, C. Seeber, and H. Prauser, *Antimicrob. Agents Chemother.* **1**, 385 (1972).
152. M. Okanishi, T. Ohta, and H. Umezawa, *J. Antibiot.* **23**, 45 (1970).
153. H. Umezawa, *in* "Advances in Cancer Chemotherapy" (S. K. Carter *et al.*, eds.), p. 27. Jpn. Sci. Soc. Press, Tokyo and Univ. Park Press, Baltimore, Maryland, 1978.
154. M. Blumauerova', E. Kralovcova, J. Mateju, Z. Hostalek, and Z. Vanek, *in* "Genetics of Industrial Microorganisms" (O. K. Sebek and A. S. Laskin, eds.), p. 90. Am. Chem. Soc. Microbiol., Washington, D.C., 1979.
155. M. Blumauerova', J. Mateju, K. Stajner, and Z. Vanek, *Folia Microbiol. (Prague)* **22**, 275 (1977).
156. E. Kralovcova and Vanek Z., *Folia Microbiol. (Prague)* **24**, 296 (1979).
157. K. Klanova, M. Blumauerova', and Z. Vanek, *Folia Microbiol. (Prague)* **22**, 286 (1977).
158. D. L. Kern, R. H. Bunge, J. C. French, and H. W. Dion, *J. Antibiot.* **30**, 432 (1977).
159. A. Yoshimoto, T. Ogasawara, I. Kitamura, T. Oki, T. Inui, T. Takeuchi, and H. Umezawa, *J. Antibiot.* **32**, 472 (1979).
160. Z. Vanek, J. Tax, J. Goldin, M. Blumauerova', N. Steinerova, J. Mateju, I. Komersova',

and K. Stajner, *in* "Second International Symposium on the Genetics of Industrial Microorganisms" (K. D. MacDonald, ed.), p. 473. Academic Press, New York, 1976.

161. M. L. Casey, R. C. Paulick, and H. W. Whitlock, *J. Org. Chem.* **43**, 1627 (1978).
162. H. J. Shaw, G. W. A. Milne, and A. Minghetti, *Phytochemistry* **18**, 178 (1979).
163. P. F. Wiley, D. W. Elrod, and V. P. Marshall, *J. Org. Chem.* **43**, 3457 (1978).
164. V. P. Marshall, E. A. Reisender, and P. F. Wiley, *J. Antibiot.* **29**, 966 (1976).
165. V. P. Marshall, J. P. McGovren, F. A. Richard, R. E. Richard, and P. F. Wiley, *J. Antibiot.* **31**, 336 (1978).
166. P. W. Rueckert, P. F. Wiley, J. P. McGovren, and V. P. Marshall, *J. Antibiot.* **32**, 141 (1979).
167. V. P. Marshall, E. A. Reisender, L. M. Reineke, J. H. Johnson, and P. F. Wiley, *Biochemistry* **15**, 4139 (1976).
168. J. Karnetova, J. Mateju, P. Sedmera, J. Vokoun, and Z. Vanek, *J. Antibiot.* **29**, 1199 (1976).
169. A. A. Aszalos, N. R. Bachur, B. K. Hamilton, A. F. Langlykke, P. P. Roller, M. Y. Sheikn, M. S. Sutpin, M. C. Thomas, D. A. Wareheim, and L. H. Wright, *J. Antibiot.* **30**, 50 (1977).
170. B. K. Hamilton, M. S. Sutpin, M. C. Thomas, D. A. Wareheim, and A. A. Aszalos, *J. Antibiot.* **30**, 425 (1977).

Index

A

Acetate
  as biogenetic precursor, 8, 347
  labeled, 347
4-Acetyl-1-ethoxycarbonylcyclohexene,
    ethylene ketal, starting intermediate
    for anthracyclinone synthesis, 78
Aclacinomycin A
  assay in plasma, 330
  bioactivity, 321, 329
  clinical evaluation, 331
  N-didemethyl, 322
  4'''-dihydro, 321, 330
  effect on nucleic acid synthesis, 326
  5'''-*epi*, 321
  isolation, 321
  metabolism, 329
  N-monodemethyl, 321
  structure, 321
Aclacinomycin B
  bioactivity, 321, 329
  isolation, 321
  structure, 321
Aclacinomycin Y, 322, 328
Acosamine
  as antibiotic constituent, 194
  synthesis from nonsugar precursors,
    201
  synthesis from L-rhamnose, 200

synthesis of derivatives thereof, 86
D-Acosamine
  N-acetyl, methyl α-glycoside, synthesis
    of, 226
  N-acetyl, methyl β-glycoside, synthesis
    of, 227
  in daunorubicin analog, 224
  synthesis, 225
Actinomadura carminsta, 333
Actinosamine, 194
Actinosporangium sp., 323
L-Aculose, 322
Acute leukemias, 14, 25, 28, 150, 331, 332,
  335
AD 32
  biological activity, 249, 326
  cardiotoxicity, 252
  metabolism, 251
Adryamycin, *see* Doxorubicin
Adriamycinone
  bisanhydro derivative, 20
  carbon-14 labeled, 38
  conversion to doxorubicin, 87
  7-deoxy, 21
  13-dihydro, 143
  doxorubicin metabolite, 34
  from doxorubicin, 20
  in *S. peucetius* cultures, 17
  pentaacetate, 20
  structure, 20

C

M

N

MEDICINAL CHEMISTRY
A Series of Monographs

EDITED BY

GEORGE DESTEVENS

Department of Chemistry
Drew University
Madison, NJ 07940

Volume 1. GEORGE DESTEVENS. Diuretics: Chemistry and Pharmacology. 1963

Volume 2. RODOLFO PAOLETTI (ED.). Lipid Pharmacology. Volume I. 1964. RODOLFO PAOLETTI AND CHARLES J. GLUECK (EDS.). Volume II. 1976

Volume 3. E. J. ARIENS (ED.). Molecular Pharmacology: The Mode of Action of Biologically Active Compounds. (In two volumes.) 1964

Volume 4. MAXWELL GORDON (ED.). Psychopharmacological Agents. Volume I. 1964. Volume II. 1967. Volume III. 1974. Volume IV. 1976

Volume 5. GEORGE DESTEVENS (ED.). Analgetics. 1965

Volume 6. ROLAND H. THORP AND LEONARD B. COBBIN. Cardiac Stimulant Substances. 1967

Volume 7. EMIL SCHLITTLER (ED.). Antihypertensive Agents. 1967

Volume 8. U. S. VON EULER AND RUNE ELIASSON. Prostaglandins. 1967

Volume 9. G. D. CAMPBELL (ED.). Oral Hypoglycaemic Agents: Pharmacology and Therapeutics. 1969

Volume 10. LEMONT B. KIER. Molecular Orbital Theory in Drug Research. 1971

Volume 11. E. J. ARIENS (ED.). Drug Design. Volumes I and II. 1971. Volume III. 1972. Volume IV. 1973. Volumes V and VI. 1975. Volume VII. 1976. Volume VIII. 1978. Volume IX. 1979. Volume X. 1980.

Volume 12. PAUL E. THOMPSON AND LESLIE M. WERBEL. Antimalarial Agents: Chemistry and Pharmacology. 1972

Volume 13. ROBERT A. SCHERRER AND MICHAEL W. WHITEHOUSE (EDS.). Antiinflammatory Agents: Chemistry and Pharmacology. (In two volumes.) 1974

Volume 14. LEMONT B. KIER AND LOWELL H. HALL. Molecular Connectivity in Chemistry and Drug Research. 1976

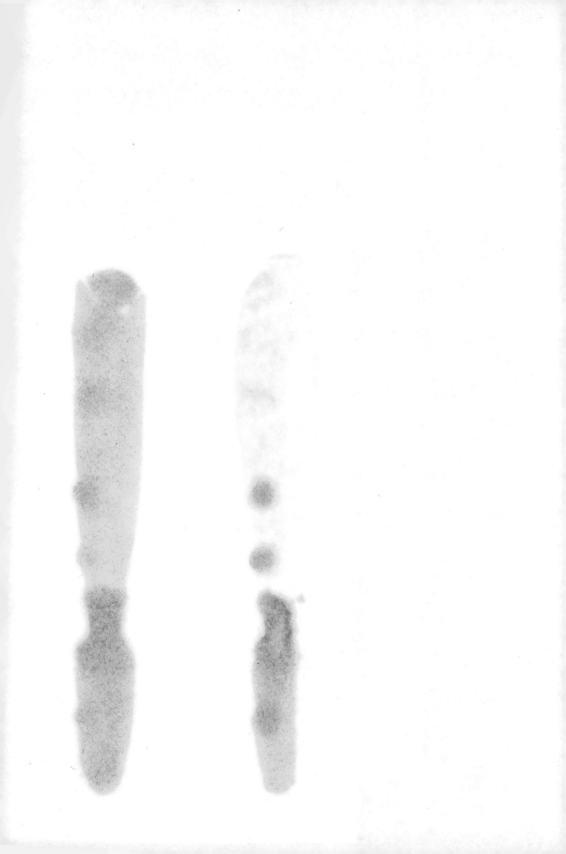